THE DAY THE SINGULARITY

UFOs & the Great Technological Quantum Leap

Steve S. Lazarus

MetaCognitive
PUBLISHING

Printed in the United States of America

First Edition

ISBN 978-1-7334475-0-8

MetaCognitive Publishing
Agoura Hills, CA
www.metacognitivepublishing.com

For my mother Sandra and my brother Bill, whose unwavering support and encouragement made *The Day After The Singularity* a reality.

TABLE OF CONTENTS

ACKNOWLEDGMENTS

First and foremost I thank my family for coming along with me on this journey, this quest for the ultimate truth about UFOs and the extraterrestrial presence. I couldn't have made the trip alone. Thanks for believing that I could get us there.

I would also like to thank Richard Hoagland for giving me the opportunity to work for the Enterprise Mission on Disclosure related projects and Dr. Steven Greer for the opportunity to collaborate with the Disclosure Project on its August 4th, 2001 press conference in Los Angeles. These experiences and others as an activist in pursuit of Disclosure led me to ask myself just what exactly were we disclosing. What are the ultimate implications of an extraterrestrial presence? This book is the result.

Special thanks to Ken Packard for his help documenting the L.A. Disclosure Project press conference. Godspeed my friend- see you in the afterlife or the 'post-Singularity' world or whatever you want to call it. I thank Suzanne Baumann for her encouragement and support in the early dark days of the project when it seemed so far from fruition.

Finally, thanks to the Disclosure Project witnesses for coming forth at great risk to tell their stories. And thanks to all my fellow travellers in the Disclosure Movement. Our Galileo moment is at hand.

INTRODUCTION

In the classic X-files episode, *Jose Chung's From Outer Space*, FBI agent Dana Scully asks novelist Jose Chung, why he wrote a book about alien abduction if he had no personal interest in the subject. Chung, artfully played by Charles Nelson Reilly, tells Scully he saw an opportunity to create a whole new genre that he calls nonfiction science fiction. The episode is silly satire, but the premise is spot-on. Nonfiction science fiction or maybe 'science faction' is more appropriate than the occult or speculation sections in which one would usually find books about UFOs in dwindling brick and mortar bookstores.

The nonfiction science fiction label is especially fitting for this book, which posits that Earth is part of a much larger, much more advanced civilization that has spread throughout the galaxy. It may sound like science fiction, but our lives are becoming more and more like science fiction every day.

If someone travelled back in time just 20 years and told the people there that we had a device that fit in a pocket that instantly connected us to the world at large, giving us access to a vast encyclopedia, allowing us to order books and movies and pizzas, get weather forecasts, box scores, and stock quotes, etc., all in real time, and that this device also enabled us to see and talk with someone else practically anywhere in world and everything else that a smartphone does, they would be laughed off as insane. Yet here we are today.

The next twenty years will make the last couple decades seem downright boring. Just around the corner are driverless cars, 3D-printed houses and factories and robots that do every chore. One can only imagine where all this is going.

Futurists tell us that as computing power doubles roughly every two years we are headed for a technological Singularity, a transcendent event in which artificially intelligent computers and robots surpass human capabilities. When the Singularity occurs no one knows what will happen next. Some fear the Terminator scenario. Others see the emergence of techno-Nirvana. Ray Kurzweil, head of Google engineering, thinks that by the year 2029 we will merge with our artificially intelligent creations and become, for all intents and purposes, immortal. The civilization that will result, the beings that we will become, are impossible for even our greatest science fiction writers to imagine. And oh by the way, this post-Singularity civilization will have the capability to colonize the galaxy.

What does this Singularity have to do with UFOs? As it turns out-everything. When UFOs first came into public consciousness in the middle of the twentieth century they were called flying saucers, which were most often described as metallic craft in the shape of a disc with a dome on top. These objects were reported by both civilian and military eyewitnesses. In the 1950s, flying saucers were a pop culture sensation. There was ample speculation about the possibility of visitors from other planets, but the general consensus was that such things just weren't possible. It was also common wisdom that a UFO cover-up wasn't possible either. As rumors about crashed disks proliferated, skeptics laughed off the suggestion of such a conspiracy. But it's not *just* a conspiracy theory; it's also a sociological theory. There was no conspiracy against Copernicus or Galileo, yet their discoveries were suppressed and denied for a hundred years. Why? Because it was universally believed at the time that the Earth was at the center of the Universe. The same sociological forces, written about by science philosopher Thomas Kuhn, come into play whenever UFO sightings compel us to contemplate the question of whether or not we're alone in the Universe, an assumption left over from the days when Earth was at the center and humans reigned over all creation. In 1950, the debate about UFOs led Nobel-prize winning physicist Enrico Fermi to the realization that while flying saucers probably weren't extraterrestrial spacecraft, we should've been visited many times by now. Fermi's reasoning was simple. The universe is incredibly immense and much older than our Earth and Sun. Someone should've come before us and they should've spread among the stars. In fact, the galaxy should have already been colonized.

Back in Fermi's day, the Singularity was too far over the horizon for anyone to see. Now that it is almost upon us it's clear that Fermi's simple formula needs another expression. Whoever came before us will have developed computing before us meaning they will have hit the Singularity before us- and they will have colonized the galaxy.

The implications of the Singularity highlight the significance of the UFO phenomenon, especially since we are now at a point in time when anyone who studies the subject seriously will quickly discover that, as historian Richard Dolan has written, *UFOs are real*. In fact, we are now in a period analogous to the last paradigm shift when Copernicus and Galileo proved that the Earth was not the center of the universe. If that period taught us anything it's that paradigms don't shift easily. Adherents to long-held worldviews don't relinquish their belief systems without a fight. Although Copernicus showed that the Earth circled the sun, the establishment refused to abandon its belief that everything in the universe revolved around the Earth- until a century later when Galileo discovered the moons of Jupiter. Even then the Catholic Church did its best to resist. Cherished beliefs die hard. There are still about a thousand flat-earthers to this day.

This time around it's the scientific wing of the establishment that can't handle the truth. Anyone who takes UFOs seriously is automatically dismissed as a crank, even astronaut Edgar Mitchell, who was dismissed out of hand when he spoke out about the Roswell Incident. And anyone who believes that so-called "alien abductees" are telling the truth, like Harvard psychologist John Mack, who studied over a hundred of them, is simply ignored, or worse, ridiculed mercilessly. The distinction between official reality and actual reality could not be more stark. For example, in 2011 over ten thousand people signed a petition on the White House's *We the People* website demanding the government acknowledge the extraterrestrial presence engaging the human race. The White House responded with the blanket denial that there was no credible evidence of extraterrestrials. Just eight months later former CIA agent Chase Brandon announced that he'd seen evidence in the CIA's archives proving the crash of an ET spacecraft was the cause of the Roswell Incident. UFO lobbyist Stephen Bassett of the Paradigm Research Group immediately submitted a new petition asking the White House to investigate Brandon's claims. The government never responded and the mainstream media chose not to investigate.[1] It was the 21st century equivalent of the Catholic Church's reaction to Galileo and his discovery of the moons of Jupiter.

As Mark Twain said, "history doesn't repeat itself, but it does rhyme." We now find ourselves in a familiar position. Almost seventy years into the modern UFO era it's clear that we face another world-altering paradigm shift. Most ufologists think that the truth will come out when a dramatic and undeniable sighting occurs or when a piece of the Roswell 'memory metal' somehow surfaces or when an Edward Snowden-type whistleblower emerges with a cache of top secret documents, but the truth will likely come out in some unexpected way.

Whatever the case, disclosure of the truth is inevitable. Imagine it's 2029, the year that Kurzweil believes we'll hit the technological Singularity, enabling us to upload our brains into computers. There's a new type of software called 'mindware' that lets us search and sort our memories much like Google helps us navigate the Internet. It's now possible to turn these memories into streaming video to share with others. Close encounter witnesses and so-called alien abductees suddenly flood the Internet instantly crushing any remaining doubt about the reality of their experiences. The establishment would surely relent in such a scenario, but it's much more likely to happen in a thousand other unimaginable ways long before then. The closer we get to the Singularity, the more difficult it will be to prevent the truth from coming out. It could happen at any time. In fact, it may be happening now. As this book goes to publication, *The New York Times* is reporting that the latest cutting-edge technology shows UFOs *are real* after all. Navy pilots attached to the aircraft carrier Theodore Roosevelt began seeing UFOs on an almost daily basis from the summer of 2014 through March 2015, after their 1980s-era radar was upgraded to a more advanced system. Without jet engines or an exhaust plume, the unidentifiable objects were somehow able to fly circles around our best Top Gun fighters, but no one in the Department of Defense is ready to call them extraterrestrial- yet.

All by itself, the UFO evidence strongly suggests that there are extraterrestrial craft in our skies and in some Top Secret Air Force hangars as well. While the definitive hard evidence that would satisfy the skeptics can be hidden under lock and key, there is other evidence that can't be suppressed. There are clues in the sky the whole world can see. Once again, the telescope is the instrument of paradigm shift. In the data gathered by the world's space agencies is rather stunning evidence that an extraterrestrial civilization hit the Singularity long ago. When one considers the UFO evidence in the context of a post-Singularity civilization that has the capability to colonize the galaxy, all the puzzle pieces fall into place.

When the ultimate Disclosure occurs we will discover that our world is the product of a much larger, much more advanced civilization that has spread throughout the galaxy. Project Blue Book astronomer J. Allen Hynek once said, "When the long-awaited solution to the UFO problem comes, I believe that it will prove to be not merely the next small step in the march of science, but a mighty and totally unexpected quantum leap."

That day is here.

PART ONE

UFOs & FERMI'S PARADOX

A purely psychological explanation is ruled out…the discs show signs of intelligent guidance, by quasi-human pilots… the authorities in possession of important information should not hesitate to enlighten the public as soon and as completely as possible.
— **Carl Jung, 1955**

Several days in a row we sighted metallic, saucer-shaped vehicles at great altitudes over the base, and we tried to get close to them, but they were able to change direction faster than our fighters. I do believe UFOs exist and the truly unexplained ones are from some other technically advanced civilization.
— **Astronaut Gordon Cooper, 1980**

It now seems quite clear that Earth is not the only inhabited planet… it seems likely that a large number of planets within our Milky Way galaxy- perhaps as many as a million- are inhabited by technical civilizations in advance of our own.
— **Carl Sagan, 1963**

We're just one tiny grain of sand on a virtually infinite beach. The notion that we're alone in the universe, that we're the only living species, is absolutely ridiculous… Our whole idea of what it means to be living on this planet, and even being a thinking human on this planet, is going to have to undergo some major revision.
— **Astronaut Edgar Mitchell, 2014**

CHAPTER 1

PARADOX

The type of UFO reports that are most intriguing are close-range sightings of machine-like objects of unconventional nature and unconventional performance characteristics, seen at low altitudes, and sometimes even on the ground.

— James McDonald, physicist, at hearings before the Committee on Science and Astronautics, U.S. House of Representatives, July 1968

Skeptics, who flatly deny the existence of any unexplained phenomenon in the name of "rationalism," are among the primary contributors to the rejection of science by the public. People are not stupid and they know very well when they've seen something out of the ordinary. When a so-called expert tells them the object must have been the moon or a mirage, he is really teaching the public that science is impotent or unwilling to pursue the study of the unknown.

— Jacques Vallee

THE LEGEND OF FERMI'S PARADOX

The key to understanding the universe and our place within it was first articulated by Italian physicist Enrico Fermi during a visit to Los Alamos National Laboratory, the birthplace of the atomic bomb, one day in 1950.

If the universe is teeming with life… where is everybody? As legend has it, this was the million dollar question that emerged from a discussion about UFOs, then more accurately known by the unfortunate term: flying saucers.

Over lunch, Fermi, a world-class, Nobel Prize winning scientist for his work on radioactivity, and his colleagues, Emil Konopinski, Herbert York and infamous military-industrial complex Grand Pooh-Bah, Edward Teller, debated the existence of the strange, disk-shaped craft, which were front-page headlines back in the day.

It suddenly occurred to Fermi that, despite the general consensus that flying saucers likely weren't real, extraterrestrial visitation should be routine. He rattled off a set of calculations regarding the probability of Earth-like planets in the galaxy, the probability of life on such planets, the probability that life-bearing, Earth-like planets might evolve intelligence and eventually technology, and so on, and concluded that we should have been visited many times by now.[1] In fact, Fermi found the absence of extraterrestrial visitation troubling. It could be that interstellar travel is impossible, he mused. Or even worse, maybe technological civilizations don't survive long enough to achieve travel between the stars, worried Fermi, who inadvertently gave birth to the cosmic riddle that has become known as Fermi's paradox.

According to the Copernican Principle, the Earth occupies no special place in the universe. In other words, our world is a typical planet orbiting a typical star in a typical galaxy in a universe that is unimaginably large and unfathomably old. The universe was around for billions of years before our Sun was even formed. It's obvious that someone must have come before us. The implications are monumental. Fermi's epiphany strongly implied that the Galaxy should already have been colonized. Indeed, Fermi paradox theorists argue that we should see evidence of a great galactic civilization.

Our technological progress has only made the absence of aliens more glaring. In 1980s astronomer John Barrow and Physicist Frank Tipler showed that a technologically advanced civilization could colonize the Galaxy in about a million years even without the ability to blow by the cosmic speed limit. The duo concluded that the apparent absence of a Great Galactic Civilization meant that we must be alone in the Galaxy because if someone came before us we should've not only been visited many times, we should be able to gaze in awe upon their planet-size engineering projects right here in our own solar system.

The advance of technology not only hinted at what was possible it also revealed the truly stunning immensity of the universe. Big numbers are difficult to envision. Words like 'billions' and 'trillions' lose their meaning.

Fortunately, the Hubble telescope has given us a pair of images that show the scale of the universe in a way that words and numbers simply can't. Available online at hubblesite.org, the *Hubble Deep Field* and the *Hubble Ultra Deep Field* are stunning images achieved by focusing the Hubble telescope on a tiny patch of empty sky for an extended period of time. Over ten days, Hubble peered into a slice of sky the equivalent of a dime on edge at a distance of 75 feet to produce the *Hubble Deep Field*.[2] The image showed there were, in fact, 3,000 galaxies in this little strip of empty space.[3] The *Hubble Ultra Deep Field* made an even deeper reach out into the void, capturing 10,000 galaxies residing in the thin edge of nothingness.[4]

The Big Picture looks like this: there are more than 100 billion galaxies in the universe that are filled with stars and planets like beaches with sand.[5] Typical galaxies hold between 10 million and one trillion stars. Planets are surely even more abundant. The total number of planets in the universe is anyone's guess but the number might be more properly expressed as somewhere just south of infinity. According to theoretical physicist Michio Kaku, the numbers are such that it's become "increasingly clear" that we are not alone in the Universe.[6]

In just our Milky Way galaxy there are hundreds of billions of stars and about a trillion planets. On his iconic TV series *Cosmos*, astronomer Carl Sagan estimated that, "There may be a million worlds in the Milky Way galaxy alone which are at this moment inhabited by other intelligent beings."[7] If only one planet in a million evolves an intelligent civilization, it would fulfill Sagan's estimate of one million intelligent civilizations in the Milky Way Galaxy.

Odds are that all these hypothetical extraterrestrial civilizations are more advanced than ours. Science tells us the universe is very old. NASA recently pegged it at 13.7 billion years.[8] In contrast, our Sun is relatively young at 4.5 billion years and our technological civilization is in its infancy. Although life on Earth arose long ago, it was simple and primitive until just recently. Civilization as we know it is only thousands of years old and advanced civilization is brand new. In a scant few generations we have gone from working in fields to working in factories to working in cyberspace. We have just arrived. In theory, many technological civilizations should've come before us by millions or even billions of years and they should've colonized the galaxy long before we came of age.

Fermi's paradox became a legend within the scientific community of such historical significance that Eric M. Jones of Los Alamos National Laboratory sought to firmly establish its factual basis in 1985 when he solicited and published the recollections of Konopinski, York and Teller, who have all since died, in a paper entitled, *Where is Everybody? An Account of Fermi's Question.* Fermi was unavailable to contribute having died in 1954.

Fermi didn't live to see the profound effect his simple epiphany had on the scientific community. Scientists Michael Hart, Carl Sagan, I. S. Shklovsky, Frank Drake, Frank Tipler, John Barrow and others built upon his basic premise.

The probability that extraterrestrial civilizations exist led to the founding of SETI, the Search for Extraterrestrial Intelligence, which has its roots in Fermi's paradox. SETI founding father, astronomer Frank Drake, expanded on Fermi's off-the-cuff calculation, which is now known as the Drake Equation.[9] The numbers astronomers assign to the variables are highly debatable, but its SETI's best guess at how many civilizations it might be able to detect as it scans the skies looking for a radio signal from an alien world much like our own.

In the 1970s, astronomer Michael Hart sparked a fresh debate about Fermi's paradox, resulting in a consensus that someone should've already colonized the Galaxy. In 1986, Barrow and Tipler showed how it could be done, basing their model for interstellar migration on mathematician John von Neumann's concept of a 'Universal Constructor,' a machine capable of building other machines, including copies of itself using raw materials gathered from the environment. Tipler and Barrow found that a 'von Neumann probe' could colonize the Galaxy without exceeding the speed of light.[10] Once such a probe reached a new star system it would set up shop, make copies of itself and launch its cloned offspring towards other stars to repeat the process. This Universal Constructor would then build a space station and grow synthetic humans in a lab. The entire Galaxy could be colonized this way in less than a million years, making the perceived absence of extraterrestrial visitors even more puzzling.[11]

Sagan's theories about the feasibility of space travel also served to highlight the apparent absence of spacefaring ETs. In his book, *Intelligent Life in the Universe*, co-authored with Russian astronomer I. S. Shklovsky, Sagan showed that travel between the stars, *and even the galaxies*, was doable.[12] So again, where were all the ET tourists? It was more than just a challenging intellectual problem for Sagan, who claimed to be deeply troubled by SETI's inability to detect an alien radio signal. Sagan's alleged angst over SETI's failures led him to obsess over one particular variable of the Drake equation: the average lifetime of a technological civilization. Sagan used the term as an argument against space travelling aliens. Perhaps technological civilizations inevitably destroy themselves before they achieve space travel? Sagan argued the Galaxy might be littered with a million *dead* civilizations. The prospect of our own nuclear Armageddon made him a passionate critic of militarism, a staunch antinuclear activist and an ardent advocate of SETI, which he defended against critics who used Fermi's paradox to rubbish the program as a waste of money. Sagan beat back such attacks by claiming that SETI's success was critical. It would mean someone had survived technological development without destroying themselves. Detection of an alien signal meant hope for the human race.

Others weren't concerned about UFOs or alien radio broadcasts. Scientist Robert Freitas, railed against Fermi paradox theorists who drew radical conclusions based on the absence of evidence, which he dismissed, in mocking fashion, as meaningless. According to Freitas, almost all advanced civilizations would be either "invisible or unrecognizable using current human observational methods."[13]

Lost in the debate were the flying saucers that sparked it. Despite the growing awareness that ET should be here, no one reconsidered whether or not UFOs were examples of extraterrestrial visitation. While it's true that such expectations don't mean that flying saucers must be extraterrestrial, the response of mainstream science, which dismisses these reports out of hand, seems incredibly irrational. Sagan biographer Keay Davidson gave a textbook example of scientific establishment bias against UFOs in the process of explaining Fermi's paradox when he wrote, "UFO sightings don't count; most good scientists rejected these as nonsense."[14]

The attitude of such "good scientists" toward UFOs is completely inappropriate. Given Fermi's epiphany, one would expect scientists to be open to the idea that some UFOs are extraterrestrial craft, rather than the near hysterical refusal to consider the possibility. Instead, what we find is that most scientists disregard UFOs entirely.

The question is: Why did Fermi, Teller, Tipler, Sagan and the others dismiss the possibility that flying saucers might be the craft of an extraterrestrial civilization? It would seem schizophrenic, on the one hand, to expect to see the spaceships of advanced extraterrestrial cultures, and on the other, to categorically reject reports of objects that appear to meet that expectation. The paradox within the paradox raises many questions: Might the legend be incomplete or even intentionally misleading? Is there more to the story, and if so, might it change our perspective about Fermi's paradox and our place in the universe in a profound way?

THE REAL FERMI PARADOX

Imagine waking up to the fresh, crisp air, flowing streams and pine-covered mountains of northern New Mexico, and spending your day creating the most destructive abomination in the history of mankind, something capable of incinerating such pristine beauty. This was the setting at Los Alamos, New Mexico in 1943 where some of the world's most beautiful minds, including Edward Teller, John von Neumann, Leo Szilard, Richard Feynman, Stanislaw Ulam, Enrico Fermi and others, gathered to create The Bomb.

The fact that the Los Alamos gang succeeded in reducing Hiroshima and Nagasaki, Japan to smoldering ash in 1945 and went on designing bigger, more insanely destructive bombs, is well known. What is generally unknown is that they appeared to be under the surveillance of a superior force- something that was inconceivable at the time.

In 1948, military personnel, pilots and civilians began seeing what appeared to be "green fireballs" streak across the night skies of New Mexico. The name "green fireballs" would turn out to be misleading for this type of luminous UFO. The so-called fireballs maintained altitude, changed directions and crossed the sky in silence. The unusual activity was of great concern to the military as it was occurring in an area of the country's most sensitive airspace. Many installations vital to the defense of the U.S. were spread throughout the majestic New Mexico landscape. The labs at both Los Alamos and Sandia were the center of the atomic bomb program. Concerned intelligence officers at Kirtland Air Force Base called in world-renowned meteor expert, Lincoln La Paz of the New Mexico Institute of Meteoritics to investigate.[15]

La Paz thought the green fireballs could be meteorites, but some observations didn't fit. He set about his investigation, interviewing witnesses in an attempt to triangulate on the impact site as he had in the past with other meteorites. Only this time La Paz couldn't find any evidence no matter how many times he and his crew searched the area. This was a man not accustomed to failure. In nearly every case involving known meteorites he'd been successful in finding fragments. La Paz began to doubt that the green fireballs were natural objects.

Between December 1948 and January 1949 sightings of green fireballs became an almost nightly occurrence. There were at least 39 reports of the phenomenon over New Mexico in this time period. In his report on UFOs, Captain Ed Ruppelt of Project Blue Book, the Air Force's official UFO investigation, wrote, "Everyone, including the intelligence officers at Kirtland AFB, Air Defense Command people, Dr. La Paz, and some of the most distinguished scientists at Los Alamos had seen at least one."[16]

La Paz saw one on December 12, 1948 and thought it was possible that the UFO had flown directly over Los Alamos. The object maintained a horizontal path and was completely silent as it traversed the sky too slowly to be a meteor. Green meteorites were not a new phenomenon in astronomy, although the color associated with those types is a pale, yellowish green. These objects were a bright, almost neon, Kelly green and their size was scary. Some were as big as the Moon and turned night into day as they passed silently without the window-rattling sonic boom one would expect, like there was with the 2013 Russian meteorite captured on ubiquitous digital video cameras screaming in from outer space, shattering windows and injuring thousands in the region of Chelyabinsk. What's more, it was clear that the phenomenon was unique to the New Mexico area. La Paz became increasingly convinced that whatever the green fireballs were, they weren't meteors, meteorites or fireballs- or natural objects.

Such suspicious activity over America's most sensitive airspace was cause for alarm. A secret conference was convened at Los Alamos on February 16, 1949. La Paz, Edward Teller, Joseph Kaplan and other scientists and military personnel gathered to discuss both green fireballs and flying saucers. Blue Book director Captain Ruppelt noted, this was a conference where there was no need to debate the existence of this particular type of UFO because everyone present had seen at least one. The debate was about whether the phenomenon was natural or artificial. Opinions were divided. La Paz and others were convinced that what they were witnessing was some form of technology. Teller thought the green fireballs might not be solid objects, but an "electro-optic" phenomenon of some sort. Whatever they were, green fireball sightings could not be explained by secret training exercises according to Kaplan, a world-renowned expert on the physics of the upper atmosphere. It's unknown if any useful conclusions about the green fireball UFOs were reached at this conference, which took place the year *before* Fermi's historic lunch at the lab.

Green fireball UFOs ignited the imagination of the Manhattan Project scientists. Ruppelt recalled a casual discussion he'd had with a group of Los Alamos scientists – whom he wouldn't name - during one of his visits. "When the possibility of the green fireballs' being associated with interplanetary vehicles came up, the whole group got serious. They had been doing a lot of thinking about this, they said, and they had a theory," wrote Ruppelt, who said this anonymous group of Los Alamos scientists thought the green fireballs might be "atmospheric test flights" launched from a mother ship high in orbit making preparations to land on an alien planet. Ruppelt assumed their theory meant they thought the green fireballs were artificial, but the scientists wouldn't go that far. They would only concede that the evidence for artificiality far outweighed the natural explanation.[17]

Green fireballs weren't the only form of UFO seen by prominent scientists in New Mexico during the time period. In the summer of 1947, Clyde Tombaugh, an astronomer who had discovered Pluto, was in the car with his wife and kids when he saw a shiny oval object hovering near the highway shoot rapidly upwards through the clouds. He went public making an official statement two years later- when he saw something else that defied conventional explanation. From his backyard in Las Cruces, New Mexico, Tombaugh officially declared that he and his family had seen a formation of rectangular yellow-green lights like windows on a plane move across the sky from the northwest to southeast in three seconds, leaving him in a state of astonishment.[18]

Like the Los Alamos scientists, Tombaugh also saw the green fireballs- three in total.[19] And like Ruppelt's Los Alamos scientists, Tombaugh was open to the Extraterrestrial hypothesis (ETH). In fact, he blasted scientists who rejected the possibility, like Harvard astronomer Donald Menzel, as *unscientific.*[20]

In the context of the intense buzz generated by UFOs in the tight-knit scientific and technical community of New Mexico, the story of Fermi's paradox seems strangely incongruous. Teller's assertion that, "we talked about flying saucers and the obvious statement that the flying saucers are not real," is difficult to reconcile in light of the UFO sightings made by the Los Alamos scientists, the conference they held to debate them, and the conclusion of meteoritics expert Lincoln La Paz that the green fireball UFOs were not natural. Given the circumstances, one can't help but wonder why the discussion centered on the premise that flying saucers weren't real? One would expect the kind of thinking demonstrated by the group of unnamed Los Alamos scientists written about by Ruppelt. Their theory about an orbiting spaceship and atmospheric tests seems a more appropriate response than ruling out the possibility of interplanetary travel. In fact, there is evidence to suggest that this type of thinking *was* going on *behind the scenes*.

In 1953 the Air Force fast-tracked a secret project to detect satellites in Earth orbit. This was, of course, years before any nation on Earth had launched any such satellites. When word got out, officials at White Sands issued a press release stating the military was looking for small asteroid-like "moonlets" that had come in from deep space and entered into orbit around the equator. Such objects would be both a danger to space travel and an opportunity for a space base- so they said.[21]

The story achieved its apex in the mainstream media when *Time* Magazine reported that astronomer Clyde Tombaugh was in charge of the search for what they called a second moon. Tombaugh, the only astronomer to officially report a UFO, was assisted by none other than Lincoln La Paz, the meteor expert who didn't believe green fireballs were natural objects, in the quest to identify objects that arrived from deep space and entered into Earth orbit. The circumstances were telling to say the least.

Time reported that Tombaugh was tight lipped about his findings, referring all questions to the military. He denied media reports about the satellites, but others, including the Adler Planetarium in Chicago, confirmed their presence. No one challenged the shaky premise that these objects that had arrived from interstellar space to settle into stable Earth orbit were natural.

According to retired Major Donald Keyhoe, the first civilian UFO researcher, the search for the so-called "moonlets" was a cover story. The military was actually looking for spacecraft.[22]

Keyhoe reported that the Air Force suffered quite a shock when it powered up its brand new long-range radar equipment, which promptly revealed a huge object orbiting the equator. What's more, not long after the first mystery satellite was detected, the new high-powered radar system tracked another sizeable object as it arrived from deep space and entered into a similar orbit.

From the perspective of the unnamed Los Alamos scientists written about by Ruppelt, such dramatic radar returns would seem to be rather emphatic evidence in support of their theory that the green fireballs were the product of orbiting spacecraft. In fact, one can't help but suspect that the informal brainstorming session held at Los Alamos was the genesis of the mission to search for "moonlets." Such a program would have been the logical next step if Ruppelt's anonymous group of Los Alamos big wigs were to test their theory that the green fireballs were the atmospheric tests of an orbiting spacecraft.

Whether or not the brilliantly green UFOs were actually such tests – they may have had more in common with Lieutenant Uhura's hailing frequency than Scotty's transporter room – their appearances over New Mexico got the attention of the scientific community, which began to investigate. Tombaugh's leadership of the project to search for moonlets, along with the participation of Lincoln La Paz, further suggest that its real goal was to search for extraterrestrial spacecraft in orbit. It's also telling that the media dropped the story like the proverbial hot potato.[23] The public heard no more about Earth's moonlets, which became just another faded memory.

The episode shows the progression of an unofficial theory about an extraterrestrial presence developed by the scientists of Los Alamos that seems to have begun with the conference held in 1949, a year before the Fermi lunchtime discussion.

It's clear that the discussion that led to Fermi's epiphany just as easily could have revolved around the possibility that the flying saucers were real. If it had, Fermi's revelation would've reinforced the ETH instead of birthing a paradox. In either case, it is antithetical to science to presume an answer before an investigation.

In the final analysis, the story of Fermi's paradox drips with irony. UFOs inspired a theory about extraterrestrial visitation, yet were rejected as such evidence, thus creating the impression that we are alone in the cosmos. What's more, it seems there's a lot more to the story. There's reason to believe that a member of the Fermi group actually *knew* that UFOs were extraterrestrial. As they say, where there's smoke there's fire- or in this case, mirrors.

OPERATION MANHATTAN TWELVE

The connection between atomic bomb makers and UFOs ran much deeper than the green fireball UFO mystery that took place in the skies over Los Alamos. World War II saw the rise of the military-industrial complex and its Top Secret operation to build the atomic bomb. The Manhattan Project was unprecedented in its use of extreme secrecy. An entire community of scientists and technicians spent over two billion dollars of the people's money absent oversight by their elected representatives and the world never knew about any of it until Little Boy and Fat Man were dropped on Japan. This effort necessitated a marriage between the scientific, military and intelligence communities. As a result, men of science and technology assumed key positions of power in the new technological cold war that spawned the arms race. Eventually, the Department of Defense employed half of all the scientists and technical personnel in the country.[24]

World War II saw not only the rise of the Marvel Comics Tony Stark Iron Man-type scientist-as-superhero, it was also, as historian Richard Dolan noted, the first time we took to the skies en masse. With our collective vision extended above the clouds and yet again by radar, something strange occurred. Both allied and enemy forces encountered what they assumed were secret weapons of the other side. Called foo fighters, these objects displayed the familiar characteristics that would later be associated with flying saucers and UFOs- they glowed, they hovered, they sped away in a flash, they made hairpin turns at seemingly impossible speeds and stopped on a dime, they appeared impervious to the rounds occasionally fired at them and they flew circles around everything else in the air. The performance of these objects was far superior to anything in any nation's arsenal. Before long, it was evident to intelligence analysts that they were neither allied fighters nor enemy devices- but what were they?[25]

Not much is known about the military reaction to these early UFO reports, which continued on long after the conclusion of the war. What is clear is that the military had been dealing with UFOs for years before they entered the public consciousness with the famous Kenneth Arnold "flying saucer" sighting in June of 1947. While searching for a downed plane near Mount Rainier Washington, Arnold saw nine oddly-shaped metallic objects he couldn't identify flying at an impossible speed "like a saucer would if you skipped it across water." Headlines about Arnold's "flying saucers" captured the public's imagination, crystallizing the mystery of unidentified craft in pop culture.

Shortly after the Arnold sighting and before the green fireball UFO reports in New Mexico in 1948, an event occurred which appears to have put an end to the mystery of the bizarre flying objects- at least for those with knowledge of the incident.

On July 6, 1947, a local rancher named Mack Brazel brought strange debris he had discovered in a pasture to the attention of the authorities in Roswell, New Mexico. Intelligence officer Jesse Marcel, Captain Sheridan Cavitt and Master Sergeant Lewis Rickett were sent to the ranch to gather the debris and return it to Roswell Army Air Field. The wreckage, much like the performance of the anomalous objects, was unlike anything the men had ever seen and was immediately identifiable as "nothing made on this Earth,"[26] as Marcel would later confess.

On July 8th, commanding officer of the 509[thth] bomb group, Colonel Bill Blanchard told Public Information Officer Lt. Walter Haut to issue a press release. Later that day the Roswell Daily Record announced that the Army had come into possession of a flying saucer.

The town of Roswell erupted as the news spread like a wildfire. Western Union, radio stations, newspapers and the AP picked up the story fanning the flames of excitement nationally and internationally. The following day, the Army retracted its claim explaining that a weather balloon was to blame for all the hysteria.[27] The story soon died and was forgotten, but the Army's first announcement was the truth. Despite extreme measures used by the government to enforce secrecy about the Roswell Incident that included death threats, the story began to leak out decades after the fact.[28]

As the end of his life approached, Major Jesse Marcel found he could no longer stay silent. In 1978, when Marcel started talking, the original weather balloon cover story started to unravel. Researchers began investigating Marcel's claims, locating other witnesses, etc., and in 1980 the first in a series of books on the affair, *The Roswell Incident,* was published.[29] Over the years, many more witnesses to the events at Roswell have followed Marcel's lead in breaking their silence. To date there are approximately 600 who have come forward in support of the first official statement that a flying saucer was recovered at Roswell.[30]

Like Marcel, many were "old timers," as astronaut Edgar Mitchell called them, who wanted to get the truth out before they died. Mitchell, the sixth man to walk on the moon, grew up in the Roswell area and was familiar with community lore. He knew many of the old timers. They sought him out to tell their story. For the people of Roswell the cover-up was a joke. Something to snicker at in amazement. They knew what had happened. An alien craft had crashed on a ranch. There was no doubt about it. Subsequently, Mitchell has spoken on the record about the fact that the Roswell Incident was indeed the result of the crash of an extraterrestrial spacecraft.[31]

Nevertheless, the Air Force has steadfastly maintained its position despite overwhelming testimony and evidence to the contrary, aided by the successful confiscation of the hard evidence, which apparently remain under lock and key in an Indiana Jones-type warehouse somewhere deep in the bowels of the military industrial complex.[32]

Absent a smoking gun in the form of a piece of the wreckage or an official government document, there seemed to be no way of compelling the government to explain what really happened at Roswell. Then, in 1984, researchers on the Roswell trail received an undeveloped role of film in the mail from an anonymous source. On the black and white 35mm film were top-secret classified documents purporting to be briefing papers for President-elect Eisenhower. Dated 18 November 1952, the briefing document describes an intelligence operation set in motion by the crash and recovery of a flying saucer near Roswell, New Mexico called Operation Majestic Twelve.[33]

Some of the country's most prestigious and powerful men were listed on its roster, including the head of the Air Material Command, General Nathan Twining, Air Force Chief of Staff and the second Director of Central Intelligence, General Hoyt Vandenberg, the first director of the CIA, Admiral Roscoe Hillenkoetter, Harvard astronomer and consultant to the NSA and CIA, Donald Menzel and Vannevar Bush, head of the Office of Scientific Research and Development and head of the *Manhattan Project*.[34]

Nuclear physicist Stanton Friedman, one of the original Roswell researchers, was excited, but suspicious of the documents. The manner in which they were leaked made it impossible to verify their origins. While not a proof of forgery, it was a significant barrier to establishing authenticity. Also, because the documents arrived on film, there were no originals on which to perform forensic tests. What's more, the researchers who received the roll of film had ties to Air Force intelligence agents of dubious intentions who were likely the source of the documents.

Friedman smelled a rat. He thought the Eisenhower briefing document might be part of a ruse designed to discredit UFO researchers on the Roswell trail. An elaborate hoax that could be exposed after gullible ufologists had publicly touted their significance. Fortunately, Friedman's reservations did not stop him from conducting a thorough investigation, which convinced him of the document's authenticity. He found the format of the Eisenhower briefing document to be consistent with comparable documents of the time period in question and the richly detailed content checked out in dramatic fashion.[35] In a documentary film aired on The Learning Channel entitled, *UFOs: 50 Year of Denial*, Stanton Friedman noted, "It's the list of 35 pieces of information not known to be true before we got the documents that turned out to be true afterwards. I've had archivists tell me they couldn't have faked those documents because there was too much detail." Since that time the number has grown to 37 pieces of information not known until the appearance of the documents.[36] Former CIA Chief of Operations Richard Bissell said of the Eisenhower briefing document, "I personally have little doubt that it is authentic."[37] The documents and the ongoing efforts to authenticate them can be found online at majesticdocuments.com as well as stantonfriedman.com.

Over the years, other Majestic documents have surfaced. In the process of authentication, many have been found wanting. It appears that, while some are probably authentic, others are most likely fraudulent.[38] Consequently, in a classic case of throwing the baby out with the bath water, most UFO researchers consider the Majestic documents to be a hoax, which may have been the goal of whomever was behind the leaking of the documents. It's a messy and confusing situation indicative of a disinformation campaign.

There is little question that the government has engaged in disinformation regarding the Roswell Incident. It has given four different explanations for the event in what appears to be an attempt to counter the mounting evidence of the crash of an extraterrestrial spacecraft.[39] As if the government's ever evolving explanation for what really happened at Roswell weren't troubling enough, the last attempt to offset the growing number of witnesses to dead alien bodies jumped the shark, so to speak, in 1997 when the Air Force claimed that the diminutive four foot tall non-human bodies reported by both civilian and military eyewitnesses were actually six-foot tall crash test dummies that, for all intents and purposes, look like an undressed mannequin one would see in a department store. Additionally, the dummies in question had the words "property of the Air Force" stamped on them and weren't in use until almost a decade after the Roswell Incident.[40] Given that the Air Force has changed its story several times and invoked such wildly implausible explanations, it would seem to be an indisputable fact that the government has engaged in a disinformation campaign regarding the Roswell Incident.

There's an old Irish folk tale about a leprechaun and his pot of gold that makes an unlikely, but apt analogy for the uses of disinformation in the Roswell Incident and the UFO phenomenon in general. The leprechaun, forced to reveal the location of his buried treasure by a common man, is bound by honor not to remove a red tie wrapped around a tree to mark the spot. When the commoner returns with a shovel to dig up the gold, he finds that the Leprechaun is gone and there are red ties around every tree. The fable illustrates a situation where a secret has been discovered and must be re-hidden by clever means. The government is much like the leprechaun in the fable, not wishing to relinquish its "pot of gold" recovered in Roswell, and using disinformation as its field of red ties to preserve its secret.

Disinformation, also known as black propaganda, is a broad term. In general, it is the art of spreading false information to mislead the public in the pursuit of an agenda. Intelligence agencies routinely employ disinformation to accomplish their goals. There are many disinformation techniques. Disinformation agents make use of misdirection not unlike a magician. A common method is to distort the truth by mixing it with lies so that the truth is presented in a way that renders it unbelievable. This appears to be the chosen method with the Majestic documents and with the UFO phenomenon in general.

Any disinformation campaign would have to include a plan to make use of mass media, and indeed, it is an indisputable historical fact that the United States government has had a mass media disinformation campaign to debunk flying saucers since 1953.

The year before had seen a serious threat to the policy of secrecy regarding flying saucers and the extraterrestrial presence on Earth. In 1952, there was a huge UFO sightings wave that generated headlines on a regular basis. The situation came to a head with sightings over Washington D.C., including the White House.[41] Newspaper headlines across the nation screamed: 'SAUCER' OUTRAN JET, PILOT REVEALS, JETS CHASE D.C. SKY GHOSTS, and AERIAL WHATZITS BUZZ D.C. AGAIN![42] The public was captivated and books and magazine articles began to appear claiming that the government knew that the unknown objects were interplanetary craft but was hiding the truth from the public. The media generated a lot of interest and excitement and the Air Force was deluged with requests for more information on flying saucers.[43] This was a big problem for the national security state.

Subsequently, in 1953, the CIA convened a panel of high-powered scientists to "study" the UFO problem and recommend policy. At least that's the way the Robertson Panel was billed. The record shows that the committee, chaired by the prestigious physicist H.P. Robertson, a Department of Defense director and covert CIA agent, was actually a tightly scripted play staged to justify a policy that had been predetermined.[44]

The Robertson Panel episode was filled with intrigue, which will be explored in greater detail in a subsequent chapter. When all was said and done, the panel concluded that UFOs were not a threat to national security, but UFO reports were. The antidote they recommended was a covert mass media campaign to debunk flying saucers, which had captured the imagination of the public. The final report advised that, "…[N}ational security agencies take immediate steps to strip the Unidentified Flying Objects of the special status they have been given and the aura of mystery they have unfortunately acquired."[45]

Accomplishing this goal meant organizing a massive propaganda campaign. "The debunking aim would result in reduction in public interest in 'flying saucers' which today evokes a strong emotional reaction. This education could be accomplished by mass media such as television, motion pictures, and popular articles," wrote Robertson's cache of military-industrial complex scientists.[46] What's more, they advocated the use of public figures including celebrities, scientists, amateur astronomers and psychologists who could help sway public opinion. It is particularly revealing that the panel made an emphasis of employing the use of psychological methods to achieve its goals.

Simply put, the Robertson Panel plan was to convince the public that the flying saucers that had captured its imagination were nothing more than a product of the imagination- an illusion.

There is no doubt that the Robertson Panel strategy was implemented. In 1966, CBS aired a "documentary" entitled, *UFOs: Friend, Foe or Fantasy*, narrated by Walter Cronkite that debunked UFOs just as the panel recommended. This was not by chance. Proof was discovered in the Smithsonian Institute archives in a letter written by one of the Robertson scientists, Thornton Page, who wrote that he "helped organize the CBS TV show around the Robertson Panel conclusions."[47]

The panel's "recommendations" for a massive propaganda campaign along with smoking gun evidence that the policy had been put into action meant that the Cronkite episode was likely just the tip of the iceberg. And so it appears.

Science journalist Terry Hansen author of *The Missing Times: News Media Complicity in the UFO Cover-up*, uncovered further evidence of the disinformation campaign during his decades long career covering the UFO phenomenon. Hansen documented the glaring difference between local and national elite media organizations in their coverage of the subject. UFO Stories reported at the local or regional level were suppressed or given short shrift by the elite national news media, which has a history of cooperating with the government on issues of national security.

The Montana UFO encounters of 1975 were a dramatic example. Locals including police and military personnel reported UFOs over *nuclear missile silos*. Like the green fireball UFOs that plagued Los Alamos in 1950, the Montana nuclear missile site UFOs represented a serious national security threat. And much like the green fireballs, such sightings were a regular occurrence. By late 1975 there had been over 130 incidents, yet the national media looked the other way. Hansen likened the events to a war that no one bothered to cover. The story was reported locally, but completely ignored by the elite national news organizations until years afterwards when the first paper with national circulation to report on it was the *National Enquirer*.[48]

The strange episode did not appear to be happenstance. Hansen discovered a pattern in the coverage of UFO sightings. Big media institutions ignored UFO reports at the same time that the infamous tabloid news rag made them front page headlines. In fact, Hansen's research led him to conclude that the *National Enquirer* may have been a psychological warfare tool created for the purpose of discrediting the UFO phenomenon and that the pattern of coverage was the result of a disinformation campaign like the one set in motion by the Robertson Panel.

Hansen found that the *National Enquirer* was started by former CIA agent Generoso 'Gene' Pope, Jr., son of an influential Italian American newspaper publisher. Pope spent a year in the psychological warfare unit before "leaving" the agency to found the *Enquirer* in 1952 at the age of twenty-five. He had powerful political connections, including ties to organized crime. Rumor had it that the mob loaned Pope the money to get the venture off the ground, but Hansen wasn't so sure. Whoever bankrolled Pope got their money's worth. When a large supermarket chain was reluctant to carry the *National Enquirer*, Pope arranged a tour of the White House for its executives that included a personal chat with President Nixon. It goes without saying that the average businessman would never be able to call upon the president of the United States to help close a deal, much less the would-be purveyor of such a tawdry and disreputable publication, unless of course, the paper served a purpose. Given Pope's shady source of funding, his high level political connections, his background with the CIA and its relationship with the Mafia, Hansen came to believe it likely that the CIA was ultimately the source of funding for the paper and that Pope may have been carrying out an assignment as a deep cover agent.[49]

For a businessman, Gene Pope had an unusual and unprofitable interest in UFOs, which drove down sales. Issues featuring UFO headlines never sold as well as those featuring celebrities, scandals and the usual fare. Nonetheless, Pope spared no expense in dispatching reporter Bob Pratt all over the globe to cover UFOs, leading Hansen to believe that Pope had an ulterior motive.[50] In light of the circumstances, it's difficult not to connect the dots. A "former" agent of the CIA's psychological warfare unit founded the *National Enquirer* shortly before the convening of the Robertson Panel and its preordained conclusions. Subsequently, one can't help but suspect that the *National Enquirer* was a product of the same high-level policy decision that led to the staging of the Robertson Panel and that Gene Pope was acting in his role of CIA psychological warfare agent despite having officially left the agency. Anyone familiar with the spy game is undoubtedly aware that the terms of employment are more in line with that of the Sopranos than they are with labor laws. As Joe Pesci's character says in the movie JFK, once you join the agency, you're in for life. Although there is no proof that Pope was acting on behalf of the CIA when he founded and operated the *Enquirer* and efforts to acquire government documents on Pope have been blocked on account of national security, there are compelling reasons to believe this was indeed the case. According to Hansen, "Any way you look at it, there are these ties between the *National Enquirer* and the intelligence community."[51]

Use of the *National Enquirer* as a psychological warfare tool is consistent with the Robertson Panel recommendations to use "popular articles" as part of its mass media debunking strategy along with the advice of "psychologists familiar with mass psychology." UFO reports published in the *National Enquirer* were tainted by their association with the sensationalistic garbage for which the rag was famous. "This psychological warfare method would effectively discredit the story once and for all because *no one* in the American intelligentsia takes the tabloids seriously. Stories that appear in the tabloids are nearly always seen as fabrications, which they often are. If an independent minded reporter tried to follow up on the story, no reputable publication would print it because of its roots in the tabloid press," explained Hansen,[52] whose research indicated that the UFO stories published in the *National Enquirer* were mostly true, even providing researchers with enough facts to generate successful Freedom of Information Act requests.[53]

It is most telling that what we might call the *National Enquirer* strategy appears to have been used to obscure the truth about the most infamous case in UFO history. When the Roswell story broke in 1980 after Jesse Marcel started to talk, the *Enquirer* was all over the story while the mainstream media remained steadfastly silent.[54] This is consistent with the disinformation campaign the government has waged against the Roswell Incident since 1947, the Robertson Panel mass media debunking campaign recommendations and the theory that the *National Enquirer* was used as a psychological warfare tool to camouflage UFOs as nothing more than flights of fancy.

The evidence for a disinformation campaign in regards to UFOs in general and Roswell in particular is clear. The extent of the campaign is somewhat less certain and largely circumstantial as is the case with the Majestic Documents and the *National Enquirer*, nevertheless, the evidence is compelling, especially in light of the historical record. If the government's disinformation campaign really used psychological warfare methods to disguise the truth with lies, then there should be independent evidence of the truth to be found- and there is. Regardless of the Enquirer's true motive for sacrificing profits to cover the UFO phenomenon or whether some of the Majestic Documents are authentic or not, the historical record shows that UFOs are real, an extraterrestrial craft really did crash at Roswell and there was a Top Secret group charged with managing the aftermath of the Roswell Incident.

One such example of independent evidence for Majestic-12 is a memo written by Canadian government official Wilbert Smith. While in the U.S. on business in 1950, Smith, an engineer, met with Robert Sarbacher, a physicist on the U.S. Defense Department Research and Development board headed by Vannevar Bush. Flying saucers were a hot topic of discussion during the meeting. Specifically, Smith had an interest in a book claiming that government scientists had recovered and analyzed crashed extraterrestrial spacecraft in the American southwest. Sarbacher told Smith that although the book *Behind the Flying Saucers* had been dismissed as a hoax, the facts were, to a significant extent, correct.

Smith wrote a Top Secret memo about the meeting. The memo stated that flying saucers were indeed real, their method of operation was unknown, the entire subject was the most classified secret in the U.S. government - higher than the H-bomb - and the whole matter, considered to be of tremendous significance, was *being studied by a Top Secret group led by Vannevar Bush.* [55] This was the same story told by the Majestic Documents.

UFO researchers have firmly established the fact of the Smith memo. A transcript of the conversation was found in Smith's papers after his death and Sarbacher confirmed the meeting and subsequent discussion about the crash of alien spacecraft before his death. The Top Secret memo written by Smith is a matter of historical record.

There are hints of a secret investigation throughout UFO history. Some evidence is explicit, like the so-called Cutler-Twining memo discovered in the National Archives that refers to an MJ-12 Special Studies Project.[56] And some evidence is explosive like *The Day After Roswell*, written by then eighty-four year old whistleblower Col. Philip J. Corso who died shortly after publication.

Corso wrote about his role in the effort to reverse engineer extraterrestrial artifacts recovered in Roswell, which was rooted in the Majestic-12 operation. In fact, a thorough review of UFO history, which will follow in a subsequent chapter, reveals ample support for Majestic-12, or a group very much like it, independently of the Majestic Documents. In other words, regardless of the document's murky provenance or its probable intended purpose as disinformation, the story that it tells is basically true. Many of the men listed in the Majestic Documents roster played key roles in UFO history, including Harvard professor Donald Menzel, who was not known to be an intelligence agent until the appearance of the documents focused research efforts on him.

World War II saw leading scientists assume starring roles in a military-industrial complex increasingly reliant on technological superiority to maintain its strategic advantage. The Roswell Incident further reinforced the importance of such world-renowned scientists. As Stanton Friedman noted, scientists who worked on the Manhattan Project likely would have been part of a secret operation regarding the crash of an extraterrestrial spacecraft.[57] Such scientists were not only the best and brightest, the most capable of understanding such advanced technology, they were also used to keeping secrets. Their work on UFOs would be hidden from public view in the dark world of compartmentalized military-industrial complex defense research just like their work on the atomic bomb. This otherworldly aspect of R & D remains largely unknown and officially unacknowledged. Nevertheless, men such as Vannevar Bush, Detlev Bronk, Lloyd Berkner, Robert Oppenheimer, Edward Teller and others involved in the Manhattan Project and related super secret military research operations also surface in the murky world of UFO matters and are featured most prominently in the Majestic Documents.[58]

Out of context, the story of Fermi's paradox seems to be a quaint anecdote about a group of prestigious scientists chewing the fat over lunch about a pop culture fad called flying saucers. The same story placed in its true context becomes somewhat incongruous. Why would scientists who had experienced frequent UFO sightings and held high-level meetings to discuss them dismiss the possibility that flying saucers could be real, especially since the meetings and discussions about the Los Alamos UFOs led to speculation about extraterrestrial spacecraft in orbit? At the very least, one would expect such scientists to be open to the possibility that flying saucers might actually be extraterrestrial craft. Under such circumstances one can't help but suspect that the true nature and significance of the Fermi paradox lunchtime discussion was mischaracterized, or at the very least, trivialized.

It's another thing altogether if the Manhattan Project scientists had knowledge of the Roswell Incident. It's not known if any of the men of the Fermi lunch discussion group were in on the secret, but some were more likely than others to have known because of the system of compartmented information used in military intelligence.

In order to limit the damage that could be done by spies, Vannevar Bush implemented a system of compartmentalization for the Manhattan Project that made classified national security information available only if one had a need to know in order to perform one's job.[59] In this system, only those at the top had full knowledge of a project or operation. Of the four men who took part in the Fermi lunch discussion, Edward "father of the hydrogen bomb" Teller, appears most likely to have had knowledge of Roswell given his elite status among Manhattan Project scientists and his intimate involvement with the UFO phenomenon including the green fireball UFO mystery in the skies over Los Alamos and other sensitive military installations in New Mexico. Further, Teller was a fanatical proponent of the SDI (Strategic Defense Initiative) "Star Wars" missile defense system, which, according to multiple sources, is a cover for a weapons system designed primarily to target and destroy alien vehicles entering the atmosphere rather than a shield against nuclear weapons. Teller has even been identified as a latter day member of Majestic-12 by defense and aerospace industry insiders.[60] It is also interesting to note that some of the Majestic Documents have been attributed to Teller, although they appear to be among the documents that are fabrications. One can't help but speculate that bogus Majestic Documents bearing Teller's name might have been the result of an effort to provide cover for him in light of all the suspicions regarding his involvement with Majestic-12 and his association with the operation to back-engineer alien technology. Regardless of the fake documents, many reasons remain to suspect that Teller might have known the truth about the Roswell Incident. Conversely, there is little reason to suspect that anyone else in the Fermi lunch group had knowledge of Roswell beyond the fact that they were Manhattan Project scientists.

If the Roswell Incident were common knowledge among the Fermi lunch group then the discussion of the "evidence for flying saucers" would have been very different. However, if only Teller were privy to Operation Majestic-12 and its objectives, it would have been standard operating procedure for him to participate in the discussion as if the crash at Roswell had never happened. Whatever the case, the debate was based on the premise that flying saucers weren't real, according to Teller. The group rejected the idea that flying saucers might be extraterrestrial because of the limitations of light speed and the great distances between the stars, he said. In other words, the Fermi group's guiding principle was the well-known and, as will be seen, highly-flawed axiom: *It can't be; therefore it isn't.* Even so, Fermi made a compelling argument that extraterrestrial visitation should be real, considering it far more likely that the speed of light could be breached than Teller.[61] Whether idle chitchat or something else altogether, the discussion famously inspired his series of calculations that imply the galaxy should have already been colonized.

SUMMARY AND CONCLUSIONS

One can't help but appreciate the irony that flying saucers, which inspired the realization that the galaxy should be occupied by a much older, much more advanced interstellar civilization, were rejected as evidence of such civilization. In spite of Fermi's calculations about the size and age of the universe, which strongly indicate that life evolved elsewhere long before we did, he and his colleagues allegedly decided that extraterrestrial flying saucers simply couldn't be real based on the belief that interstellar travel was probably impossible, which might actually say more about the limitations of our science and understanding of nature rather than the limitations imposed by the speed of light.

It is revealing that the Fermi gang's discussion of flying saucers centered on the possibility that they were extraterrestrial as opposed to a natural phenomenon or some form of secret terrestrial technology. Many mistakenly assume that if something out of the ordinary has been seen in the sky that it is most likely explainable by classified development of new technology. The Manhattan Project scientists were uniquely qualified to evaluate the state of technological progress against UFO reports, which often include maneuvers or flight characteristics that shouldn't be possible according to our understanding of physics or should be lethal to any life form aboard the craft. Many also mistakenly assume that observations of such anomalous phenomena are probably in error. The Manhattan Project scientists could not take refuge in this assumption because they had personally made such observations. They had seen the so-called green fireball UFOs make hairpin turns at impossible speeds without making a sound. Teller himself speculated about some form of optical technology to explain the sightings at a meeting held in 1949, one year before the infamous Fermi lunch discussion.

In light of the circumstances one can't help but wonder how convinced the Fermi group was of its own conclusions given that there was no mention of a discussion of alternative explanations for UFO sightings. Fermi even challenged the cornerstone of the argument against extraterrestrial UFOs. Naturally, one can't help but wonder if Fermi was skeptical of the dogma that interstellar travel was essentially impossible and, by extension, UFOs couldn't be extraterrestrial. Certainly, if one concludes, as Fermi did, that superior extraterrestrial civilizations should be zipping about the galaxy and that evidence to this effect should exist, one might consider that reports of unknown, high-performance, highly anomalous craft might be such evidence regardless of our inability to conceive of how interstellar travel can be accomplished. However, it does not appear that Fermi's revelation caused his colleagues to reconsider the possibility that UFOs might be extraterrestrial.

Even if one can somehow dismiss reports about green fireball UFOs, orbiting spacecraft and the Roswell Incident, there's proof that the Air Force knew such objects were real thanks to a secret Air Force memo declassified in 1967 known as the Twining letter. In 1947, shortly after the Roswell Incident, Gen. Nathan Twining, head of the Air Material Command and alleged Majestic-12 member, wrote the memo in answer to Gen. George Schulgen's inquiry about UFOs. Twining flatly stated in no uncertain terms that flying disks were "real and not visionary or fictitious."[62] He described the objects as metallic, disc or cigar-shaped, with a dome on top, capable of extreme rates of maneuver. In short, an official document of the U.S. government clearly validates flying saucer reports, thus giving credence to green fireball UFOs, orbiting spacecraft, Roswell and all.

If extraterrestrial spacecraft exist, as it appears, then there is no Fermi's paradox and the debate about whether or not we're alone in the cosmos is superseded by the question of whether or not the existence of extraterrestrial craft does in fact mean that the galaxy has been colonized. The implications of such a proposition are vast. One must recognize the concept of extraterrestrial visitation as quaint. The idea that we are simply being visited from elsewhere out of scientific curiosity or space tourism is entirely inadequate. If the galaxy has been colonized, an extraterrestrial presence more likely signals occupation of some sort. One can easily imagine the great difficulty such a revelation would present to the authorities who likely do not understand the situation well enough to inform the public. There are a myriad of issues that could cause great societal stress depending on the exact nature of our relationship to the greater interstellar civilization. Our collective worldview hasn't experienced such a shock since the flat Earth days before the Galileo revolution when the Earth was thought to be the center of the universe around which everything else revolved. In fact, this would likely be the greatest existential shock of all time.

In debating the Fermi paradox, some have argued that the absence of evidence for extraterrestrials is insufficient proof that we are alone in the universe. Conversely, one must consider that the existence of extraterrestrial craft is equally insufficient to conclude that the galaxy has been colonized. It's certainly a matter for debate. As will be seen in the following pages, there are many aspects of the UFO phenomenon that are difficult to resolve in terms of extraterrestrial visitation that come into focus through the lens of interstellar civilization. For example, the sheer volume of UFO sightings, which amounted to thousands per year, made little sense in terms of extraterrestrial visitation and caused famed Air Force Project Blue Book astronomer J. Allen Hynek and protégé Jacques Vallee to consider an alternative to the Extraterrestrial hypothesis that included intelligences from other dimensions of reality.[63] But heavy traffic fits the model of interstellar civilization. If an advanced galactic society has spread throughout the cosmos and has bases or colonies in the local neighborhood, which in all probability includes Earth, one would expect such regular traffic.

In the final analysis, the Fermi paradox is the product of an informal discussion that resulted in rather profound conclusions. It is important to note that the Fermi group's premise that UFOs weren't real was not the result of a scientific study or empirical process. The true value of Fermi's epiphany resides not in its judgment against UFOs or its implication that we are alone in the universe, but in the realization that the galaxy should be occupied by an older and much more advanced interstellar civilization. In light of the astonishing implications of Fermi's epiphany, the obvious statement, to use Teller's parlance, would be that the UFO phenomenon demands more than a casual discussion or cursory investigation. Clearly, a thorough review of UFO evidence over the last 60 years, which will follow in subsequent chapters, is in order. Ultimately, the message of Fermi's paradox is that if the core of the UFO phenomenon is indeed extraterrestrial, it is likely the result of an interstellar civilization that has spread among the stars and a sign that the galaxy has been colonized.

CHAPTER 2

ROSWELL

The evidence points to the fact Roswell was a real incident, and that indeed an alien craft did crash, and that material was recovered from that crash site.
— **Astronaut Edgar Mitchell, 1997**

It is my thesis that flying saucers are real and that they are space ships from another solar system. I think that they possibly manned by intelligent observers who are members of a race that may have been investigating our earth for centuries. I think that they possibly have been sent out to conduct systematic long-range investigations, first of men, animals, vegetation, and more recently of atomic centers, armaments and centers of armament production.
— **Professor Hermann Oberth, 1954**

LIGHTSPEED AND BEYOND

In their recollections of the lunchtime conversation in 1950 that led to the Fermi Paradox, Konopinski and Teller relate two very revealing anecdotes. In the first, Konopinski recalls that when he joined the group the discussion was about flying saucers, which evoked the memory of a cartoon he had just seen in New Yorker magazine. The cartoon was a comical attempt to explain the disappearance of public trashcans in New York City. The panel depicted a parade of little green men carrying trashcans up a ramp and into a flying saucer. Fermi amused Konopinski with the comment that it was a reasonable theory since it accounted for two separate phenomena: flying saucer reports and the disappearance of the trashcans.

Teller, on the other hand, began his account of the day's conversation with the proclamation that they had been talking about flying saucers and the obvious statement that they were not real. The two anecdotes illustrate how science is and isn't supposed to work. Fermi jokingly demonstrates the logic and reason of an objective and unbiased mind, while Teller's statement, which, to be fair, was a perfectly natural assumption for a scientist at the time, nonetheless reflects prejudicial bias. Not to confuse the issue, speculation is a fair practice but not to be mistaken for actual scientific fact. It's a virtual certainty that upon investigation an alternative explanation would be found for the disappearing trashcans and, in 1950, one would have certainly expected that an alternative explanation for reports of flying saucers would be found. However, this did not happen.

In the time period it was generally agreed upon that the speed of light was an absolute limit that made the great distances between the stars an insurmountable barrier. Interstellar travel was thought to be impossible. This was viewed as obvious by anyone with an understanding of Einstein and special relativity. Scientists assumed that people who reported flying saucers were simply mistaken. With the exception of Earth, our solar system appears quite inhospitable to life. Extraterrestrial visitors just couldn't be. Today, with theories about wormholes, superstrings, extra dimensions, time travel, etc., belief in the speed of light as an absolute limit is fading. The notion of interstellar travel is still, as Edgar Mitchell has observed, a "thorny" issue, but in 1950 the light speed limit was generally accepted as an ironclad argument against the ETH. Complicating matters, if flying saucers were real and were not from Earth then many of our scientific, philosophical and religious beliefs were incomplete at best, if not flat-out wrong. In light of the circumstances, it is easy to understand why the idea of extraterrestrial spacecraft would be dismissed out of hand absent hard evidence.

It is intriguing that the Fermi lunchtime discussion included a debate between Fermi and Teller over just such hard evidence of faster-than-light travel. Specifically, Fermi challenged Teller on the possibility that unambiguous evidence of an object that could exceed the speed of light would be discovered "within ten years."[1] Teller set the odds at 10^{-6}, or about a gazillion-to-one in other words, while Fermi opted for the much more likely figure of ten percent. The difference between Teller's estimate and Fermi's is as puzzling as it is striking. Fermi's figure bordered on scientific heresy, so much so that it amounted to a subtle suggestion that the ultimate law could be broken.

In light of the circumstances, one can't help but ponder the meaning of Fermi's estimate in conjunction with his epiphany that we should see evidence of extraterrestrial activity. Was Fermi simply playing the contrarian pushing back against his colleague's skepticism and the popular assumption that: It can't be; therefore it isn't? Or were his arguments a reflection of a privately held belief that UFOs might be extraterrestrial? Did Fermi have knowledge of the Roswell Incident? Ten years is a very specific and short time period for an utterly fantastic and revolutionary, paradigm-busting, discovery. If one had secret knowledge of the recovery of an extraterrestrial spacecraft at Roswell three years prior to the discussion, one might speculate that the discovery would eventually become common knowledge within a reasonable time period. Or could the debate between Fermi and Teller have been an inside joke between colleagues? Were they speaking in code? Was the unlikely exchange merely the product of whimsy during a casual discussion? Whatever the case, it's worth noting that Teller claimed to be much more pessimistic than Fermi about the prospects for a superluminal artifact, yet he may have actually known of the existence of just such an object.

GROUND ZERO

Flying saucers became a public sensation in late June 1947 when pilot Kenneth Arnold saw nine unidentified objects flying in formation at a high rate of speed near Mount Rainier, Washington. There'd been other sightings that month but it was Arnold's that crystallized the idea of the mysterious craft thanks to his observation that they flew like a saucer skipping across water. Newspapers confused his description of the craft's flight motion with its appearance and the term "flying saucer" was born.

At first, most thought the strange craft were likely secret guided missiles or experimental military aircraft of some sort. No one considered the possibility of visitors from other planets.[2] Just when speculation about ETs began is unknown, but it's possible it started in the wake of the Roswell Incident, which happened about two weeks after the Arnold sighting.

Although officially regarded as an urban legend, the Roswell story is well known. Many important books have been written about Roswell, including *The Roswell Incident* by Charles Berlitz and Bill Moore, *Crash at Corona* by Stanton Friedman and Don Berliner, *Witness to Roswell* by Thomas Carey and Don Schmitt and perhaps the most important of all, *The Day After Roswell* by Col. Philip Corso and Bill Birnes.

The investigation that began when Jesse Marcel could no longer stay silent has now amassed several hundred first, second, and third-hand witnesses. [3] Because military intelligence operates on compartmented information – one only has access to information necessary to perform one's job – Roswell witness testimony is like a jigsaw puzzle. The picture assembled by researchers shows the military cover-up of the recovery of a crashed extraterrestrial craft and its transport from a hangar in Roswell Army Air Field to the Air Technical Intelligence Center at Wright Field in Dayton, Ohio.

The case for UFO reality doesn't revolve around a single event, but the Roswell Incident is central to understanding the UFO phenomenon and the secrecy and denial that come with it. UFO incidents in general are fleeting and ghost-like in that when they are over there is usually nothing left but the memories and accounts of astonished eyewitnesses, which are open to interpretation. Sometimes there is radar evidence as well as physical trace evidence, photos and video, but they too are subject to interpretation. On the other hand, the Roswell Incident, with its crashed disk, debris field and alien bodies, leaves no such ambiguity. After Roswell, the core nature of the UFO phenomenon was no longer in doubt. For all intents and purposes, the Roswell Incident is the Rosetta stone of ufology.

The story unfolded on Sunday July 6, 1947 when rancher Mac Brazel brought strange debris to the attention of the Roswell Sheriff's office and eventually Roswell Army Air Field. Air intelligence officer Jesse Marcel, then a Captain, and Army Counter Intelligence Corps Captain Sheridan Cavitt accompanied Brazel back to the ranch 75 miles northwest of Roswell to inspect the debris field. Marcel was the head intelligence officer at the world's only atomic bomber squadron, the elite 509th bomb group. He was there in case the wreckage was "ours," and Cavitt, the head of counterintelligence, was sent in the event it was one of "theirs," meaning foreign. [4]

It was immediately obvious to Marcel that what he was looking at was neither "ours" nor "theirs." It was truly foreign, or as he put it, "nothing made on this Earth." [5] The scene of the crash at the ranch actually consisted of two separate sites- a debris field in a pasture and an impact site at a bluff about two miles southeast where bodies were discovered. Marcel reported back to the air base with a carload full of debris. Meantime, reports phoned into the Sheriff's office and fire department by civilians indicated another crash site much closer to Roswell just to the north of town. This site was the final resting site of the flying disk and most of its crew.[6]

Cavitt, who, unlike Marcel, never confessed his true role in the Roswell Incident before his death, made several trips to inspect the wreckage taking with him his underling Master Sergeant Lewis "Bill" Rickett, who became a key witness to Roswell.[7] Rickett's experiences show that Lincoln La Paz had good reason to suspect the green fireballs of Los Alamos were artificial. According to Rickett, the Air Force hired La Paz to determine the speed and trajectory of the flying disc at the time of impact and it was his job to assist La Paz in his investigation. Rickett spent the following month escorting La Paz around New Mexico in the effort reconstruct the crash scene. In the process, they discovered an area where the sand had been turned to glass indicating that something had crashed and skipped off the ground. Apparently unaware that bodies had been recovered, La Paz deduced that the object was an unmanned alien probe from another planet.[8] His testimony is supported by other witnesses who have also reported La Paz was involved with the Roswell Incident.[9]

Rickett's testimony not only placed La Paz at the scene of the Roswell Incident, it helped researchers Schmitt and Cary plot the path of the disc, which exploded over the Foster/Brazel ranch creating the original debris field before impacting at a bluff and spewing more debris, including bodies that were discovered by Brazel. It then skipped back into the air and flew another 30 miles, eventually crashing back to Earth and coming to rest at the third site approximately 40 miles from Roswell.[10] Retrieval operations at both sites followed.

Samples of the exotic wreckage were immediately shipped to Washington D.C.[11] One can only imagine the reactions in officialdom, but human nature being what it is, one would expect that it might not be too different than the townsfolk in Roswell. According to one local resident, news of the crash spread through town like a wildfire. Within a half hour, the news was common knowledge of a population of approximately 25,000 people. Rumors flowed like spirits in local watering holes and gathering spots, but there was no official word. The local radio stations and media were silent. A Serviceman stationed at the base described the mood around town as, "anxious... perhaps scared would better describe it."[12] Certainly, fear would seem a perfectly natural reaction given the astonishing circumstances. Just seven years prior, the Orson Welles radiobroadcast of *War of the Worlds* caused widespread chaos and panic among the public. This precedent is often the focus of speculation about the primary reason for the decision to cover-up the Roswell Incident. There are other, less obvious, reasons that factored into the decision to undertake a whitewash, which will be fully explored in later chapters. Whatever the reasoning, the decision was, in fact, made to cover up and deny the apparent crash of an extraterrestrial spacecraft. The endeavor presented a challenging task. Civilians had discovered the wreckage and alerted the sheriff's department and, in turn, the local radio station. The genie was already out of the bottle, so to speak, and putting it back in was likely going to require extraordinary measures and an unconventional strategy.

On July 8th, two days after Marcel had returned to the RAAF with crash debris that was immediately shipped to Washington, Public Information Officer Walter Haut was directed by Colonel Bill Blanchard to issue a press release announcing that the Army Air Force had come into possession of a flying saucer. Haut did as told and the news hit the wire services including the AP, which quoted the press release in full, igniting media frenzy.[13] The evening edition of the Roswell Daily Record for Tuesday July 8, 1947, carried three front-page stories on the incident with the headlines: *RAAF Captures Flying Saucer On Ranch in Roswell Region.* According to the *New York Times*, within an hour of the original press release, the story began to change.[14]

Blanchard sent Marcel and the crash debris to Wright Field in Ohio.[15] Wright Field was home to the Air Force's Air Technical Intelligence Center, an outfit set up to reverse engineer foreign technology captured on the battlefield. ATIC would later become the Foreign Technology Division.[16]

After takeoff, Marcel's flight was diverted to Fort Worth, Texas. While he was still en route, Blanchard's superior, General Roger Ramey, the Commanding Officer of the Eighth Air Force at Carswell AAF in Fort Worth, began to promote the weather balloon cover story. Ramey gave statements to the press describing the object as a weather balloon three to five hours before Marcel arrived with the wreckage. Meanwhile, the curtain came down on the Roswell Incident enveloping it in a blanket of secrecy.

On the morning of July 8th, hours before the official announcement hit the news that the military had recovered a flying saucer, the Army grabbed Mac Brazel and held him for five days against his will, trashing his civil rights in the process. What's more, Brazel was subjected to harsh interrogation techniques in an apparent attempt to force his cooperation with the weather balloon cover story.[17] Meanwhile, the FCC ordered local radio station KGFL to deep six an interview it had taped with Brazel. Owner George Roberts was told that the station's license would be revoked if it broadcast any portion of the Brazel interview on the grounds that the Roswell Incident was a matter of national security. If there were any doubts about the government's intentions they were erased by Senator Dennis Chavez, who insisted the station comply with the FCC's demands. The threats worked. The station dropped the story and surrendered the recording of the interview with Brazel to the Army.[18]

Behind the scenes, the government did its best to kill its official statement about the recovery of a flying saucer. Military officials raided local news organizations in New Mexico. They confiscated copies of Haut's original press release along with any material that contradicted the weather balloon story.[19] Lydia Sleppy, a secretary at a local radio station, was a first-hand witness. She received an urgent report of the flying saucer crash, little bodies and all, but was prevented from spreading the report any further. She alerted ABC News headquarters in Hollywood to expect a "high bulletin" story, but before she could finish transmitting, the Teletype machine was interrupted by an urgent message from the FBI ordering her to cease all transmissions immediately. The message read: ATTENTION ALBUQUERQUE: DO NOT TRASMIT, REPEAT, DO NOT TRANSMIT THIS MESSAGE. STOP COMMUNICATION IMMEDIATELY. NATIONAL SECURITY MATTER.[20]

Bill Moore, one of the original Roswell researchers, discovered an anecdote that showed just how effective the Pentagon's media strategy was at stuffing the Roswell genie back in its bottle.[21] English actor Hughie Green heard the reports of a flying saucer crash on the radio in July 1947 as he was driving across the country, but the story faded out completely by the time he reached the East Coast.[22]

The gears of the cover-up were in motion when Jesse Marcel arrived in Fort Worth, unaware that he'd been cast to play the leading role in the Army Air Force's weather balloon cover story. Without explanation, Marcel was made to pose with a crumpled weather balloon and ordered into silence by General Roger Ramey as a reporter from the Fort Worth Telegram took pictures.[23] Bewildered, Marcel simply followed orders as Ramey rewrote history. What's more, he was kept out of the press conference that followed the photo op and ordered not to speak to reporters.

At the press conference, Ramey said the whole affair had been caused by the misidentification of a common weather balloon and that the flight scheduled to take the mangled object on to Wright Field had been canceled as a result. This wasn't true. In fact, some of the crash debris had already been shipped to Washington and there would be two more flights carrying more wreckage and the bodies to Fort Worth and ultimately Wright Field.[24]

Although it was true that Marcel's original flight didn't make the trip and Marcel himself was sent back to Roswell, the crash debris that he brought with him was loaded onto another plane destined for Wright Field. Eyewitness testimony about the secret shipment of flying saucer debris is further supported by an FBI memo that refutes Ramey's claim that the flying disk was just a weather balloon.[25]

As the retrieval operation continued in secret, the front page of the July 9th edition of the Roswell Daily Record carried the headline, *General Ramey Empties Roswell Saucer – Ramey Says Disk is a Weather Balloon.* The media blindly accepted Ramey's blatantly absurd explanation. "As far as the press and public were concerned, that was the end of the tale of the crashed 'flying saucer.' No one thought to question why something so commonplace as a weather balloon had caused so much commotion. Or how two officers of an elite AAF unit could possibly have failed to recognize it. Or how this small, flimsy contraption, which could hardly have come to Earth violently, could have strewn its pieces over 'a square mile' of sheep ranch," wrote principal Roswell investigator Stanton Friedman about the weather balloon cover story.[26] In fact, locals really couldn't have made such a mistake. Fallen weather balloons were so common that they were regularly gathered up and deposited in an old water holding tank.[27]

A weather balloon is nothing more than rubber, tin foil, balsa wood, and twine, all commonplace materials. Even a classified Mogul balloon, which the Air Force would eventually substitute for the original weather balloon cover story, was made of the same common, off-the-shelf material that couldn't possibly be mistaken for advanced technology much less an extraterrestrial spaceship.[28] For all intents and purposes, a balloon was a balloon that would have fallen to the ground and lay in a heap like all others that had been retrieved and dumped into the old water tank. It couldn't crash in any true sense of the word. What's more, Mac Brazel had twice before found weather balloons on the ranch and was adamant that what he discovered was no such thing.[29] There was simply no reason to take any special notice of a balloon - any kind of balloon - much less the hysterical reaction to the one alleged to have caused the Roswell Incident.

The Air Force finally admitted that the weather balloon story was a lie in 1994 when it claimed that a top secret Project Mogul balloon train designed to listen for signs of Soviet nuclear testing had somehow crashed near Roswell, causing the infamous incident. In the process of reaching this conclusion, the Air Force ignored most of the evidence, including the date of the crash and the common sense fact that a balloon was still a balloon and could not possibly be mistaken for a spacecraft from another world.[30] Despite its classification, a Mogul balloon was comprised of the same common off-the-shelf material as a weather balloon. It was Mogul's mission that was secret not its components.

In the final analysis, the Mogul balloon cover story suffered from most, if not all, of the same fatal deficiencies as the original weather balloon explanation.[31] In effect, the Air Force replaced one cover story with another and, in the process, admitted that its iconic picture of Major Marcel posing with a weather balloon was a hoax. Simply put, there's no doubt there was a cover-up at Roswell.

Ironically, one of the pictures that resulted from the hoaxed photo op staged by Ramey shows evidence of the original narrative about the crash of a flying saucer- a circumstance that could not have been foreseen by anyone in 1947. In several pictures Ramey appears with Marcel and his Chief of Staff Col. Thomas DuBose, who told investigators that the weather balloon was substituted for the real crash debris in order to "get the press off the General's back."[32] Computer enhancement supports Dubose's testimony.

In one of the photos the text side of a memo in Ramey's left hand is visible. Although his thumb blocks a portion of the message as does folds in the paper, several phrases emerge that hint at the original story, including "acknowledges that a 'disk' is next new find," and "victims of the wreck," which are consistent with the original press release about the crash of a flying saucer. Pictures and analysis can be found at the Roswellproof.com website.[33]

While the march of time made it possible for technology to reach back into the past to provide fresh clues, it also enabled those like Jesse Marcel who might fear harsh reprisals to tell their stories at the end of their lives, or from beyond the grave like RAAF Public Information Officer Walter Haut, whose press release about the recovery of a flying saucer at Roswell in 1947 stunned the world.

Over the years Haut never said anything further about Roswell other than he was ordered to make the infamous press release by his boss Colonel Bill Blanchard. But after his death in 2005, Haut had a lot more to say in a sealed affidavit released by his family and published in Schmidt and Carey's *Witness to Roswell*. In fact, Haut's posthumous testimony is a key piece of the Roswell puzzle.

Marcel's confession alerted researchers to the original press reports, which led them to Mac Brazel and the debris field at the Foster ranch. But as the investigation unfolded eyewitnesses reported another crash site that went unmentioned in the official press release.[34] Haut described how Blanchard ran a Pentagon plan to divert attention away from the more important site just north of Roswell where the alien disk had finally come to rest by acknowledging media reports about the debris field discovered by Brazel at the Foster Ranch.

Haut said Blanchard swore him to secrecy after leading him to see the object recovered from the site just north of town in a heavily guarded hangar. It was a metallic, egg-shaped disk 12 to 15 feet long and wide and about six feet high. Laid out on the floor were little bodies about the size of a ten-year old child with disproportionately large heads. Haut concluded his affidavit stating his belief that the incident was the result of the crash of a spacecraft from another world piloted by an alien crew.[35]

Haut had seen the wreckage and the bodies before they were shipped out of Roswell. Brigadier General Arthur Exon heard rumors about them after they arrived at Wright Field. Despite such secrecy that would compel Haut to withhold the truth from his own family until after his death, rumors continued to circulate within the military about a flying saucer crash. Exon, the highest-ranking officer to confirm the Roswell Incident, was stationed at Wright Field in July 1947 when flights arrived from Roswell on or around the 9th. Although he didn't see the bodies or the crash debris himself, he heard about them from colleagues who told him about "extraordinary" materials they'd analyzed. Exon later flew over the crash site near Roswell and saw deep gouges in the ground at two separate locations where the ET craft slammed into the Earth.[36]

The rumors weren't limited to just New Mexico and Ohio, the two focal points of the recovery operation. In early 1950, the Air Force took note of stories about crashed saucers, little bodies and mysterious metal that appeared in newspapers in Denver and Kansas City. Even *Time Magazine* got into the act in its January 9th issue with rumors about crashed saucers and little humanoid bodies in New Mexico.[37]

The stories don't appear to have gained any traction or made much of an impact. The rumors were like all the previous weather balloons that had fallen out of the sky in New Mexico prior to the Roswell Incident- they caused no reaction beyond the custodial effort to deposit them in a trash bin.

Rumors are one thing; claims of fact are another. In September 1950, columnist Frank Scully published a controversial book called *Behind The Flying Saucers*. Scully claimed that the scientific community had been co-opted by the defense industry and that the U.S. government had indeed recovered a crashed spaceship along with dead alien bodies somewhere in the southwest. The book was immediately dismissed as nonsense by the establishment media.

After an investigation conducted primarily by UFO researchers, the general consensus was that Scully appeared to be the victim of a hoax. At the root of the story was a con man with a significant criminal history hyping a phony oil detection scheme allegedly derived from recovered ET technology. In light of the Roswell Incident, a hoax scenario about a flying saucer crash in the southwest complete with little alien bodies seems more than twisted irony or simple coincidence. In his landmark work, *UFOs & the National Security State*, historian Richard Dolan noted that, "the crashed disc thesis, simply by association with Scully's book remained peripheral to UFO studies."[38] In other words, the Scully "hoax" acted as a deterrent against the investigation of reports of UFO crashes. It achieved the effect of a classic disinformation operation in which the truth is released in a way that renders it unbelievable. If the book was indeed the result of a disinformation campaign, Scully was either a willing participant or a simple dupe exploited by intelligence agents. Whatever the case, the end result was the same- stories involving UFO crash retrievals were disregarded. There were notable few exceptions like UFO researcher Leonard Stringfield, a former Army Air Force intelligence officer whose background made him a trustworthy confidant for those in the military who had participated in UFO crash retrievals or had heard the rumors about them.[39] In general, as a result of Scully's book, the UFO community ignored reports of crashed discs and did not take them seriously until Jesse Marcel and Stanton Friedman broke the spell.

Although it was condemned by mainstream society and rejected by the UFO community, Scully's book was regarded much differently in certain defense industry circles. This was the book that Canadian government official Wilbert Smith inquired about during a visit to the Pentagon with defense research scientist Robert Sarbacher, who confirmed it as accurate about the basic facts. This meeting led Smith to write his famous secret memo that UFOs were the most highly classified secret in the U.S. government administered by a group headed by Manhattan Project scientist Vannevar Bush.

The year 1950 was also the year of the Fermi paradox. Between January when *Time Magazine* published rumors about a flying saucer crash in New Mexico and September when Scully published *Behind the Flying Saucers* Manhattan Project scientists Fermi, Teller, Konopinski and York held their infamous lunchtime debate about the subject. This chain of events suggests that discussion of flying saucers was much more than just a passing fancy among the tight knit community of top defense industry scientists. It appears that knowledge of the real Roswell Incident was somewhat of an open secret within the upper echelons of the military-industrial-complex- at least it appears to have been for elite scientists connected to Vannevar Bush and the Manhattan Project.

The Roswell story went forgotten for thirty years until 1980 when the Friedman investigation resulted in the publication of *The Roswell Incident*. This time the so-called myth didn't die a quick death. Instead, the story gained momentum, so much so, that by 1993 New Mexico congressman Steven Schiff was compelled to make an official inquiry with the Pentagon, which had no interest in telling the truth about Roswell. After getting the "run-around," Schiff accused the Pentagon of stonewalling and asked the General Accounting Office to look into the official records of the Roswell Incident.

The GAO found that all administrative records of Roswell Army Air Field from March 1945 through December 1949 had been destroyed without explanation and, in addition, all outgoing messages from October

1946 through December 1949 were missing. These were permanent records meant to be preserved. In this case, the absence of evidence was evidence of a cover-up.[40]

Schiff, who died of cancer in 1998, said the government couldn't explain why the records were destroyed or who destroyed them. Although his efforts appeared in vain, the pressure that Schiff brought to bear on the Air Force made it admit that its original weather balloon explanation was just a cover story. Unfortunately, instead of coming clean, the Air Force doubled down, essentially swapping one lie with another. This time instead of hoaxed photos, the Air Force cooked up its own report on Roswell, blaming the incident on a Project Mogul balloon train. Project Mogul, as has been shown, was on par with the original cover story and was totally inadequate to explain the Roswell Incident.

The Air Force, which hadn't said anything new about Roswell in almost fifty years, made three official statements between 1993 and 1997. In 1993, the Air Force finally abandoned the weather balloon cover story for the Mogul balloon explanation in its report entitled, *The Roswell Report: Fact Versus Fiction in the New Mexico Desert.* In 1995, it padded and reissued the report and in 1997, the 50th anniversary of the Roswell Incident, it issued what it claimed was its final report, which didn't include the great bulk of the eyewitness testimony about the crash of an alien spacecraft.

The entire case for the Mogul balloon explanation is based on Mack Brazel's retraction, the dubious testimony of CIC officer Sheridan Cavitt and the notes of a scientist who worked on Project Mogul. Other evidence to the contrary was completely ignored.[41]

In Brazel's case, the Air Force used testimony it coerced from him. Brazel, who told friends and relatives he'd been abused and humiliated while held at RAAF, warned his family not to believe what it read about him in the paper. He was made to visit local media outlets, including the *Roswell Daily Record,* under the duress of military escort. It was in this context that he recanted his original statement.[42]

Before he was kidnapped by the military, Brazel told the local authorities he found the wreckage in the first week of July. After his detention, he changed the date to June 14th, a timeframe that lent plausibility to the balloon cover story. Before he was detained, Brazel spoke about "unfortunate little creatures" that died in the crash. Afterwards he made no mention of dead alien bodies and he described the wreckage in terms consistent with Ramey's balloon explanation, although he remained adamant that what he found was not a weather balloon.[43]

The government used the carrot as well as the stick to get Brazel to cooperate. According to friends and neighbors, shortly after his release the dirt-poor rancher bought a brand-new truck, and despite barely having been able to eek out a living, left the Foster Ranch to start his own business much nearer to his home in Tularosa, New Mexico. In short, it seems that Mac Brazel, who remained silent about the Roswell Incident until his death, was bribed as well as threatened. Rumors were that his employers at the Foster Ranch were also paid for their cooperation.[44]

The Air Force's other star witness, CIC officer Sheridan Cavitt, was best known to civilian Roswell investigators as a hostile witness. Marcel said Cavitt was with him at the debris field, but Cavitt denied any involvement. In fact, he denied ever having been stationed at Roswell. But that was a lie. After being confronted with proof that he had been at RAAF, Cavitt denied being there at the time of the incident. But that was another lie. After once again being shown proof to the contrary, Cavitt admitted that he'd been there but didn't remember what happened. However, when questioned by Air Force investigators preparing to foist the 1993 Mogul balloon report upon the world, Cavitt's memory suddenly became crystal clear. He admitted that he had been to the debris field and was involved in the recovery of a Mogul balloon.[45] Although Cavitt never recanted before he died, there are signs that he at least considered coming clean. Friends and family begged him to tell the truth before it was too late but the most that he would ever say was that he wasn't ready. His wife explained to civilian investigators Schmitt and Carey that he was chosen for his assignments because of his ability to keep secrets.[46] Cavitt completed his mission and took the secret to his grave.

Regardless of Cavitt's special superpower to maintain a cover story to the exclusion of all other considerations, the Air Force's explanation for the Roswell Incident is very obviously a transparent lie. The Air Force relied upon a media compliant on issues of national security and the sheer force of its authority to carry the day. How else can one explain the rubber-stamp acceptance of the Mogul balloon explanation? Historian Richard Dolan noted 10 serious flaws in the Air Force's latest balloon theory, each one an indictment all on its own. Collectively, these flaws constituted an airtight case against the Air Force's "theories," which were obviously nothing more than self-serving lies.[47]

If there was any remaining doubt about the absurdity of the government's claims about Roswell, it was dispelled by the Air Force's final official report released in 1997 entitled *The Roswell Report: Case Closed*. In the report, the Air Force argued that eyewitness accounts of child-sized alien bodies recovered at crash sites near Roswell were actually crash test dummies dropped from high altitude in experiments that laid the groundwork for manned space flight. The Air Force hyped this explanation despite the fact that the six-foot tall adult-sized mannequins in question were not in use for a decade after the Roswell Incident and were never dropped in the vicinity of the crash sites. To account for the disparity between the dates, the Air Force spokesman explained to the press that witnesses were suffering from "time compression," a psychological effect that distorts one's memory over the years causing it to become compressed and leading one to confuse dates- in this case, leading such witnesses to connect human-looking mannequins used in the late 1950s with the Roswell Incident that occurred in 1947.[48] Curiously, the Air Force did not have a similar body-compression theory to explain the disparity between the eyewitness accounts of child-sized aliens and the adult-sized crash test dummies.

If the Air Force's arguments were thin at first glance, they became transparent when put under the microscope. To make its case, the Air Force contradicted its own experts. Project High Dive officer, Lt. Col. Raymond Madison told the Associated Press that there was no way that simple mannequins could have been mistaken for aliens. He said each was stamped "property of the Air Force" with a reward notice. Not even the skeptics have embraced the story.[49]

When the Air Force rolled out its crash test dummy explanation it was so implausible that even its own sycophantic press reacted with guffaws of laughter - a natural reaction perhaps - nevertheless, the mainstream media dutifully reported the Air Force's gospel despite its involuntary bellyaches.

The Air Force huffed and puffed and claimed that the case was closed, but the 50th anniversary of the Roswell Incident brought with it another, much different disclosure from a key military-industrial complex insider whose story opened a window into Roswell from the inside. Much like the posthumous affidavit of RAAF Public Information Officer Walter Haut revealed an inside account of the process that led to the original Roswell press release heard around the world, Col. Phillip J. Corso's memoirs provided a view of the Roswell Incident from inside the military-industrial complex, Majestic-12 and the cover-up.

THE DAY AFTER ROSWELL: AN INSIDER ACCOUNT

In 1997, retired Army Colonel Phillip J. Corso blew the whistle on the Roswell UFO cover-up with the *New York Times* bestseller, *The Day After Roswell*, a bombshell disclosure about his role in a secret program to reverse-engineer alien technology recovered at Roswell.

Corso, who died not long after publication, had an impressive resume. He was an officer during World War II, an intelligence officer during the Korean War on General Douglas MacArthur's staff, a four-year member of President Eisenhower's National Security Council staff and the head of Foreign Technology in Army Research and Development in the 1960s. He retired with nineteen medals and ribbons and served as National Security consultant to Senators Strom Thurmond and James Eastland.[50]

One would expect the publication of such a book by a former Pentagon official with Corso's background and credentials to be controversial- and it was. However, as it seems with all things ufological, events unfolded in a manner somewhat contrary to expectations.

Weeks before the book hit the shelves, controversy erupted over its foreword written by Senator Strom Thurmond, who lavished Corso with high praise. "The Colonel had a great deal of credibility and expertise not only as a military officer but also in the fields of intelligence and national security," said Thurmond of his decision to hire Corso back in the 60s.[51] When word of the book and its endorsement by the powerful Senator became public, Thurmond's staff quickly disavowed it, alleging that the Senator was led to believe he was contributing a foreword for an autobiography and not an exposé about the government's UFO cover-up.[52] "I know of no such 'cover-up' and do not believe one existed," said Thurmond in an official statement implying that Corso had snookered him into lending credibility to the incredible, which he knew would not be forthcoming if the Senator was aware that the subject was going to be Roswell and the UFO cover-up.[53]

Liz Hartman, director of publicity for Pocket Books, a division of Simon & Schuster, rebuked Thurmond's claims in placing blame for any confusion over the book's topic on his office and his staff. "We absolutely stand by the book," said Hartman.[54]

The incident was seen as a major embarrassment for the senior Senator, who would die six years later. Yet, the controversy over the foreword may have actually spared Thurmond a great deal more difficulty. By the time it hit the shelves, *The Day After Roswell* had been tarnished. The mainstream media treated the story as if it were a joke and no one seemed to notice that the Senator's name also appeared in the pages following the foreword. According to Corso, Thurmond and his boss, General Arthur Trudeau, were old friends. He would often find the Senator in Trudeau's office and on these occasions, Roswell was a topic of discussion.[55] Corso made it clear that Thurmond was in on the secret as well as the ongoing efforts to reverse engineer alien technology. The press, however, did not follow up and Thurmond never faced any further questions about *The Day After Roswell.*

The mere allegation cast doubt on Corso's story. Skeptics, debunkers and even many UFO researchers rejected him as a genuine whistleblower because of the accusation that he acted unethically in pulling a 'bait and switch' on Senator Thurmond. However, a 1999 French UFO study known as the COMETA report, conducted by the Institute of Higher Studies for National Defense, a government-financed strategic planning agency comprised of high level officials, including retired generals, raised a third possibility that the entire affair could've been part of an intelligence operation written about by Corso in the book. COMETA said, "The author [Corso] allegedly had not told him [Thurmond] that the book was about UFOs... But it is difficult to believe that the foreword writer, the third in line in the U.S. government to succeed the President, and the publisher, Simon & Schuster, were not acting in full knowledge of the facts at the time of the first printing."[56]

In 2001, COMETA's suspicions gained steam when *UFO magazine* published the release form signed by Senator Thurmond in its October issue. According to the terms stated in the release, Corso had the "irrevocable right and permission to use and to publish the material described below, in any and all editions of the book presently entitled Roswell Book."[57]

The release made it clear that the book was about Roswell, although it hadn't received its final title at the time. Regardless, Corso critics, which included ufologists Kevin Randle and Stanton Friedman, held firm in their opinions despite the hard evidence to the contrary. Karl Pflock, a CIA intelligence officer who was a well-known Roswell debunker, attempted to cast doubt on the validity of the release form. He had previously written a book called, *Roswell: Inconvenient Facts and the Will to Believe* in which he went to great lengths to debunk the ET crash, including Corso, in favor of the Air Force's Top Secret Balloon story.

Pflock claimed that *UFO magazine*, published by Corso's co-author Bill Birnes, hoaxed the release form. He claimed that Thurmond's copy was blank where the title 'Roswell Book' had been added to the version published by *UFO magazine*.[58] Even if true, it's not clear how a blank release signed by Thurmond helped his case that he and his staff believed they were providing a forward for a memoir based on Corso's conventional military career called, *I Walked With Giants*. The idea that the Senator would sign, in effect, a 'blank check' seems highly unlikely given his stature and the expectation of due diligence by the staff of such a high office. Again, as the report emphasized, considering the parties involved, the claim of ignorance by the Thurmond office is implausible at best. One suspects that if there had been any Photoshop chicanery, the CYA shoe was likely on the other foot. Whatever the case, Senator Thurmond's office withdrew authorization of the foreword and it has not been published in any subsequent printings of *The Day After Roswell*.[59] Nevertheless, COMETA found Corso's "remarkable" career along with Senator Thurmond's tribute to be significant despite the controversy. It's unfortunate that readers of future editions will not have the opportunity to weigh the Senator's words which conclude, "We should all be grateful that there are men and women like Colonel Corso-people who are willing to dedicate their lives to serving the nation and protecting the ideals we all hold dear- and we should honor the sacrifices they have made in their careers and in their lives."

THE 'FOREIGN' TECHNOLOGY DESK

Corso began his career in the military as a draftee out of Pennsylvania. He was chosen for Officer Candidate School and soon found himself embroiled in the Second World War in command of an intelligence unit in allied-occupied Europe where he oversaw the establishment of civilian government in Rome.[60] He would go on to serve on the staff of General Douglas MacArthur during the Korean War as Chief of Special Projects in 1950. He was in charge of tracking POW camps and would later testify in front of Congress about POWs that had been left behind by the government.[61] In 1953, Corso joined Eisenhower's National Security Council staff at the White House and served for four years before leaving to become the Battalion Commander at White Sands Missile Range.

In 1961, Corso became head of the Foreign Technology desk under General Arthur Trudeau at the Pentagon. It was during this period that he was assigned the task of exploiting the extraterrestrial technology recovered at Roswell. He would eventually conclude his career in military intelligence after his tenure in Foreign Technology.

After leaving the military, he became an aid and national security consultant to Senators Strom Thurmond and James Eastland. He also worked as an investigator For Senator Richard Russell on the Warren Commission in 1964.[62] It was, as the COMETA report noted, a remarkable career indeed. A brief summary and scans of Corso's official military record can be found online at Wikipedia.com and at paradigmresearchgroup.org.[63]

In 1947, Corso had just returned from Italy and was busy climbing the ladder of military intelligence when the Roswell Incident occurred. He was stationed at Fort Riley, Kansas at the time and wouldn't learn about the crash until much later in his career. His retelling of the incident is based on memos and military reports that he'd read over the years during stints at the White House on Eisenhower's National Security Council staff and at the Foreign Technology desk at the Pentagon as well as the accounts of others.[64]

Corso made clear that his concern was not the crash itself, but the retrieval operation and subsequent effort to reverse-engineer extraterrestrial technology, hence the title, *The Day After Roswell*. While not a first-hand witness, he did have a brush with the event in its immediate aftermath.

While serving as the post duty officer at Fort Riley, a shipment arrived on a temporary stop en route to Wright Field. Despite the fact that the shipment was classified, rumors about its contents led several men to break security. Upon making his rounds, Corso was alerted by a clearly shaken subordinate who insisted that he take a look for himself. Inside one of the crates was a bizarre looking humanoid body in a thick, glass casket, floating in a clear, bluish gelatinous liquid. Corso's description of the being was consistent with other witnesses. It was child-sized with a significantly oversized head, large, almond-shaped eyes that slanted downward towards its pointed chin, almost no nose, no ears, a slit for a mouth and its pale grey skin appeared completely hairless. It had six fingers but no thumb. In short, it was very obviously not human. According to the shipping manifest, this being was the "occupant" of a craft that crashed in Roswell, New Mexico.[65]

Corso replaced the lid on the crate and did his best to put the disturbing image out of his mind in the hopes that what he had seen was somehow not real. His experiences at the White House and the Pentagon dashed his hopes.

At the White House, Corso saw many National Security memos describing the incident and its exotic hardware.[66] But it wasn't until 1961 when he went to work for General Arthur Trudeau at the Foreign Technology desk in the Army's Research and Development Division that he became fully familiar with the Roswell Incident.

The Army divided its weapons research into two categories: foreign and domestic. Corso's assignment was to recommend ways to incorporate ideas gleaned from other countries into our own weapon programs. Once at the Pentagon under Trudeau, Corso learned that he would be developing some truly 'foreign' technology. He was given a filing cabinet containing Roswell artifacts and asked to devise a plan to make use of the technology. The framework for the plan outlined by Trudeau required extreme stealth. According to Corso, Trudeau's greatest fear was that the CIA would discover the operation.[67] During the great spy wars of the new Cold War era, the KGB had penetrated the CIA and vice-versa. As a result, they acted like one agency to a large extent. Corso cited his experiences in Korea as an example. According to Corso, KGB moles within the CIA who had access to MacArthur's battle plans enabled the Soviets to capture our best technology when it was deployed in battle.[68] Evidently, extensive mutual infiltration had sparked an evolution towards cooperation in the field of espionage. Drawing upon years of experiences and numerous off the record discussions with spies, Corso concluded that the prevailing attitude of the intelligence community was that everyone else was too stupid to keep the world safe and that leveling the playing field would prevent nuclear war.[69] Consequently, neither the Soviet nor U.S. militaries trusted their own spy agencies. Trudeau certainly didn't trust the CIA, which he believed would give the Roswell technology to the Soviets.[70]

Corso knew that the CIA had been hunting the Roswell treasure trove since the early 1950s.[71] The incestuous relationship between the CIA and the KGB meant that any operation to reverse engineer the technology had to be hidden from the CIA. One of the primary objectives of the original Roswell operation devised by General Twining was to hide the alien technology from Soviet spies that had been put on the Roswell trail. Therefore, Corso made a thorough review of the original Majestic-12 plan, field reports, scientific analysis, autopsy information and other documents that came with Roswell file that he had inherited.[72] Understanding how the original plan was supposed to work and what had led the artifacts now in his charge to end up in an undocumented filing cabinet in the Army's Foreign Technology Division was crucial. Combined with his knowledge of the Roswell Incident gleaned from his days at the White House, Corso came to understand the genesis of the Majestic-12 group and its operation.

THE PLAN

It's difficult to imagine a much more challenging crisis than the one that confronted the government in 1947 in the wake of the Roswell Incident. The world was still recovering from the most devastating war in history, punctuated by the unleashing of the atomic bomb. When the dust cleared, approximately 70 million people had been killed and over 1600 cities destroyed. In its immediate aftermath, a new 'Cold War' between the Soviet Union and the U.S. began in earnest. Competition between the two budding superpowers for German weapons technology was intense with each side grabbing as much as it could. Corso himself was involved. He was a participant in Operation Paperclip, a secret effort to smuggle top German scientists including Werner von Braun, Willy Ley and others, through Italy into the United States in 1944.[73]

The struggle essentially ended in a draw with neither side able to gain a significant advantage over the other. The Roswell Incident threatened this state of technological parity. The Soviets certainly understood its significance. According to Corso, Army Counterintelligence agents uncovered a Soviet intelligence operation focused on military bases and personnel associated with the Roswell crash retrieval. It was clear that Soviet spies were hot on the Roswell trail and the defense establishment was determined not to let exotic extraterrestrial technology fall into enemy hands. They needed to come up with a plan, fast.[74]

According to Corso's colleagues on Eisenhower's National Security Council staff, Secretary of Defense James Forrestal and Central Intelligence director Roscoe Hillenkoetter told President Truman that the solution was a "working group" of well-connected, good ole boys who would run a "new Manhattan Project." Like its predecessor, this operation would have to be hidden from our own government in order to hide it from the Soviets. Essentially, the plan was to create a government within the government. The problem was that such a far-reaching operation would be difficult, if not impossible to conceal, which meant that he entire scheme would be dependent on camouflage to hide its activities. Truman was skeptical. He challenged the assumption that the truth need never be disclosed to the public.

From the beginning, the Roswell Incident was treated as military intelligence. The recovery of the flying disc was regarded by the Army as an operation conducted in a wartime theater under battle conditions.[75] Disclosure of any kind was not a consideration for men like Forrestal and Hillenkoetter. But in their zeal to gain a decisive advantage over the Soviets in the Cold War, they overlooked a possibility that hadn't escaped Truman. Flying disc reports just kept on coming. What was to prevent whoever or whatever they were from landing on the White House lawn? Or in front of the Kremlin? Flying disc pilots, wherever they were from, made it clear that nothing on Earth could prevent them should they choose to do so. Truman thought panic in the streets was likely to be much worse than if they'd simply come clean in the first place.

There were other questions: Was it even possible to run a research project of this magnitude in secret? And what about the extraterrestrial visitors? What did they want? Were they preparing for a planetary invasion? There were many unknowns and great risk no matter which direction was chosen at the Grand Fork in the Road.

Truman also doubted the government-within-a-government camouflage scheme. He didn't see how it could work without spinning out of control. But the threat posed by what appeared to be extraterrestrials forced his hand.

Twining briefed Truman in the aftermath of the Roswell Incident, warning him that flying disc activity over sensitive military installations showed hostile intent. If we had to mount a defense against an interstellar invasion we would have to understand the enemy and their technology. Therefore, the general recommended an investigation of the entire flying disc phenomenon, with special emphasis on the hardware recovered at Roswell. Twining's plan eased Truman's concerns with a contingency plan for disclosure. After all, the masses would have to be prepared for the possibility of interplanetary warfare, which convinced the President to green light the new Manhattan Project.[76]

Such was the genesis of Operation Majestic-12, authorized by President Truman on September 24, 1947 in a memo addressed to the Secretary of Defense, James Forrestal. The Truman-Forrestal memo is one of the Majestic documents authenticated by researchers.[77]

The twelve-man working group created by Truman was comprised of six civilians and six military personnel. The civilian team included leaders in aeronautics and astronautics as well as the first three directors of Central Intelligence. The military faction had representatives from each branch of the newly reconfigured military.[78]

Corso's military-industrial complex dream-team roster matched the Eisenhower Briefing Document:

Adm. Roscoe Hillenkoetter – Third Director of the Central Intelligence Group and first Director of the CIA.

Secretary of Defense James Forrestal – Former Secretary of the Navy and first Secretary of Defense of the reformed armed services.

Lt. Gen. Nathan Twining – Head of Air Material Command; Air Force Chief of Staff and eventually Chairman of the Joint Chiefs of Staff.

Professor Donald Menzel - Harvard astronomer and
Naval Intelligence cryptography expert; consultant for both the CIA and NSA.

Dr. Vannevar Bush - Head of NACA (precursor to NASA; Director of the Office of Science Research and Development; head administrator for the Manhattan Project; Chairman of the Joint Research and Development Board.

Dr. Detlev Bronk - Chairman of the National Research Council, President of National Academy of Sciences; specialist in aviation physiology.

Gen. Robert Montague - Commander of Fort Bliss responsible for White Sands Proving Ground in New Mexico.

Gordon Gray - Secretary of the Army, Chairman of the Psychological Strategy Board of the CIA.

Adm. Sidney Souers – First Director of the Central Intelligence Group; Director of the National Security Council.

Gen. Hoyt Vandenberg – Second Director of the Central Intelligence Group succeeding Souers and preceding Hillenkoetter; Air Force Chief of Staff.

Dr. Jerome Hunsaker – Aerodynamics pioneer; succeeded Bush as Director of NACA

Dr. Lloyd Berkner – Pilot; polar explorer; first executive secretary of the Joint Research and Development Board under Bush.

Majestic-12 took on a monumental task. The group sought to exploit the alien technology as a defense against what they thought might be hostile ET invaders and to win the cold war against the Soviets- all while both hiding the truth from the public and preparing the public to eventually face the truth.

Nathan Twining personally investigated the Roswell Incident, supervised the recovery effort that culminated in Wright Field and briefed President Truman. According to Corso, Twining was also the mastermind of the operation. "What was really needed, Twining suggested, was a method for gathering the information about continuing UFO activity - especially crashes, high probability sightings by pilots or the military, or actual physical encounters with individuals - and surreptitiously filtering that information to the group while coming up with practical explanations that would turn unidentified flying disks into completely identifiable and explainable phenomena. Under the cover of explaining away all the flying disk activity, the appropriate agencies represented by members of the working group would be free to research the real flying disk phenomenon as they deemed appropriate. But through it all, Twining stressed, there had to be a way of maintaining full deniability of the flying disk phenomenon while actually preparing the public for a disclosure by gradually desensitizing them to the potential terror of confronting a more powerful biological entity from a different world. It would have to be, General Twining suggested, at the same time both the greatest cover-up and greatest public relations program ever undertaken... It will be a case where the cover-up is the disclosure and the disclosure is the cover-up. Deny everything, but let the public sentiment take its course. Let skepticism do our work for us until the truth becomes common acceptance," wrote Corso of Twining's Majestic-12 strategy.[79]

CAMOUFLAGE THROUGH LIMITED DISCLOSURE

Until 1961, the Army hadn't attempted to harvest its parcel of Roswell technology stashed at the Foreign Technology desk for fear of revealing the Big Secret. With Corso onboard, Trudeau decided the time had come to pursue what he called the "grand endgame development scheme." Corso's first order of business was to study the reports in the Roswell filing cabinet that Trudeau had hand-delivered to his office. The files showed him how Twining's plan was supposed to work and how the Army had come into possession of the Roswell artifacts.[80]

According to Corso, after the initial recovery operation at RAAF, the Roswell spacecraft and debris were shipped to Wright Field in Ohio for preliminary examination and the bodies sent to Bethesda Naval Hospital and Walter Reed Army Hospital for autopsy. The disk remained in possession of the Air Force at Wright Field, while the artifacts were funneled to the appropriate military branches for further evaluation.[81]

Corso found that Majestic-12 accomplished its goals by employing a strategy he called "camouflage through limited disclosure" and that the Foreign Technology desk itself was the key to understanding Twining's plan. The size, scope and nature of the operation made it impossible to completely conceal, so Majestic-12 had to camouflage its activities. Project Blue Book was a prime example of the camouflage strategy. The Air Force used the Blue Book investigation as a cover to gather intelligence on extraterrestrial activity. "While the Blue Book field officers attributed commonplace explanations to the reported sightings, the entire project was a mechanism to acquire photographic records of flying saucer activity for evaluation and research. The most intriguing sightings that had the highest probability of being truly unidentified objects would be bumped upstairs to the working group for dissemination to the authorized agencies carrying on the research," wrote Corso.[82]

The cover-up/camouflage scheme was used even within the military. Twining created a lower level security classification to facilitate the exchange of information with other commands not cleared all the way to the top.[83] Twining wrote the first report for this lower security classification in response to a query about flying disks made by Brigadier General George Schulgen, chief of the Requirements Intelligence Branch of Army Air Force Intelligence. The Twining/Schulgen letter was declassified in 1967 and is one of the most important documents in UFO history.[84] It was also one of the most valuable documents Corso found in his Roswell filing cabinet in 1961, providing him with vital clues necessary to understand the operations of Majestic-12.

In the report, dated September 23, 1947, Twining left no doubt about the existence of flying disks, which he said were "real and not visionary or fictitious." He described the craft as "circular or elliptical in shape, flat on bottom and domed on top" with a "metallic or light reflecting surface." He said the unknown objects were capable of extreme maneuverability and speed without making a sound. Twining also said, somewhat cryptically, that there was a lack of "crash recovered exhibits" that would prove the existence of the craft beyond all doubt. Roswell debunkers often seize upon this statement to make an intellectually disingenuous argument against the Roswell UFO crash. But according to Navy physicist Bruce Maccabee, there's good reason to believe that Twining was speaking in code for the lower classification level and that he was actually hinting at the Roswell crash. "Subject matter, material, information, whatever you want to call it, which is very highly classified is not mentioned, and sometimes cannot even be alluded to in documents of lower classification. Statements can be made at the secret level that draw the reader away from the Top Secret truth." Maccabee said Twining could have easily sent Schulgen the opposite message through a Top Secret channel.[85]

Corso read the memo in similar fashion, noting that despite Twining's claim about the lack of hard evidence, he initiated a full-scale investigation - with a Code Name, priority and security classification - that will issue reports every month as the investigation unfolds and disseminate the data to the Army, Navy Atomic Energy Commission, Joint Research and Development Board, Air Force Scientific Advisory Group, NACA, and the RAND and NEPA projects. Historian Richard Dolan noted that these were all agencies with strong connections to Vannevar Bush, head Manhattan Project administrator and alleged Majestic-12 leader. For Corso, Twining's distribution list was a roadmap for the dissemination of the Roswell artifacts, which explained how the Army had come into possession of its share.[86]

Corso also found coded passages in the general's report that hinted at Majestic-12's plans to exploit the flying disk recovered at Roswell. Twining argued that if the United States were to build such a craft it would be "extremely expensive" and a threat to draw resources away from other projects, therefore development would have to take place independently. To Corso, this was nothing less than a veiled suggestion that an effort to reverse-engineer the Roswell craft would require a completely separate program outside of the existing weapons-development infrastructure. A program like the one put into operation out at Area 51, which Corso thought fit the model recommended by Twining, especially Lockheed Skunk Works' development of the Stealth fighter and B2 bomber.[87]

Another document Corso said was critical to his understanding of Operation Majestic-12 was a report written in December 1948 called *Analysis of Flying Object Incidents in the U.S.* It was one of the first examples of the Majestic-12 camouflage scheme in action. "UFOs are never referred to as extraterrestrial objects but as elements of 'foreign technology,' which was actually the subject of the report," wrote Corso.[88]

For Majestic-12, foreign technology was the perfect cover. The media never bothered with foreign technology, which included everything from French helicopter blades to Russian MiGs. Reporters found the subject exceedingly dull as well as highly classified.[89] Within the existing infrastructure, this was the perfect spot for research into the flying disk phenomenon and development of the Roswell technology. "Here, the materials could be deposited for safekeeping within the military while Army and Air Force brass decided what our existing industrial and research technology allowed them to do," wrote Corso. "Just don't call it extraterrestrial; call it "foreign technology" and throw it in the hopper with the rest of the mundane stuff," he said. Likewise, Majestic-12 operations were conducted in camouflaged projects. Corso said Project Sign, Grudge, Blue Book, Blue Fly, Twinkle, Horizon, HARP, Rainbow and SDI were all camouflaged projects with a connection to alien technology.[90]

IN TECH WE TRUST

In the process of researching and formulating their plan, Trudeau and Corso concluded that the original Majestic-12 group had gone defunct. Because Majestic-12 was classified Above Top Secret and didn't officially exist, it couldn't call upon other areas of the government for resources. In order to fund its operations it had to create lower classified subgroups to carry out its research and development in piecemeal. As the operation grew it became more and more unmanageable until Majestic-12 lost control just as Truman feared it would.

A power struggle between the military and intelligence factions tore the group apart. "Its functions had been absorbed by the groups beneath it. But nobody bothered to tell anyone because a super group was never supposed to exist officially in the first place. That which did not exist officially could not go out of existence officially. Hence, right through the next forty years, the remnants of what once was a super group went through the motions, but the real activities were carried out by individual agencies that believed on blind faith that they were being managed by higher-ups," wrote Corso, about the demise of the original Majestic-12 group and Trudeau's decision to set his own policy.

According to Corso, Trudeau's top priority was to hide the development of the Army's Roswell hardware from the CIA, which had been penetrated by the KGB. Essentially, as far as the military was concerned, the CIA was the enemy. Because several intelligence directors were Majestic-12 members, including the CIA's first director, Admiral Roscoe Hillenkoetter, the group's secrets were compromised. Fortunately, as far as Trudeau and Corso were concerned, the agency lost track of Army's Roswell stash in the confusion of the cover-up, freeing them to develop it as they saw fit.[91]

Corso's plan to harvest Roswell was simple- follow General Twining's blueprint. "What they did was organize according to a business plan even though the operation was something that hadn't been done before. That's the camouflage: don't change a thing but use your same procedures to handle this alien technology," wrote Corso. It was business as usual. "If we don't want anybody to think we're doing anything out of the ordinary, we don't do anything out of the ordinary."[92]

Following Twining's lead, Corso seeded the alien artifacts into weapons development programs already in progress rather than starting new projects that would certainly draw unwanted attention. The existing defense contract became a cover for development of the Roswell technology.[93]

Corso matched various Roswell artifacts to ongoing defense projects with the help of his scientific brain trust, which included John von Neumann, Hermann Oberth, Wernher von Braun, Robert Sarbacher, and Hans Kohler- all world-class scientists who he'd chosen because they'd been exposed to the Roswell Incident through their connection to the Research and Development Board chaired by Vannevar Bush

These were some of the greatest minds of the time, possessing as Corso said, the "cold precision of an engineer with the speculative vision of a free thinker."[94] Mathematician John von Neumann was a principal member of the Manhattan Project. He stood out as a genius among geniuses and made major contributions to a broad range of fields including quantum mechanics, game theory and computer science. Oberth, a physicist and engineer, was one of the founding fathers of rocketry and astronautics. Von Braun, who got his start as an assistant to Oberth, would go on to be known as perhaps the greatest rocket scientist in history. He designed and built the V-2 rocket as well as the Saturn V Superbooster that took the Apollo spacecraft to the moon. Sarbacher, a key figure in UFO history, and Kohler were somewhat lesser known but highly regarded. Sarbacher was especially valuable in that he was part of Twining's original team.[95] This meant that Sarbacher was in part responsible for the Roswell artifacts that ended up in Corso's charge and thus could provide unique insight into the decision that resulted in the Army's Roswell haul as well as to provide guidance for development of the technology.

Unlocking the riddles of the wrecked disk, crash debris and alien bodies presented a significant challenge for Corso and his dream team of power scientists. Many of the basic necessities one would expect to find in the craft and in the extraterrestrials themselves were missing. The craft appeared to have no engine, no power supply, no fuel, no navigational controls and no protection against the tremendous G-forces its flight maneuvers appeared to generate.[96] Further, there were no facilities for food storage or food preparation or waste disposal. Autopsies revealed that the beings themselves also lacked digestive and waste systems.[97] It was a complete enigma. Yet, after thorough analysis, a picture began to emerge that allowed Corso to understand how the craft operated and to see opportunities to adapt the alien technology to our own.

One would expect the technology of a civilization capable of interstellar travel to be far in advance of our own and the Roswell craft certainly met expectations. As the Majestic-12 brain trust discovered, the craft wasn't missing an engine and power supply because *the craft itself was the engine and power supply*. In fact, the spaceship appeared to be a giant capacitor in which the pilots themselves were part of the circuit.[98]

Engineers at Norton Air Force base, where the disk was eventually hangared, found the most refined copper and purest silver along the underside of the craft that they'd ever seen. They couldn't replicate the alloy. According to Corso, "The metal was remarkable for its conductivity, as if the entire craft was an electrical circuit offering no resistance to the flow of current."[99]

Flight suits worn by the Roswell extraterrestrials provided engineers with a vital clue. The diminutive humanoid pilots were wrapped from head to toe in a fabric so form fitting that Corso suggested that the term "flight skins" was more appropriate. Most amazing was the pure conductivity of the fabric, which was atomically aligned in such a way as to provide incredible tensile strength and flexibility that also vectored current and neutralized cosmic rays. The latter attribute was the key to the mystery of the missing power supply and engine, as well as the interface between the pilot and the ship, which lacked control sticks, wheels, throttles, pedals, cables, flaps, and rudders or any sort of traditional navigational control.

Another key component was a flexible plastic headband embedded with electroencephalographic-like conductors and sensors that the extraterrestrial pilots wore on their heads. The headband picked up electrical signals from the pilot's brain and translated them into system commands that flowed through the flight skins and into the ship's panel through an indentation in the shape of the ET's hand. The result was that the ship was controlled by the pilot's thoughts. In effect, the ship became an extension of the ET's body.[100]

Although it wasn't understood whether the craft generated its own power or merely stored it, it was clear that it had a huge capacity to conduct current. The tremendous electrical potential of the Roswell spaceship, which lacked any sort of traditional engine, hinted not only at its source of power, but its method of propulsion. According to Corso, the ET disk reminded the scientists who examined it of the work of the great Serbian genius, Nikola Tesla. It was Tesla who invented AC electricity and whose discoveries led to radio, television, fluorescent and neon lighting, radio control devices, robotics, X-rays, radar, microwaves, etc.

Tesla essentially invented the modern world. And it was Tesla who was rumored to be developing antigravity craft. In fact, according to Corso, it was Tesla's research that enabled the Roswell disk scientists to understand the extraterrestrial spacecraft recovered at Roswell.[101]

The general consensus was that the disk converted an electromagnetic field into an antigravity field.[102] "The craft was able to displace gravity through the propagation of magnetic waves controlled by shifting the magnetic poles around the craft so as to control, or vector, not a propulsion system but the repulsion force of like charges… the craft itself stored the energy necessary to propagate the magnetic wave that elevated it, allowed it to achieve escape velocity from the Earth's gravity, and enabled it to achieve speeds of over seven thousand miles per hour. The pilots weren't affected by the tremendous g-forces that build up in the acceleration of conventional aircraft because to those inside, it was as if gravity was being folded around the outside of the wave that enveloped the craft. Maybe it was like traveling inside the eye of a hurricane," wrote Corso about the exotic technology the alien craft.[103]

The Colonel didn't have access to the actual disk itself, but other items that hinted at how the craft worked found their way into his Roswell filing cabinet including long, thin, flexible glass-like filaments that conducted light that looked like wiring, quarter-sized, hexagon-shaped plastic wafers with etchings like circuitry, eyepieces that intensified light, metallic fiber that couldn't be torn or burnt and resumed its original shape after being bent or crumpled and a pen-like device that produced a beam that could burn through objects.[104]

With the help of his scientific team, Corso was able to supercharge existing weapons development programs. Von Braun, Sarbacher and company also helped him maintain security by guiding him to contractors in the defense industry who could be trusted with the Roswell secret.[105]

Once Corso placed specific items in his Roswell inventory with ongoing defense projects, the operation was a go. He offered technical reports on the material, and sometimes the device itself, to the appropriate contractor, who would then treat it like any other piece of foreign technology.[106]

For example, the eyepieces that magnified light were inserted into an ongoing project at Fort Belvoir inspired by the German's attempt to develop night-vision. Both the US and Soviet Union initiated night-vision programs after discovering that the Nazi's had tried unsuccessfully to deploy what were essentially clunky infrared viewers on the battlefield in WWII.[107] The benefits were obvious. To be able to see in an environment where the enemy was blind would be a tremendous tactical advantage for any military force. Of all the artifacts in Corso's parcel of Roswell material, the eyepieces worn by the extraterrestrials that enabled them to see in the dark were the easiest to understand and exploit. To anyone who looked through them, their purpose was obvious.[108]

Fort Belvoir was the perfect spot to seed the Roswell eyepieces. Corso delivered them to the technology development consultant for the night-vision project who then passed them on to one of his contractors for development. The lucky recipient, Martin Marietta Electronics, was granted the right to own the patent on the device it reverse-engineered from the eyepieces that they were told had come, not from an extraterrestrial spacecraft, but from a foreign country- no questions asked. Trudeau provided funding for a budget submitted by the tech consultant, Corso assigned a liaison from Army R&D to oversee its development and the project was off and running.

Fort Belvoir's night-vision project was such an effective cover that there was barely a ripple in the history of its development. If one looked back the only hint of the Roswell tech's impact was a boost in funding, the appearance of General Trudeau's name as a benefactor and a sudden acceleration of the program after 1961.[109]

The project to supplement Fort Belvoir's night-vision research with extraterrestrial technology was a tremendous success, especially for Martin

Marietta, which would eventually become Lockheed Martin. By 1963, after Corso and Trudeau had left the Pentagon, night-vision was already making its way into the field in Europe and Vietnam.

According to Corso, other projects enhanced by Roswell technology also bore fruit, including efforts to develop fiber optics, integrated circuit chips, super tenacity fibers and lasers. The Roswell technology was also critical to the development of brain wave guidance systems, particle beam weaponry, SDI, depleted uranium projectiles, HARP and electromagnetic propulsion systems.[110]

MEDIA SILENCE

One might expect such revelations from a key military-industrial complex insider to be worthy of front-page headlines. One might also expect society to value teachers over professional athletes, but life on Earth doesn't work that way. *The Day After Roswell* made the *New York Times* best-seller list, but not the front-page headlines. It never made the nightly news and there was virtually no serious coverage in the mainstream media. The most prominent coverage the story received was on Dateline NBC, which gave it short shrift. With a tone of bemused skepticism, a segment entitled "Space Cadets" featured an interview with Corso, focusing on one of his biggest revelations that some of our most advanced technology had its roots in alien artifacts recovered at Roswell. Corso told Dateline he had no direct contact with any of the contractors and that these companies were never told that the foreign technology they were asked to reverse-engineer was extraterrestrial in origin. Dateline contacted the companies named by Corso. Predictably, all rejected his claims, denying any knowledge of the Colonel or the Roswell Incident. That was the extent of Dateline's report. Corso was portrayed as a crazy old man with a tall tale, leaving little doubt that the piece was nothing more than a stunt meant to discredit him.

Had Dateline actually investigated the story there were plenty of opportunities. As Tim Clodfelter of the Winston-Salem Journal noted in his review of *The Day After Roswell*, "This book is a godsend, one that finally gives the details and names the names." For starters, Dateline could've looked into Corso's scientific team. Had they done so, they would have discovered that in 1983 the late Robert Sarbacher had gone on record about the crash and retrieval of an extraterrestrial spaceship and the subsequent investigation led by alleged Majestic-12 member Vannevar Bush. Sarbacher also confirmed witness's description of the debris of which he said, "Certain materials reported to have come from flying saucer crashes were extremely light and very tough. I am sure our laboratories analyzed them very carefully."[111]

Dateline also could've have found support for both the reverse-engineering program and the night-vision project. General Arthur Trudeau's memoirs, available through the Army War College and online at Google Books, provide confirmation of the Army's quest to develop exotic technology, including HARP and Project Horizon. Although Trudeau never mentions UFOs or Roswell, which one would hardly expect given the circumstances, his memoirs support the general narrative of Corso's story, including the necessity of expanding military operations in space and on the moon, the support of Senator Thurmond, the role of the German "Paper Clip" scientists, the use of foreign technology and the development of applied engineering.[112] Corso emphasized the latter term in his Dateline interview in which he said, "We called it applied engineering. What we meant by that was give this information to industry that wants it and encourage them to take credit for it and take the patents."[113]

In addition to Trudeau's memoirs, Fort Belvoir's published history includes a chapter entitled, "conquest of the night," in which General Arthur Trudeau is credited for the development of the night-vision goggles used in Vietnam. According to Corso's co-author Bill Birnes, Fort Belvoir's recognition of General Trudeau as instrumental in the development of night-vision from the unwieldy German design dependent on large amounts of power to the night-vision goggles worn by our troops in Vietnam constitutes no less than "extrinsic" proof of *The Day After Roswell*. Birnes conceded that "of course nobody will ever say UFOs… aliens… they never said that because that was not supposed to be discussed and it wasn't, they simply said that the technology was brought to them from Army R&D along with a very sizable budget for funding and under Trudeau's urging they developed it."[114] At present, a simple Internet search returns other publications and defense documents that also cite Trudeau as the primary benefactor of night-vision development.[115]

Sarbacher's admission, Trudeau's memoirs and the written history of Fort Belvoir represent just a few of the opportunities missed by Dateline to verify substantial aspects of Corso's story. These were the low-hanging fruit.

The difference between investigations conducted by independent researchers like Carey, Schmitt and Friedman and others, and the establishment media could not be more striking. Consider the Dateline example in contrast with an independent research effort that has tracked the Roswell retrieval operation from the desert to Wright-Patterson AFB to the labs of Battelle Memorial Institute.

In an updated edition of *Witness to Roswell*, researchers Tom Carey and Don Schmitt published the findings of associate Anthony Bragalia, who uncovered smoking-gun evidence of the Roswell material at Battelle Memorial Institute in Ohio.[116]

Battelle's involvement with UFOs is well known. The Air Force hired Battelle to undertake a study of UFO sightings, which resulted in the little-known but highly significant *Project Blue Book Special Report 14*. Battelle's close proximity to Wright-Patterson Air Force Base and its expertise in metallurgy and materials science made it an ideal spot to conduct research on the Roswell artifacts. Researchers suspected the holy grail of hard evidence ended up in the labs of the applied science and technology development company.

Bragalia scoured the scientific literature at Battelle for any signs of the Roswell material and hit the jackpot. What he found was references to highly classified reports made to Wright-Patterson AFB on the development of a new metal alloy with Roswell-like properties. The reports show that in the immediate aftermath of the Roswell Incident, Battelle began researching and developing what first-hand witnesses described as 'memory metal.' According to multiple witnesses, one of the most amazing attributes of the Roswell debris was the so-called memory metal that recovered its original shape after being distorted or crumpled by those who handled it.

History shows that prior to 1947, the military had never pursued an alloy with the ability for "shape recovery" as they called it. The Battelle project to pursue a Roswell-like memory metal resulted in the development of Nitinol, a Nickel-Titanium alloy. Bragalia's research essentially substantiated the statements about the materials recovered at Roswell made by General Arthur Exon and Robert Sarbacher.[117] Bragalia's contribution to the Roswell investigation highlights the difference between the efforts of private researchers, who lack the resources of big media but are driven to uncover the truth, and the establishment media, which have ample resources to investigate but are not inclined to conduct an honest search for the truth.

There were many more opportunities for follow up investigation in the text of *The Day After Roswell*. Whether or not one agrees with Bill Birnes that Fort Belvoir's written history constitutes proof of Corso's story, taken collectively, these examples show there was more than enough information potentially available to Dateline to actually present a meaningful piece rather than the thinly-veiled anti-UFO/Roswell propaganda that aired. The failure to fully investigate Corso's story was typical of mainstream media UFO related "exposés," which never dig below the surface of the issue or follow up on investigative leads.

One cannot fully appreciate just how lacking the treatment given to Corso by the fourth estate until one considers his remarkable career and credentials. This was a man who had served on General MacArthur's staff in Korea, had served on President Eisenhower's National Security Council staff, had served as National Security Advisor to Senators Strom Thurmond and James Eastland, had testified before the House National Security Committee about American POWs held in North Korea, had testified before a Senate committee on Internal Security about the penetration of the CIA by the KGB, had appeared on *Prime Time Live* as a cold war expert on U2 flights over Russia and had been decorated with nineteen medals and ribbons during his twenty-one year military career.[118] Corso was a true military-industrial complex insider and a man not to be easily dismissed. Yet that was the reaction of the mainstream news media.

When UFOs did make the nightly news it wasn't because of Corso. Instead, the headlines were given to a cult called Heaven's Gate, whose followers committed mass suicide in the belief that their souls would hitch a ride on a spaceship following behind the comet Hale-Bopp. Mainstream media bias of this sort is standard operating procedure. Stories that paint the UFO phenomenon in a ridiculous light are emphasized while serious stories that reveal an uncomfortable and potentially frightening reality are shunned. A serious, in-depth interview with Corso could only be heard when most of the country was asleep and unable to listen to late night radio talk shows like Art Bell's *Coast to Coast AM*.

In general, the Colonel's tell-all was greeted as just another tall tale in our increasingly strange world. Many dismissed it out of hand, trained by decades of ridicule and denial by the print and broadcast media. Debunkers seized upon small errors and inconsistencies in Corso's story and argued about hypothetical situations from their armchairs fifty years after the fact. Several prominent researchers within the UFO community, including Stanton Friedman, sided with the skeptics, perhaps fearing the sting of an intelligence operation designed to discredit them, not unlike the Majestic Documents episode of the previous decade. Whatever the case, the charges didn't stand up under close scrutiny.

Skeptics branded him a real life "Walter Mitty," pretending to be more important than he really was because of his claim to have been part of President Eisenhower's National Security Council. At first glance, the accusation appeared to have some merit, but upon investigation, it was at best disingenuous and misleading. According to Dr. Michael Salla of the Exopolitics Institute, the dispute was much ado about nothing. Salla reviewed Corso's service record, a declassified FBI report and Corso's personal notes.[119] He found that during the time period in question, Corso was a member of the Psychological Strategy Board and its successor, the Operations Coordinating Board, which were attached to the National Security Council. The PSB, and later the OCB, reported directly to the NSC and was responsible for implementing its decisions. Salla also discovered that Corso's sworn testimony before Congress in 1992 on POW/MIA affairs listed him as "Lt. Col. Philip [sic] Corso (USA, Retired) National Security Council Staff, Eisenhower administration." In other words, Corso served on the NSC *staff* as opposed to the NSC itself. It was a distinction that the Colonel had made in his notes and in the text of *The Day After Roswell*. His critics seized on the rare instances when the word "staff" had been omitted. Whether it was due to editorial error or a simple form of shorthand, Salla found that Corso's debunkers misrepresented the facts and overstated their significance. Corso was indeed a member of President Eisenhower's National Security Council staff.

Salla also found that other accusations hurled at Corso were just as misleading and trivial. Critics charged that he hadn't headed the Foreign Technology desk for the full two years as he claimed. Salla found that, although Corso only held the title 'officially' for three months, he was in fact the head of the Foreign Technology Desk under General Trudeau for the full two years just like he said he was.

Others used his public statements about having been formally associated with Majestic-12 to attack his credibility. Again Salla found such attacks unwarranted. His research suggested that the PSB, and by extension the OCB, to which Corso was assigned, was likely created to perform certain functions for Majestic-12. National Security advisor and Secretary to the Army, Gordon Grey, who was named in the Eisenhower Briefing Document, created the PSB. What's more, one of the Majestic Documents made note that the group had convinced President Truman to greenlight the board.[120] Although the question of the authenticity of this document has not been settled beyond doubt, the founding of the PSB on April 4, 1951 is an obscure detail that lends support for its credibility.[121] Salla wrote of the relationship between the PSB and Majestic-12, "Both the PSB and the OCB were based on developing psychological warfare strategies. Given the role recommended by the 1953 Robertson Panel to debunk UFO sightings and Gordon Gray's original role in setting up the PSB, it can be concluded that one of the functions of the OCB was to develop appropriate psychological warfare strategies to deal with the public response to the UFO phenomenon. Corso was most likely referring to his service on the PSB/OCB as the basis for his claims to have been formally associated with MJ-12." Lloyd Berkner's influence on the CIA's Robertson Panel and Gordon Gray's relationship with the PSB/OCB firmly establishes a connection between Majestic-12 and both bodies that further supports Salla's conclusions.

As a result of his research into the accusations levied upon Corso, Salla concluded, "the ad hominem attacks on Corso's reflections on the significance of his historical role in a secret Army program to seed civilian industries with extraterrestrial technologies are at best a distraction. At worst, such ad hominem attacks are more evidence of Corso's critics crossing the Rubicon between objective criticism and debunking."[122]

The simple fact is that Colonel Philip J. Corso was who he said he was. The mainstream media called him an expert when he spoke on U2 spy missions over Russia during the Cold War. But when he spoke out about the recovery of a crashed extraterrestrial spacecraft in Roswell and the subsequent integration of extraterrestrial technology into our culture, he was instead subjected to absurd levels of criticism. When confronted with the debunker's accusations shortly before his death, Corso fired back, "I ask them this- were you there with me? Were you part of this? Were you cleared? Did you have the clearances? They can't answer those questions- all they do is criticize with no evidence."[123]

The news media shunned Corso despite the fact that he had twice before blown the whistle on controversial stories that turned out to be true. On the first occasion, he appeared in front of Congressman Bob Dornan's committee to investigate missing POW's in Korea. Corso testified that POW's had been sent to the Soviet Union to be exploited for intelligence purposes and then subjected to terminal experimentation reminiscent of Mengele and the Nazi's. The story, including his testimony, was covered by ABC's 20/20 with Hugh Downs and Barbara Walters, The U.S. News and World Report and later published in a book called, *The Men We Left Behind*, by authors, Mark Sauter and Jim Sanders. This was a case where Corso was proven to have exposed a government cover-up. Henry Kissinger and General Brent Scowcroft had previously told Dornan's committee that there were no reports of missing POWs. Corso knew otherwise. He was the original source of the intelligence. His testimony was confirmed when the missing reports suddenly turned up.[124]

The second time Corso exposed a controversial government cover-up involved what he called the "secret war" that transpired in the shadows of the Cold War. Several pilots on spy missions were shot down and presumed dead during operations deliberately designed to probe the Soviet's air defense system. In other words, the best of the best were simply human sacrifices in an unacknowledged war. Corso often quipped that in his experience he didn't know of any cold wars, they were all "hot wars" with real bullets and real casualties.[125] In this instance, he appeared in an exposé on ABC's Primetime Live with Chris Wallace. Yet, when the Colonel blew the whistle on Roswell, the mainstream media dropped the story like a hot potato.

When the Roswell Incident did receive mainstream media attention on its 50th anniversary, it was the Air Force that was given center stage to peddle its infamous crash-test-dummies-super-secret-weather-balloon story. Despite the laughter heard at the press conference, the media dutifully reported the Air Force's version of events as if it were cold hard fact. When *Coast to Coast AM* radio show host, Art Bell, asked Col. Corso for his reaction to the Air Force's press conference, Corso was completely befuddled. He said, "I can't even conceive why they did something like this... If I'd have done something like that I think General Trudeau would've thrown me out of the top window of the Pentagon."[126]

DEEP IMPACT

Had the media made a sincere effort to investigate Corso's revelations about Roswell - as it did when he blew the whistle on the more down-to-earth scandals involving POWs and spy flights over the Soviet Union during the Cold War - it would have blown the lid off the UFO cover-up. Nevertheless, Corso's memoir reignited the modern disclosure movement, which began with the Rockefeller Initiative that failed to gain traction until the publication of *The Day After Roswell.*

In 1993 Laurance Rockefeller of the Rockefeller family dynasty launched an initiative to convince President Bill Clinton to become the "disclosure President."[127] Clinton was known to have a burning interest in UFOs. When he took office he had good friend Webster Hubbell, whom he appointed to the justice department as an Associate Attorney General, look into two questions for him. Clinton wanted to know who really killed Kennedy and if UFOs were real. Hubbell never found the answers and the Rockefeller initiative was all but dead by 1996.[128]

Two years later, not long after the publication of *The Day After Roswell,* long-time White House reporter Sarah McClendon helped to resurrect the movement with a press release that flatly declared, *Lid Coming Off Government Cover-up on UFOs.* "Unidentified Flying Objects, a term given for many years to unexplained sightings of craft in the skies over every state in the Union, are actual visitors from other worlds, believe a community of scientists and technicians employed by government," wrote McClendon about the burgeoning disclosure movement. The woman who had grilled many a President demonstrated her fearlessness once again in reporting Laurance Rockefeler's previously unpublicized campaign to persuade President Clinton to end the UFO cover-up. She said that, although the Clinton administration ultimately failed to deliver, hundreds of military-industrial complex insiders were "willing to swear under oath that alien craft are repeatedly penetrating our airspace."[129]

McClendon announced that the group led by Dr. Steven Greer, who had briefed the sitting director of the CIA, James Woolsey, was seeking an official disclosure by the U. S. government and that, according to Col. Philip J. Corso, author of *The Day After Roswell,* the government was in possession of the definitive hard evidence.

McClendon's efforts to lead the mainstream media appeared in vain. The establishment laughed off *The Day After Roswell*. Even so, it was taken very seriously in certain high-level circles- most notably, by the community of government scientists and technicians willing to stand with Corso and testify before Congress to the reality of an extraterrestrial presence. This group of insiders was emboldened, perhaps even compelled, by Corso's disclosures to come forward with their own. Although The Disclosure Project was never afforded the opportunity to testify before Congress, the movement came to fruition in 2001 with a historic press conference at the storied National Press Club in Washington D.C., which will be covered in detail in the following chapter. Were it not for Corso and *The Day After Roswell*, it's possible, maybe even probable, that the Disclosure Project press conference would not have taken place and the disclosure movement would have withered and died.

In general, there appeared to be broad support for Corso from the military wing of the military-industrial complex beyond the hundreds of insiders who came out to stand with him. According to Corso's co-author Bill Birnes, during the book tour, at Army and Air Force bases around the country, military personnel who had served in the Pentagon after him, came out to tell him they knew from their own experiences what he'd written was true. In fact, claimed Birnes, the Pentagon ordered more copies of *The Day After Roswell* than any other bookstore.[130]

Military support for Corso extended beyond the U.S. military. In 1999, a French UFO study conducted by high-level officials, including retired generals from the French Institute of Higher Studies for National Defense, a strategic planning agency financed by the government, concluded that the Extraterrestrial hypothesis was the best explanation for high-quality UFO sightings made by reliable witnesses. The study known as the COMETA report argued that Corso's story might well be true despite the controversy over his book.[131] The quasi-official stamp of the French government was of such significance that independent journalist Leslie Kean was able to publish a sober article about the COMETA report in the Boston Globe, an arm of the mainstream media usually off limits to pro-UFO stories.[132]

In 2003, Corso's influence reached the most senior levels of government when the former Canadian Minister of Defense, Paul Hellyer, was inspired to read *The Day After Roswell*, after watching the late Peter Jennings' ABC special *UFOs: Seeing Is Believing*. Hellyer was blown away.

He knew he had to speak out. On September 25, 2005 at an exopolitics symposium at the University of Toronto, he delivered a remarkable speech about UFOs and Corso's story. "Two or three of my friends have asked me if I didn't think *The Day After Roswell* could be just some brilliant work of fiction. My answer was no. Not even with the imagination of someone like Yann Martel, author of *The Life of Pi*, could anyone fake it. The book is replete with too many real names, real places and real dates to be fiction," said Hellyer, who added that a retired U.S. Air Force General he'd asked about Corso's book told him unequivocally, "Every word of it is true, and more."[133]

Canada's former Minister of Defense caught the attention of the mainstream media, which couldn't completely ignore the story given his stature as a senior government official. He made the rounds on cable news and, although the interviews were polite, the tone was skeptical, and nothing ever came of it. The media didn't investigate anything he said. There was no follow up. Having become a show about entrapping pedophiles, Dateline NBC never updated their report on Corso, never revisited his story in the wake of Hellyer's endorsement. "UFOs are as real as the airplanes that fly over your head," he told the audience in Toronto, his words flashing instantly around the world here in the digital age. He said that although he'd become personally fascinated by UFOs, it was the policy implications that compelled him to go public. According to Hellyer, we've gotten ourselves into a classic catch-22.

The military designated the extraterrestrials as "enemy aliens" in the immediate aftermath of the Roswell Incident, and because there was nothing any earthly Army, Navy or Air Force could do to counter such a technologically superior adversary our leaders covered up the evidence and denied their existence in order to prevent panic in the streets. The original policy is still in place today. Only now the military has weapons, including lasers and particle beams, reverse-engineered from the ET's own technology for use against them. The former Minister of Defense didn't think this was such a good idea. He hit on the key policy question: "Are they really enemy or merely legitimate explorers from afar?" There's never been a public debate, he said, because it's impossible to discuss a problem "that doesn't officially exist."

Hellyer called for an end to "the greatest and most successful cover-up in the history of the world" so that there could be an open debate about extraterrestrial policy. He also warned that the current wild west shoot first and ask questions later approach to extraterrestrial relations was dangerous and could land us in an interstellar war. He warned against the weaponization of space, denouncing the Bush administration's plans to build a moon base originally proposed by Corso's boss, Arthur Trudeau. Corso devoted an entire chapter to Project Horizon, a plan to put an Army base on the Moon in order to mount a defense against extraterrestrials.[134]

In concluding one of the most memorable speeches ever made by a senior government official, Hellyer cited a little-known book by Alfred Webre, International Director of the Institute for Cooperation in Space (ICIS), former head of the 1977 Extraterrestrial Communication Study for the White House under President Jimmy Carter and author of *Exopolitics: Politics, Government and Law in the Universe*. In *Exopolitics*, Webre wrote that we weren't alone in the universe, but we were isolated from the universe. It seems we are black sheep kept in quarantine until we are morally and spiritually mature, a shortcoming Hellyer made painfully clear in his criticism of the plan to build a moon base against extraterrestrials. "It seems that once again the military view has prevailed and the project will go forward at a cost of $100 billion. That is a lot of money- enough to save the lives of millions of earthlings dying of malnutrition and lack of medical treatment." said Hellyer, who endorsed Webre's proposal for a "Decade of Contact," an era of openness that included public hearings, public-funded research and education about extraterrestrial reality. "Who knows? That could be just the antidote the world needs to end its greed-driven, power-centered madness," opined the former Minister of Defense at the conclusion of his speech.

Hellyer has continued to speak out ever since. His numerous cable talk show appearances can be found on YouTube. He also joined with the ICIS, the Toronto Exopolitics Symposium and the Disclosure Project in calling for hearings in Canadian Parliament. These groups sought to present evidence of the extraterrestrial presence and to make policy recommendations, including Webre's plans for the Decade of Contact. The effort became known as the Canadian Exopolitics Initiative. With the name of the hon. Paul Hellyer, distinguished Canadian statesman, attached to the initiative, the Canadian Senate could not ignore the proposal anymore than the mainstream media could ignore his speech made in Toronto. It could, however, follow the media's lead and shirk its responsibility. In November

2005, the Canadian Senate answered the ICIS with the feeble explanation that it was too busy to hold hearings on ETs.[135] Also in November of 2005, a motion of no confidence in the government was passed in the House of Commons that resulted in the dissolution of parliament and a new minority government led by the conservative party. No hearings on the Canadian Exopolitics Initiative have ever been held.

It was perhaps the closest the issue of Disclosure had ever come to public recognition in a governmental body such as the Canadian parliament. Despite the fact that the Disclosure movement has not yet achieved its ultimate goal, it has gained a momentum that many like activist Stephen Bassett believe will ultimately result in official Disclosure. In the final analysis, the Roswell Incident is the smoking gun that proves that genuine UFOs are craft from another world. The insider account of the incident provided by Col. Philip Corso ignited a disclosure process that appears destined to fully mature. *The Day After Roswell* will be remembered as perhaps the catalyst that brought about Disclosure and ushered in the new era in interstellar civilization.

SUMMARY AND CONCLUSIONS

Ever since an alien spacecraft crashed in Roswell, the government has been pretending the event never happened while secretly exploiting the technology that fell into its lap. Despite what Paul Hellyer called the most successful cover-up in human history, compelling evidence continues to surface more than half a century later. Evidence such as the posthumous affidavit signed by Air Force public relations officer Walter Haut and the development of Nitinol from the Roswell memory metal at Battelle Memorial Institute documented by Anthony Bragalia.

The Top Secret committee of military-industrial complex scientists and statesmen assigned to manage the ET issue adopted a schizophrenic policy of secrecy and gradual acclimation to the truth. Through a military lens the potential threat posed by a superior force clearly necessitated the development of the alien technology to whatever degree possible. ET tech also had the potential to tip the balance of the Cold War with the Soviet Union as well as to act as a boon to industry, which generated windfall profits through defense development contracts and through spin-off commercial products. This set of circumstances formed the framework for a secret policy that has become institutionalized over time.

Although the effort to bury the truth with lies, intimidation and death threats was successful for roughly thirty years, by the mid 1990s the basic story of the UFO crash was so widely known that it had become a part of pop culture. The plot of 1996 alien invasion flick, *Independence Day*, which became a worldwide sensation, revolved around the Roswell Incident and the operation to study the alien disk stored at Area 51.

When the policy of secrecy collapsed under the weight of mounting evidence, the government did what it always does: Lie and deny. Aided by its system of compartmentalization – only those at the top knew the full story – each leak that occurred amounted to just a small piece of the puzzle. Meticulously assembled by researchers, the puzzle pieces revealed only a glimpse of the big picture, but the missing pieces left holes to be exploited by the debunkers, naysayers and guardians of the secret. The story may have been well known by the mid 1990s, but it was not universally believed. In general, it was regarded much like other stories that go viral on the Internet only to be exposed as an urban legend by the likes of snopes.com. What was missing were the revelations of an insider high enough in the chain of command to provide a comprehensive overview of the event, the government's reaction to it, and the operation that resulted from it. Col. Philip j. Corso filled in that blank. Just as the Roswell Incident is the Rosetta stone for understanding UFOs, Corso's *The Day After Roswell* is the primer for understanding the government's response to the UFO phenomenon.

Corso named names. He was there. Former Canadian Minister of Defense, Paul Hellyer confirmed the truth of his story. Yet it has been unfairly dismissed and is lightly regarded, even within the UFO community. Nevertheless, it has had a significant impact on the rise of the Disclosure movement. In fact, *The Day After Roswell* may very well be a product of the original Majestic-12 plan. The French COMETA report concluded the near simultaneous release of *The Day After Roswell* and the Air Force's final debunking attempt called *The Roswell Report: Case Closed* was consistent "with Corso's theories" about the Majestic-12 acclimation program in which *the cover-up is the disclosure and the disclosure is the cover-up.* Here was the perfect example. What's more, Corso worked for Majestic-12 while on Eisenhower's National Security Council staff and he resurrected the original Majestic-12 blueprint under Trudeau. Thus, one could argue that *The Day*

After Roswell was the product of the long since defunct Majestic-12 public relations campaign.

It's unclear what entity, if any, filled the void left by Majestic-12. Because of the system of compartmentalized secrecy, no one knew what had happened to the top-level group and no one was in charge. It's possible there are other rogue operations like the one run by Corso and Trudeau, especially in light of the circumstances that brought about the end of the original Majestic-12 operation.

Mistrust between the military and the intelligence community, which Corso attributed to conflicting agendas regarding the balance of power in the world, is a major theme of *The Day After Roswell*. It's clear that Corso didn't trust the CIA. As far he was concerned, the CIA was the enemy. Complicating matters, the intelligence community had been involved with the Roswell Incident from the beginning. For all intents and purposes, the power struggle that derailed the original Majestic-12 plan resulted from an attempt by the CIA to hijack the operation and steer it off course. Corso and Trudeau were determined to right the ship. They used the original Majestic-12 camouflage scheme to shield the CIA from the Army's efforts to make something useful out of its Roswell spaceship sprockets and gears.

The success of Corso's Majestic-12 reboot was surely a colossal embarrassment for the CIA. Thus, it's no surprise to find the agency's fingerprints on debunking efforts launched at Corso. One of his most prominent debunkers was Karl Pflock, a former CIA intelligence officer. COMETA found that Pflock used disinformation techniques to debunk the Roswell Incident. He also refused to recant his charges that Corso hoodwinked Strom Thurmond into providing a foreword for *The Day After Roswell* even after the emergence of documentary evidence refuting his claims.

The schism that developed between the military and the intelligence community over the Roswell technology and the UFO phenomenon in general likely exacerbated the institutional chaos and confusion to which all large organizations like the government are prone. The government is anything but monolithic. There are countless agencies and departments with competing and conflicting agendas. Imagine the chaos when the left hand doesn't know what the right is doing in an organization with thousands of arms. What's more, to have a schism in such a highly compartmentalized operation that was growing out of control and becoming unmanageable undoubtedly led to further confusion in the subgroups created by Majestic-12. As a result of this institutional dysfunction, the government's handling of the UFO problem has often appeared incoherent and muddled. It is little wonder that private researchers attempting to make sense of the UFO mystery and the government's response to it have had little success. In this context, to paint a picture of conflict between the military and the CIA over the Roswell/ET issue is to paint a picture with too broad of a brush. Obviously, the Air Force is complicit in maintaining the cover-up. More accurately put, the military remnants of the original Majestic-12 operation were, and possibly still are, in conflict with what's left of the intelligence faction. Even this scenario may be an over simplification. There could be rival operations with competing agendas within both the military and the CIA. This could explain why the CIA seems to have been involved in both leaking the Roswell story and covering it up at the same time, which could also be the result of an acclimation program if it was still operational. It is impossible to know exactly what is going on in a conflict taking place behind the scenes in the highest strata of national security. The Corso episode provides one example of a clandestine conflict between the military and the intelligence community over the Roswell Incident and ET policy in general.

In the middle of this epic Above Top Secret power struggle between the military and intelligence communities was the scientific community, especially the Manhattan Project scientists, who were, of course, the logical choice to handle such a problem as the Roswell Incident. Leaks were rare, but when they happened they were highly significant. DoD scientist Robert Sarbacher and meteor expert Lincoln La Paz connected the Manhattan Project scientists to UFOs and Roswell, which put the Fermi paradox in a whole new light.

Science's most famous lunchtime gabfest did not take place in a vacuum. It happened in the midst of a UFO sightings wave at Los Alamos that led to meetings and debates. It happened in the aftermath of the Roswell Incident and the inception of the Majestic-12 operation run by Manhattan Project scientist Vannevar Bush. In such a context one can't help but think there was much more to the Fermi confab than has been publicly admitted. Perhaps the discussion was an attempt among colleagues to hash out the implications of extraterrestrial visitors? Fermi's epiphany, which was the genesis of SETI, the Search for Extraterrestrial Intelligence, would certainly have been of great interest to Majestic-12. In a universe teeming with life, Twining's plan to gather intelligence on extraterrestrial activity would have to include an attempt to monitor or intercept ET communications. In fact, SETI was likely one of those hidden-in-plain-sight Majestic-12 operations Corso wrote about in *The Day After Roswell*.[136]

SETI uses a worldwide array of radio telescopes to scan the heavens for the hailing beacon of an ET civilization. It's advertised as an attempt to answer the question of whether or not we're alone in the universe, but that may be a cover story used to camouflage its true purpose, just like Blue Book used its public UFO investigation as a pretext to gather intelligence on ET activity. When one considers the Roswell Incident, Majestic-12, Blue Book, SETI and the rest of it in its entirety, one can help but wonder if the Fermi paradox itself is an invention of the Majestic-12 operation.

In conclusion, there is no Fermi paradox. What's more, Roswell is the Rosetta stone for understanding the flying saucer phenomenon. The recovery of an ET spacecraft set in motion a policy of secrecy, cover-up and denial that has been in place since 1947. Roswell is also unique among UFO incidents, which are usually fleeting events lacking a definitive resolution, in that it ends the debate about UFOs. Once in possession of the hard evidence, the Majestic-12 scientific team had the means to confirm that the craft and crew were extraterrestrial. The private investigation led by Friedman, Schmittt, Carey and others shows that unambiguous proof in the form of hard physical evidence, said to be lacking by a hostile scientific establishment, exists under lock and key. Roswell renders moot all arguments about secret American or foreign technology, misidentifications, hoaxes and natural phenomena. The Roswell Incident makes it unambiguously clear that that there is a superior extraterrestrial civilization above and beyond ours.

The only remaining question is whether the existence of spacefaring ETs does indeed mean the galaxy has been colonized. Is one confirmed instance of extraterrestrial visitation enough to justify such a conclusion? Is Roswell just the tip of the iceberg? Are we merely being visited by "legitimate explorers from afar" or are we embedded within a much more highly advanced galactic civilization? What does disclosure of the extraterrestrial presence really mean?

CHAPTER 3

DISCLOSURE

He went on to further explain that this was the material that had come from a New Mexico crash in 1947 of an extraterrestrial craft and that was discussed at length… I did not have any more contact with the subject matter of UFOs until after I came in contact with the President [Eisenhower].
— **Brigadier General Stephen Lovekin, on his training and experience in the subject of UFOs, 2000**

For those people that say that if these UFO's existed, they would some day be on radar and that there'd be professionals who would see it, then I can tell them that back in 1986 there were enough professional people who saw it.
— **FAA Division Chief John Callahan, 2000**

THE RUN-UP TO DISCLOSURE

After the initial excitement over *The Day After* Roswell waned amidst skepticism, debunking and disbelief, Colonel Corso must have felt like he was back out in the lonely New Mexico desert by himself in the middle of the night. Much like the mysterious green fireballs that briefly turned night into day, the light from his revelations was swallowed up by the return of the darkness. The Air Force maintained its "case closed" stance. No one in the government or the media questioned the Air Force about anything in Corso's book despite the GAO's finding that permanent records at Roswell Army Air Field had been destroyed without explanation. The media quickly turned its back on the story and congress failed to make any kind of official inquiry or arrange hearings as they had when Corso had blown the whistle on the Korean POW controversy. The lack of an official response to Corso's revelations was especially puzzling in light of President Clinton's public display of interest in UFOs and the Roswell Incident.

When Clinton took office he appointed good friend Webster Hubbell to Associate Attorney General at the Department of Justice and made a special request. "Web… If I put you over at Justice, I want you to find the answers to two questions for me. One, who killed JFK? And two, are there UFOs?" wrote Clinton's buddy in his autobiography, *Friends in High Places*. Unfortunately Hubbell got nowhere. "I had looked into both but wasn't satisfied with the answers I was getting," Hubbell wrote of his failure to fulfill Clinton's request.[1]

It wasn't the only time President Clinton expressed an interest in UFOs. At public appearance in Northern Ireland in 1995 he used the occasion to answer a letter from a kid in Belfast who had written him about the Roswell Incident. "No, as far as I know, an alien spacecraft did not crash in Roswell, New Mexico in 1947. And, Ryan, If the United States Air Force did recover alien bodies, they didn't tell me about it either, and I want to know," said Clinton.[2]

In 1998 the Lewinsky scandal revealed further evidence of Clinton's lust for knowledge about Roswell. During the investigation the Clinton White House was forced to produce a list of books in the President's personal library. Researcher Grant Cameron noted the catalog submitted by Clinton was very telling for what was on it and what wasn't. The President's literary collection included *UFO Crash at Roswell* by Kevin Randle and Don Schmitt, but not the Air Force's "case closed" attempt to debunk the matter once and for all. Clinton's choice of source material regarding Roswell reflected his buddy Web Hubbell's experience. It seems Clinton didn't buy the Air Force's case closed report and wasn't satisfied with the answers he was getting either.

Also missing from Clinton's personal collection was *The Day After Roswell*, but it's hard not to believe that it must've been hidden under a couch cushion somewhere. The President had to know about Corso's book given his relationship with prominent White House correspondent Sarah McClendon, who reported on it in her coverage of the Rockefeller Initiative.[3]

While the Establishment was busy pooh-poohing Corso, famed White House correspondent Sarah McClendon, a legend in Washington since World War II, gave the story the sober treatment it deserved with *Lid*

Coming Off Government Cover-up on UFOs.[4] According to McClendon, Rockefeller provided information for the President and first lady and arranged briefings for members of the Clinton administration, including Science Advisor Jack Gibbons, Personal Advisor Bruce Lindsay, National Security Advisor Anthony Lake and Vice President Al Gore. Steven Greer personally briefed Clinton's CIA director James Woolsey. Greer led a growing movement of government insider witnesses seeking to blow the whistle about UFOs, which were as McClendon reported, "actual visitors from other worlds." She said the witness pool included Colonel Philip Corso, whose recent book about the Roswell Incident completely refuted the Air Force's explanations. What's more, McClendon reported that Corso and hundreds of others like him were willing to swear under oath before Congress that extraterrestrial craft are "repeatedly penetrating our airspace."

In what should've been a major scoop, McClendon outed to the Rockefeller Initiative as the reason Clinton asked his good buddy Web Hubbell to find out if UFOs were real. This was just the type of backstory that should've sparked media frenzy. Instead, the establishment simply ignored McClendon as it had Corso. Unfortunately, Clinton did too, at least publicly.

It seems absurd that a President seeking the truth about UFOs could overlook a Pentagon whistleblower of Corso's stature. Perhaps the controversy over Senator Thurmond's foreword made Corso politically radioactive or maybe Clinton didn't really want to know the truth? Whatever the case, he never publicly acknowledged Corso, who died of a heart attack at age eighty-three less than a year after publication of *The Day After Roswell.*

Even more disturbing, Clinton's strange behavior may have had something to do with a secret he told McClendon, something she alluded to when she wrote that Web Hubbell had been "boxed in" at the Justice Department when he attempted to get the truth about UFOs. According to Greer, McClendon said that when she asked the President point blank if he would make the truth about UFOs public Clinton said he couldn't because of a secret government within the government over which he had no control.[5]

This was precisely the scenario that Corso had written about. Truman didn't see how such a government-within-the-government scheme could work and he was afraid things would spin out of control.[6] Truman's successor, Dwight Eisenhower hinted that Truman's worst fears had come to pass in his infamous farewell address warning about the unwarranted influence of the military-industrial complex. The Presidency had lost control of the issue. Clinton was simply out of the loop. He must've gotten the chills when he read *The Day After Roswell* and realized that he was living the nightmare that Truman feared.

The President wasn't alone on the hot seat. Disclosure advocates targeted Congress as well. In July 1998, two weeks before Corso's death, McClendon followed up on her initial report with *Pressure is building for Congressional Hearings on UFOs*. The veteran White House correspondent reported that scientists at Stanford, MIT, Cornell, Princeton and elsewhere were studying UFO evidence and members of congress were beginning to respond to briefings they'd taken.[7] A staff member for Congressman Dan Burton said there was a possibility that Congressional hearings would be held. McClendon then hinted at the utterly fantastic significance of UFO disclosure when she reported Greer's claim that ET spacecraft didn't run on gasoline. UFO technology had the potential to end our addiction to oil, reverse environmental damage and save hundreds of billions of dollars every year. But nevermind all that. The mainstream media was busy with its breathless, wall-to-wall coverage of the Monica Lewinsky scandal, including the grand jury testimony of Linda Tripp and the infamous blue dress. Again the establishment media chose to ignore McClendon's reporting on the biggest story in the history of this civilization.

COMETA BY THE TAIL

The mainstream media looked down its nose at Corso, but as he warned, others were taking the extraterrestrial phenomenon far more seriously. In 1999, a major new study was published in France called, "*UFOs and Defense: What must we be prepared for?*"[8] High-level officials including retired generals and scientists participated in a three-year study known as the COMETA report. COMETA was an acronym for "Committee for in-depth studies." The foreword was written by the former President of the French equivalent of NASA, Andre Lebeau, who compared UFOs to meteorites.

Reports of flaming stones falling from the sky were once thought to be nothing more than the product of folklore until a really big meteorite shower brought the phenomenon out of the realm of mythology and into the annals of science. Like meteors and the science of astronomy, UFOs can only be studied through observation. They can't be subject to reproducible experiments, which are considered the bedrock of the scientific method. Unlike astronomy, where the scale of events makes broad observation the equivalent of reproducible experiments, UFO sightings are much more discrete incidents that invite suspicion. Complicating matters, the onset of the space age made observations of anomalous atmospheric phenomena much less unambiguous. There were plenty of manmade objects and human activities to muddy the waters. Establishing the facts about UFOs was difficult to be sure, but the biggest obstacle in the study of the phenomenon was what Lebeau called its "irrational environment," which he said had caused the scientific community to relegate the subject to the realm of mythology.

In other words, all the hype about the possibility of extraterrestrial visitors was a turn off to the scientific community. Lebeau argued that the existence of such extraterrestrial-mania was actually a strong reason for science to apply its methods to the problem. It was in this spirit, he said, that COMETA had done its best to strip the UFO phenomenon of its "irrational layer" with a thorough assessment of the facts.

COMETA presented its report to President Jacques Chirac and Prime Minister Lionel Jospin before it was made public.[9] The study was based upon roughly 500 unexplained UFO reports, including sightings made by pilots where UFOs were seen both visually and on radar.[10] COMETA considered the full spectrum of possible explanations for the small percentage of well-documented, close-range encounters with unknown, high-performance craft that appear to be under intelligent control. COMETA found that no simple or mundane explanation could resolve all the evidence.

Skeptics and debunkers have long claimed that UFOs are only unidentified because of a lack of evidence and that all cases could be explained in conventional terms if only there were more data. COMETA found that the opposite was true. High-quality UFO sightings are more difficult to explain. COMETA labeled this type of report as Unidentified Aerial Phenomena – Category D. According to the committee, UAP-Ds remained unexplainable "despite the abundance and quality of the data." These are sightings in which the witnesses experience the phenomenon up close and personal, sometimes mere feet from an object that is on or near the ground. UAP-Ds comprise about 5 percent of all UFO reports after misidentifications, mistakes and hoaxes are filtered out.[11] They represent the core of the UFO phenomenon.

Skeptics and debunkers also claim that UFOs that appear to be alien technology are really just classified earthly technology. COMETA rejected this explanation because no government would allow civilians and foreign authorities to see technology it was trying to keep secret. COMETA concluded, "In fact, if it were a question of terrestrial craft, these could only be American and, despite all precautions to maintain secrecy, this would be known. The first prototype stealth aircraft flew at the end of 1977; the existence of stealth aircraft became known about ten years later, in 1988. But credible, confirmed UFO sightings began in 1944."[12] After considering a wide range of possibilities including psychological and parapsychological phenomena, mass hallucinations, disinformation attempts, holographic imagery, secret weaponry and unknown natural phenomena, COMETA concluded that the only explanation that could explain all the data was the Extraterrestrial hypothesis.[13]

COMETA's conclusions brought the study full circle. Speculation about ETs alienated the scientific community so COMETA tried to set things straight with a sober study to establish the facts about UFOs, which ironically resulted in its endorsement of the ETH. COMETA wasn't brave enough to claim it had proven its case, but it did say the physical reality of UFOs under the control of intelligent beings was "almost certain." And it did its best to dispel the myopic assumption that UFOs couldn't be ET craft by noting such previous egregious examples of establishment myopia: *"You cannot breathe in tunnels," "Science is almost finished," "Something heavier than air cannot fly," etc.* It would therefore be presumptuous to claim to foresee, based on our knowledge and our current accomplishments, what might be technologies that are only slightly more advanced than our own - or our own technologies in one or two centuries. Let us consider that only 150 years ago, engines, electricity, the existence of the atom, and Hertzian waves were unknown."[14]

Like Fermi, COMETA thought ETs were likely thousands of years more advanced than we are, which meant they would have developed in ways beyond our wildest dreams. To such a civilization, interstellar travel may be as routine as intercontinental travel is to us. Travel between the stars may only be impossible in the same way that heavier-than-air flight was impossible right up until the Wright Brothers took to the skies at Kitty Hawk. Advances in physics hint that the faster-than-light travel will follow suit. Carl Sagan raised the possibility that wormholes could be used as an interstellar shortcut in his novel *Contact*. Sagan envisioned an interstellar superhighway made from a network of wormholes that enabled direct contact between advanced interstellar civilizations. So far such speculation has failed to persuade the scientific community to change its belief that UFOs can't be extraterrestrial spacecraft, but change seems inevitable. COMETA showed that it wasn't just science fiction about the far-flung future that made extraterrestrial UFOs possible. Our current understanding of science shows that an extraterrestrial civilization just a hundred years more advanced than us could have settled in the asteroid belt. COMETA noted a model for interstellar colonization developed by astronomers, Jean-Claude Ribes and Guy Monnet that could make us the mysterious UFO pilots of another world in about a century. Ribes and Monnet envisioned the construction of large habitats in space that would orbit Earth, reside within asteroids and eventually migrate to other star systems using anti-matter propulsion, which will be feasible in about a hundred years or so. In this scenario, star colonists from Earth will "visit the planets of the receiving system aboard craft that are perceived by any possible natives the same way we perceive UFOs today," wrote COMETA.[15]

If we will be able to colonize another star system within a century or two, then an extraterrestrial civilization thousands of years more advanced than we are could have already moved into ours. Such a civilization could have placed a colony in the asteroid belt between Mars and Jupiter, which in turn could be responsible for UFO sightings. The possibility led COMETA to conclude that the Extraterrestrial hypothesis was plausible and that such intractable skepticism was no longer warranted.

COMETA's study included a historical review of research in the US, the UK and Russia. In the US, COMETA found glaring contradictions between the truth on the ground and official statements from on up high. For instance, the Air Force claimed to have ended its investigation of UFOs with the closing of Project Blue Book in 1969. Only it wasn't true. Official documents uncovered through FOIA requests showed that military UFO reports considered a threat to national security were never a part of the public Blue Book system and the investigation of such reports continued in accordance with military regulations AFR 200-2 and JANAP 146.[16] These regulations, which COMETA characterized as an "impressive repressive arsenal," were tools of secrecy that made it illegal for military personnel and even civilian pilots to reveal their experiences to the public under the penalty of a hefty fine and a 10-year prison sentence.[17] Throughout it all, COMETA noted, the authorities in the US consistently maintained that the UFO phenomenon was not a threat to national security and wasn't evidence of extraterrestrial activity.

COMETA found further layers of contradiction in the shuttering of Project Blue Book. The Air Force justified its decision to close Blue Book on a study it commissioned known as the Condon report, directed by University of Colorado physicist Edward Condon, who concluded there was nothing to UFOs that warranted further study.

The Air Force welcomed the report despite harsh criticism from the American Institute of Aeronautics and Astronautics that Condon's conclusions contradicted findings in the body of the study.[18] And it wasn't just the analysis of staff scientists that contradicted Condon. The report included the Twining letter written in the immediate aftermath of the Roswell Incident that showed the Air Force knew that flying saucers were "real and not visionary or fictitious."[19] The memo not only showed the government was lying about UFOs it also revealed some pretty big clues about the secret UFO operation, according to Corso.[20] It was also the first time the Twining letter was made public, which was beyond ironic.

How could the scientific report used to kill the UFO for all time contain such compelling contradictory evidence? Was this some sort of black propaganda Jedi mind trick or was it a product of the disclosure-by-cover-up scheme written about by Corso and Birnes? Whatever the case, the Twining letter added weight to the AIAA's criticism that Condon's conclusions didn't jibe with the rest of his report.

COMETA found that Condon's "strange conclusions" were symptomatic of the US government's policy of "increasing secrecy" and "constant disinformation" about UFOs of which Roswell was a primary example. COMETA concluded that the Air Force's "clumsy attempts" at explaining the incident and its unauthorized destruction of official records meant the US military was "hiding something important" just like it had with its deadly plutonium experiments.[21]

COMETA found the government used two distinct disinformation techniques to keep the big secret. The first, which it called "simplified disinformation," was effective on those who would believe any alternative explanation because they couldn't wrap their minds around the possibility of an extraterrestrial presence. COMETA used Blue Book astronomer J. Allen Hynek's infamous "swamp gas" explanation for high-profile UFO sightings in Michigan back in the 60s as an example of simplified disinformation.

Enhanced disinformation was more sophisticated. The government used enhanced disinformation like a magician used misdirection. COMETA fingered the alien autopsy hoax that aired in the mid '90s as a prime example of such a "well-orchestrated manipulation." The film not only helped debunk the Roswell Incident, it knocked the GAO's report about the illegal destruction of Roswell's official records out of the headlines, causing the more substantial news fly under the radar.

COMETA found disinformation in *The Roswell Report: Case Closed*, the Air Force's ultimate attempt to rid itself of the Roswell controversy once and for all. "Simplified disinformation is apparent in the Air Force report: testimonies on the debris have been cut down so as to give credence to the Mogul balloon hypothesis," wrote COMETA, adding, "It is also found, more subtly, in *Roswell in Perspective*, a book by 'ufologist' Karl Pflock, a former CIA and DoD employee: affidavits mentioning the tear-proof and crease-resistant material are given in full in an appendix, but they are ignored or cited only in shortened form in the text."[22]

COMETA had good reason to single out Pflock. His career as an ufologist was suspect at best. Historian Richard Dolan found substantial evidence that Pflock had been part of a CIA effort to infiltrate NICAP, the country's first civilian UFO investigation, which resulted in the ousting of its director, Major Donald Keyhoe, who had identified the CIA as the heart of the UFO cover-up.[23] Ergo, it should come as no surprise that Pflock was also a Corso debunker. Corso not only spilled the beans about Roswell he exposed the conflict between the CIA and the military within Majestic-12 over UFO policy and the Roswell technology.[24] Corso flat-out stated the CIA was the enemy. It's hardly surprising that an "ex-CIA ufologist" known for using disinformation techniques would do whatever he could to debunk an effort to expose the truth about Roswell.

Such shenanigans led COMETA to make the commonsense argument that the witnesses who reported the crash of an ET spacecraft should be taken seriously.[25] Of all the Roswell witnesses Corso was certainly one of the most important and COMETA treated him as such. "Some of these claims are surprising at the very least, but the entire contents of the book cannot be easily dismissed when one considers the remarkable career of its author and Senator Thurmond's tribute to him," wrote COMETA, who dismissed the controversy over Thurmond's forward as contrived.

In fact, COMETA was sufficiently impressed with the Colonel and his tell-all to consider the possibility that the publication of *The Day After Roswell* was the result of the Majestic-12 disclosure-by-cover-up scheme. "As soon as the book came out, the U.S. Air Force published a second report on Roswell again denying the plausibility of the hypothesis of the crash of an extraterrestrial craft... This reaction is not incompatible with Colonel Corso's theories: it may be intended to reassure those whom Corso's revelations might worry," wrote COMETA.[26]

The Disclosure-by-cover-up scheme neatly resolved what COMETA characterized as the strange position of the U.S. government in regards to UFOs, which led the committee to ask perhaps the most important question: "Why would, and how could, such an important secret be kept all the way up to the present, despite everything? The simplest response would be that the United States wants to maintain at any cost military technological superiority over rival countries," concluded COMETA about the value of the extraterrestrial technology pulled from the Roswell desert.[27]

COMETA found many more reasons that might justify the official policy of denial ranging from public hysteria to the Cold War to the insecurity of political figures unable to provide explanations or solutions, among others.

The extraterrestrial presence raised many questions. Without answers it could be difficult, even undesirable, to deal with the UFO problem in an official capacity. For instance, government disclosures might undermine confidence in the military, which couldn't defend against an Independence Day-type alien invasion. As Corso said, "we simply denied all extraterrestrial activity because no aliens meant no military responsibility to counter their threat."[28]

COMETA considered the military implications and found invasion unlikely because it would've occurred long ago, long before the Army recovered an ET spacecraft, long before Trudeau and Corso set about reverse engineering the Roswell technology and long before we had developed the ability to mount a defense of the planet. In fact, an invasion could've occurred before we'd even discovered the atom.

COMETA noted the lack of evidence of a hostile intent. Yet, the stealth with which UFOs conduct their activities hinted at a subversive purpose. "If they are observing us, it is necessary to note an apparent contradiction between the interest that they show in us and their furtiveness. Rather than observe us, it seems that they want to show themselves to us and to gradually acclimate us to the idea of their existence," wrote COMETA, suggesting that ETs might have undertaken an effort to engage us, not for the purpose of imposing their will upon us, which wouldn't be difficult given their obvious superiority, but to warn us off the use of nuclear weapons.[29]

UFO demonstrations over nuclear missile bases led COMETA to conclude that ETs might be warning us that nuclear war was an existential threat. They may also be wary of our intentions to bring nuclear weapons into their territory. COMETA argued that if extraterrestrials have established bases on the moon, Mars, the asteroid belt or elsewhere in the solar system, they might feel threatened by our behavior. The committee warned that even though ETs hadn't intervened in our affairs in the past they might in the future. In other words, if extraterrestrials do feel threatened by our nuclear arsenal and we continue to ignore their warnings, we might bring about our greatest fears in confronting a more powerful biological entity from a different world, to use Corso's words.

In its conclusion, COMETA made recommendations based on the near certainty of extraterrestrial UFOs. Unlike the Condon Report, its conclusions and recommendations accurately reflected the analysis in the body of the study. COMETA recommended a general education campaign targeting industries and institutions most likely to be directly impacted by extraterrestrial activity such as the aviation and air defense industries. In stark contrast to the Condon report, COMETA also proposed further study of the UFO phenomenon, and finally, the committee called for a European alliance to undertake a diplomatic mission to engage the United States on the UFO issue.[30]

COMETA delivered an explosive report, essentially reversing the travesty of science that was the Condon study. Unfortunately, it wasn't considered newsworthy by the mainstream broadcast networks in the U.S. It took a monumental effort by freelance journalist Leslie Kean to finally convince one of the nation's newspapers of note, *The Boston Globe*, to publish a sober article about the French study. Over a period of months, Kean submitted the article to approximately 20 papers receiving little interest before the Globe agreed to publish her report.[31] Like Sarah McClendon, Kean brought honest straightforward reporting to the UFO subject without ridicule and quips about little green men that have plagued articles on UFOs since the 50s. What's more, Kean brought a depth of reporting to the subject not usually seen in the mainstream media. She sought out Astronaut Edgar Mitchell, who had become increasingly outspoken on UFOs over the years, for his reaction to the COMETA report. Mitchell said, "It's significant that individuals of some standing in the government, military, and intelligence community in France came forth with this," adding "The only thing that's lacking is the official stamp."[32]

The COMETA Report gave the disclosure movement some real momentum. It looked as if McClendon was right and the lid was truly coming off the dark days of the UFO cover-up. It seemed as if the disclosure-by-cover-up plan was beginning to mature and skepticism was giving way to common acceptance of the truth as Twining had foreseen. But human imagination is limited. Twining was unable to anticipate just how difficult acknowledgment of such a paradigm-altering reality could be. To understand how UFOs fit into our world, one has to take a cold, hard look at the world we're trying to fit them into.

THE BELTWAY MERRY-GO-ROUND

In the mind of the general public, the cultural "official stamp" can only come from one place- Washington D.C. The building symbolic of all that is officialdom is, of course, the White House. The processes by which official decisions are made flows in sometimes unorthodox and organic ways from this ground zero of our culture. In the past, unofficial venues sometimes served as a catalyst for what would later become official policy. One such place was the famous Willard Hotel. The hotel has hosted every president in some capacity from 1853 up until the present. In *The Atlantic Monthly* during the civil war, writer Nathaniel Hawthorne wrote of the Willard, "This hotel, in fact, may be much more justly called the center of Washington and the Union than either the Capitol, the White House, or the State Department." President Ulysses S. Grant often fled the pressures of the Oval Office to the lobby of the Willard for a cigar and a brandy. Power brokers would approach him seeking his influence on behalf of a special interest or cause. Grant called them "lobbyists," a term with roots in seventeenth century England which referred to citizens who would gather in a lobby near the House of Commons to express their views to members of parliament.

Today, lobbyists are perhaps the most powerful influence on government. Recently, the number of lobbyists in Washington has exploded. Between 2000 and 2005, the number of lobbyists in Washington D.C. doubled to approximately 35,000- almost 70 lobbyists for every congressman.[33] One recent estimate has lobbyists numbering over 90,000. Lobbyists have become hired guns who will seek to influence congress and the chief executive on behalf of whatever entity is willing to pay to advance their interests. Large corporations seeking legislation favorable to their bottom line deploy lobbyists like a vast capitalist army. According to author, Kevin Phillips, the failure of the government is far beyond simplistic talk of gridlock. A class of elitists has stolen political and economic influence from America's grass roots. Phillips stated that since the 1940s, an elite special interest group has increasingly overwhelmed Washington. This elite group, now thoroughly embedded, is resistant to change, effectively short-circuiting the proper functioning of government.[34] The recent Citizen's United Supreme Court ruling that corporations are people and money is free speech has further enabled the elite takeover of Washington D.C. The concept of the common good has become an anachronistic romantic illusion replaced by an unbridled capitalist orgy.

Congressmen are for sale and the payola is everywhere. The Enron, Abramoff and Randall "Duke" Cunningham scandals made explicit the fact that government is up for sale to the highest bidder. Despite these scandals, which took place in the first half of the 2000s, the atmosphere of corruption has only worsened. Lobbyists played a central role in the great economic crisis of 2008. The financial industry lobbied the Clinton administration to undo regulations that had been in put in place in the aftermath of the Great Depression setting the stage for another epic economic crisis. After the bank bailout in 2008, this enabled financial institutions deemed "too big to fail" to engage in high-risk speculation with the implicit guarantee of the government. In effect, this meant that big banks were free to gamble with taxpayer money. It was the best of all possible worlds. Banks that would get to keep the winnings when their bets paid off would also be allowed to dump losses on the American people when their bets went bad.[35]

In the aftermath of the economic collapse of 2008, lobbyists prevented the reinstitution of meaningful financial regulations. Former Bloomberg economic reporter and MSNBC news talk show host Dylan Ratigan, author of *New York Times* bestseller *Greedy Bastards*, called efforts at financial reform a con job and compared Wall Street to the mob and the Federal Reserve to the Godfather.[36]

Internationally renowned trends expert and director of the Trends Research Institute Gerald Celente was even more explicit about the role played by lobbyists in our political system. "In 2008, financial and real estate interests spent $345.4 million to buy politicians and control legislation. Washington called it "campaign financing" and "lobbying." Anywhere else it was called "bribery," wrote Celente.[37]

In 2010 health industry lobbyists successfully "lobbied" the government to kill the highly popular single-payer and public-option, preventing any real meaningful healthcare reform. In the process, they won a mandate that would require the public to buy their products thus delivering a windfall of new customers. Former insurance industry executive turned whistleblower Wendell Potter warned the House Democratic Steering and Policy Committee that if Congress "fails to create a public insurance option to compete with private insurers, the bill it sends to the president might as well be called the Insurance Industry Profit Protection and Enhancement Act."[38]

The Enron and Abramoff scandals along with the failures to reform the financial and health insurance industries call into question the true state of our union. Rolling Stone reporter Matt Taibbi wrote of the implications of the health care reform debacle, "The cost of all of this to society, in illness and death and lost productivity and a soaring federal deficit and plain old anxiety and anger, is incalculable – and that's the good news. The bad news is that our failed health care system won't get fixed, because it exists entirely within the confines of yet another failed system: the political entity known as the United States of America."[39]

Lobbyist bribery has become standard operating procedure with ties reaching all the way up to the White House. Vast schemes to grab as much money as possible, legally or illegally, are launched in Enron-like boardrooms across America. Corporate profits and thievery have replaced any pretense of government serving the common interest. In this atmosphere, there are no large corporations lobbying for the truth about UFOs.

In fact, there is only *one* UFO lobbyist in Washington and he has no corporate sponsors. Activist Stephen Bassett, executive director of both the Paradigm Research Group and the Extraterrestrial Phenomena Political Action Committee (X-PPAC), is the only lobbyist on Capital Hill advocating for disclosure of the truth about UFOs. He can't "lobby" in any modern sense of the word because he doesn't have the millions in corporate backing it takes to be heard in Washington these days.[40] And he faces an army of lobbyists whose corporate interests may not only be indifferent to disclosure but may be hostile to it. In the context of Corso's testimony about the operation to seed the alien technology recovered at Roswell into private industry, there appear to be corporations with a vested interest in suppressing knowledge about the extraterrestrial presence. Not to mention the fossil fuel industry lobby, which has perhaps the biggest incentive of all to pretend there are no ET spaceships traversing our skies.

It is little wonder that Corso expressed serious doubt that the publication of *The Day After Roswell* would result in congressional hearings. Corso was skeptical that any congressman would take up the cause as House Republican Bob Dornan had with the Korean POWs- a controversial subject, but much less so than UFOs.[41] To such a public figure, there is simply too much downside in taking the risk of being branded a nut in an environment in which the public has been conditioned to rubbish anyone seriously addressing the UFO issue. In light of Washington D.C.'s Capitol Hill Con Game, aptly described as a *Griftopia* by Taibbi, one might ask oneself what congressman is going to risk being thrown off the gravy train currently circling the beltway like the monorail at Disneyland? Under these conditions it seemed disclosure of the truth about UFOs on the national stage was a complete impossibility- or was it?

URGENT DISCLOSURE

The Willard Hotel, the unofficial hub of power of Washington D.C. used by lobbyists to sway presidents and other power brokers to their causes in bygone days, was also the birthplace of the National Press Club, whose constitution and bylaws were passed in a meeting at the Willard in 1908. Every president since Teddy Roosevelt has been a NPC member and most have spoken from its podium, occasionally using the forum to launch a campaign for the presidency. The "Journalist's Creed" written by the founder of the first school of journalism, Walter Williams, is featured prominently on the club's website. "I believe that the public journal is a public trust; that all connected with it are, to the full measure of responsibility, trustees for the public; that acceptance of a lesser service than the public service is a betrayal of trust," wrote Williams. It was in this spirit that longtime White House correspondent Sarah McClendon, Dr. Steven Greer and a group of military-industrial complex whistleblowers known as the *Disclosure Project*, gathered in the ballroom at the storied National Press Club on May 9th, 2001 to make history.

Greer took the podium flanked by witnesses who had been in Air Force Intelligence, the Federal Aviation Administration (FAA), the Central Intelligence Agency (CIA), the Defense Intelligence Agency (DIA), the National Reconnaissance Office (NRO), Army, Navy, and the Marine Corps. The group also included corporate witnesses who'd been contractors to the government working on black budget projects. It was an impressive panel to say the least. In fact, the press conference delivered by Greer would've surely ended the UFO cover-up had he been president.

In the main ballroom filled to capacity, *Hill Street Blues* actor, Jon Cypher introduced Greer as a brave man who'd given up a lucrative career in medicine to pursue the truth about UFOs. Indeed, the emergency room doctor seemed an unlikely figure to lead a movement of military-industrial complex insiders. A married man with four daughters, Greer had been Chairman of the Department of Emergency Medicine at Caldwell Memorial Hospital in North Carolina. He'd had a successful, rather conventional life. First-hand experience with the UFO phenomenon drove him to risk his status and the future well-being of his family.

In 1990, Greer founded the Center for the Study of Extraterrestrial Intelligence (CSETI), a nonprofit research and education outfit not to be confused with SETI, the program to search for ET radio signals. According to Greer, white papers he wrote based on his research, including *Extraterrestrial contact: The Evidence and the Implications* became a hit within the aerospace industry. By 1993 his work was well known in certain circles and he developed a network of military, political and scientific contacts. It was then that he began to gather witnesses in pursuit of official UFO disclosure.[42]

Following Cypher's inspired introduction, Greer took the stage to applause and announced that 21 of over 400 Disclosure Project witnesses had come to prove that we were not alone in the universe. He thanked Sarah McClendon, seated in the front row, for sponsoring the press conference and began dropping bombshell after bombshell. He said he'd personally briefed the head of DIA, head of intelligence joint staff, members of the senate intelligence committee, members of congress, members of European leadership, the Japanese cabinet and others including CIA Director James Woolsey.[43]

Anyone unfamiliar with UFO matters – such as the mainstream media - was likely confused. Why would a CIA Director require a briefing from a civilian on the subject of UFOs? In fact, such counterintuitive, Alice in Wonderland through-the-looking-glass effects are typical in UFO affairs. One would expect journalists attending a press conference at the storied National Press Club to follow up and investigate such a juicy claim in the spirit of the Journalist's Creed, but Big Media left it to independent investigators like Grant Cameron to ferret out the backstory.

Cameron made FOIA requests to the Office of Science and Technology at the Clinton White House and received nearly a thousand pages of UFO related documents, which have been published on his website presidentialufo.com. Cameron's work shows how the most powerful office in the world has dealt with its biggest secret.[44]

The narrative he uncovered painted Woolsey was an outsider with little experience. Career bureaucrats at the CIA treated him as a political appointee who was nothing more than a temporary figurehead. What's more, the Clinton Administration had asked him to cut seven billion dollars from the intelligence budget in the wake of the demise of the Soviet Union and the end of the Cold War. As a result, Woolsey was not a popular guy. They weren't going to just give him the Big Secret. When Woolsey asked he was given the official public relations standard line that Project Blue Book shut down in 1969. The CIA made it clear to Woolsey and Clinton that if they wanted information about UFOs they'd have to go through other channels.

The Clinton administration went looking for UFO information at a time when Greer's work was just beginning to get noticed. Woolsey's close personal friend John Peterson, a former NSC staffer and the director of a Washington think tank called *The Arlington Institute,* approached Greer after a lecture at Colorado State University and offered to arrange a secret briefing for his buddy Woolsey using a dinner party as a cover story.

According to Greer, the CIA director was in a state of panic once he realized extraterrestrial UFOs were a reality – not because of the existence of the UFOs themselves – but because he'd been kept out of the loop. When Greer pressed him to force disclosure Woolsey resisted claiming he couldn't release "what I don't have access to."[45]

After meeting with Greer, Woolsey ordered a review of all CIA files on UFOs in an ill-fated attempt to get access. The agency he supposedly led rebuffed him again with a fresh debunking effort that claimed more than half of all UFO sightings in the 50s and 60s were caused by U-2 and SR-71 spy planes. But the report didn't give a single example of such a case. Ufologists universally rejected it prima facie. Woolsey had gotten nowhere. In December 1994, he resigned from his post.

As Sarah McClendon noted, this was happening behind the scenes. No one was reporting on it. Greer didn't go public with the briefing until after Woolsey resigned and Webster Hubbell made Clinton's interest in UFOs public.[46] Unfortunately, Woolsey tried to deny the briefing by using the dinner party cover story. He never denied meeting with Greer or discussing UFOs, but he claimed it was just dinner table chitchat. Greer fired back, calling the former CIA director turned lobbyist a liar who had betrayed his responsibilities as a public servant. Woolsey never responded.

The episode was a golden opportunity for journalists. Greer and his team briefed others in the Clinton administration, including Deputy White House Counsel Bruce Lindsey, one of Clinton's close personal friends. Briefings and materials were also provided for the president's Science and Technology Advisor Jack Gibbons and National Security Advisor Anthony Lake, as well as Vice President Al Gore and his staff. And, although Greer never briefed Clinton personally, he forwarded briefing materials specifically for the president.

The full magnitude of the UFO issue must have dawned on Clinton at some point. When pressed by Sarah McClendon about UFO secrecy, Clinton expressed frustration over a "secret government within the government" over which he had no control. Word eventually came back to Greer through an intermediary that although the Clinton administration shared the project's objectives they were unable to help. Greer was told that the President was afraid he'd end up like Kennedy if he tried to end UFO cover-up. The message back from Clinton was, "I can't do this, but you can."[47] Shortly thereafter, Greer began preparing for disclosure without the official stamp of the government just as he warned Woolsey he would. This unofficial civilian disclosure initiative came to fruition as the Disclosure Project press conference at the National Press Club.

Amidst flashbulbs and video cameras, Greer explained that the Disclosure Project had identified over 400 witnesses and more than 100 of them had been interviewed and their testimony recorded on 120 hours of videotape. The video testimony had been distilled down to four hours as well as published in a 570-page book called Disclosure- all made available to the media. Detailed versions of each of the witnesses' press conference testimony could be found in the book.

Greer said that Disclosure Project witnesses felt a sense of urgency to disclose the truth about UFOs. Many of them worked in black budget projects that were taking in between 40 and 80 billion dollars a year and sitting on technology that could change the world. "It has the most profound implications for the human future, U.S. National Security and for world peace. Specifically, technologies connected to UFOs and extraterrestrial vehicles, if declassified, and used for peaceful energy generation and propulsion would solve the looming energy crisis definitively, would end global warming, would correct environmental challenges that the Earth is facing," said Greer, explaining that UFO disclosure wasn't just an issue of great academic importance, it was also one of great practical urgency.

Worldwide, calls are growing louder to address global warming induced climate change. Since 1988, the Intergovernmental Panel on Climate Change (IPCC) has been studying the effects of industrialized civilization on Earth's climate. The results are in and the news isn't good. Human activities are the driving force behind potentially catastrophic climate change.[48]

Unfortunately, any proposal to reverse global warming by reducing or replacing oil, coal and natural gas represents an existential threat to an energy industry that contributes mightily to the army of lobbyists in Washington.[49] Predictably, the issue has become politicized. Despite the overwhelming scientific consensus, climate change deniers oppose any action to reduce greenhouse gasses, variously claiming that the science is unsettled or that global warming is a completely natural phenomenon unrelated to our polluting activities or that it's a hoax perpetrated by the IPCC to keep the research funds rolling in. But climate change is neither a liberal plot nor a cash cow for climate scientists. It's clear that our environment is suffering death by a thousand cuts.

In 2004, a Pentagon report leaked to the media found that climate change was a threat to destroy civilization. In fact, researchers warned the Pentagon to brace itself for rising sea levels, mega-droughts, famine, disease, population migration, widespread rioting and even the possibility of nuclear war over dwindling resources, including food, water and oil. Much of Europe will sink beneath rising seas and Britain's climate will become like Siberia's, said Authors Peter Schwartz and Doug Randall, who flatly stated that climate change "should be elevated beyond a scientific debate to a US national security concern."[50]

The Pentagon knows, of course, that the resource wars have already begun. By 2007 it was pretty much common knowledge that non-existent weapons of mass destruction were merely a pretext for the Iraq war which was really about oil, or to be more specific, "peak oil."[51] When half of Earth's oil has been extracted we'll have reached peaked production after which there will be an inevitable decline. What's more, since we've already gobbled the low-hanging fruit the rest will be much more difficult to harvest.[52] The BP oil spill in the Gulf of Mexico illustrates the challenges of drilling the ocean floor a mile beneath the surface. The catastrophe is a good example of how much more difficult drilling for oil will be going forward and it may be a sign that we've already hit the peak, which will be difficult to recognize until well after the fact.

Concern for the future of the planet and the sustainability of civilization weren't the only reasons Disclosure Project witnesses felt an urgent need to tell the world the truth out about UFOs. The militarization of space was a much more immediate problem that drove Sarah McClendon, Greer and the Disclosure Project witnesses to the National Press Club podium. Greer said Disclosure Project witnesses would testify that extraterrestrial civilizations have made it clear time and again they don't want us to weaponize space, which is territory they occupy. Greer's warning dovetailed with COMETA's that our destructive ways might eventually provoke a cosmic intervention. One can only imagine the potential consequences of ignoring the warnings of such a far superior civilization.

After making a strong case that UFO disclosure was of critical importance, Greer launched a preemptive strike against institutional media bias toward UFOs and UFO witnesses. "I expect people to be skeptical, but not irrationally so," he said, scolding a media that likes to portray those who report UFOs as an unreliable collection of drunks, morons, hoaxers and attention-seekers.

In fact, Disclosure Project witnesses were some of the most credible eyewitnesses imaginable. These were professionals entrusted with national security. Some handled nuclear weapons. They weren't a gang of rednecks auditioning for the next Jackass sequel as one might assume based on reaction of the mainstream media. These were people with credentials who could establish who they were. Greer said he'd been to the Vatican to speak with respected Italian theologian, Monsignor Corrado Balducci, who agreed it was downright crazy to dismiss the testimony of such witnesses. As far as revelations went this was shock and awe. With a smile, Greer warned the assembled media this was a serious event not to be mocked with wisecracks about Little Green Men. He told the press they'd hear testimony that the military had recovered and studied ET spacecraft as well as their non-human pilots. What's more, antigravity technology that had been reverse-engineered was in use in secret black budget programs and that all of it was kept secret from Congress and from at least two administrations. As a result, the Constitution had been subverted and national security compromised as these black projects grew in power.

After railing against the societal distortions caused by UFO secrecy, Greer addressed stereotypical fears about evil aliens. "There is no evidence, I wish to emphasize, that these life forms from elsewhere are hostile towards us, but there is a great deal of evidence that they are concerned with our hostility. There are times when they have neutralized or rendered inert the launch capabilities of intercontinental ballistic missiles. Witnesses here today will describe those events to you. They have shown clearly that they do not want us to weaponize space and yet we are proceeding down that dangerous path," said Greer, doing his best to dispel fears of a Hollywood-style Independence Day alien invasion.

It was a lot to digest, especially for the uninitiated. The picture Greer painted clearly demanded presidential attention. Clinton was unable or unwilling to act, but by the time of the Disclosure Project press conference, George W. Bush was president. Some believed Bush might be willing and able to take on Disclosure. His father, President George H. W. Bush, was a former director of the CIA. Unlike Woolsey, Bush was an insider whose relationship with the agency was such that it named its headquarters in

Langley Virginia, *The George Bush Center for Intelligence.* The lack of access that plagued Clinton would not be a problem for the Bush administration. What's more, both Bush presidents promised to make the truth about UFOs known when asked during their presidential campaigns.[53] George H. W. Bush admitted knowing a "fair amount" about UFOs, and W pointed to his running mate Dick Cheney. "It will be the first thing he will do. He'll get right on it," he said.[54]

Passing the buck to Cheney was reasonable since he'd been Secretary of Defense under W's father. Months later Cheney gave a campaign speech in Roswell that led many in the UFO community to believe Bush's promise was sincere. Cheney added even more fuel to the fire during a call-in radio show when UFO researcher and founder of Presidentialufo.com, Grant Cameron asked him about Bush's pledge and whether he had ever been briefed on UFOs. Cheney replied, "Well, if I had been briefed on it, I'm sure it was probably classified and I couldn't talk about it."[55]

Whether or not Cheney had been briefed on UFOs – and it's a good bet he had been - Disclosure wasn't his first order of business once in office as Bush had promised. In front of the establishment media at the National Press Club, Greer put Bush and Cheney on notice. The Disclosure campaign would continue until the following goals were met:

• Open hearings in the U.S. Congress.
• Permanent ban on the weaponization of space and prohibition against targeting objects of extraterrestrial origin.
• Declassification and release of UFO technology for general use in the generation of free, non-polluting energy and repair of environmental damage caused by industrial civilization.

In concluding his opening remarks, Greer suggested it was time to become mature adults in the cosmic neighborhood. "This is the end of the childhood of the human race," he said, yielding the stage to the witnesses.

THE WITNESSES: "I'm prepared to go to Congress, to swear before Congress, that everything I've said is true."

It's one thing to understand that there are 400 military-industrial complex insiders willing to bear witness to events involving UFOs and extraterrestrials. It's another thing altogether to actually hear the testimony of these individuals backed by their promise to testify under oath before Congress. Each Disclosure Project witness made this pledge after telling his or her story. What's more, these witnesses, some of whom worked in black budget projects known as USAPs or Unacknowledged Special Access Programs, had signed secrecy agreements. Greer insisted that these programs were unconstitutional absent congressional oversight, which made all such secrecy agreements null and void. Nevertheless, these brave individuals came forward to testify at great personal risk.

Below is a sampling of the witness presentations at the Disclosure Project National Press Club press conference. Each witness only had a few minutes to tell their story, but the full details could be found in the briefing materials made available to the press.

JOHN CALLAHAN, FAA DIVISION CHIEF

Retired FAA official John Callahan, former head of the accidents and investigations division, was first to the podium following Greer's introduction.[56] Callahan was involved in a major UFO event during his time at the FAA. In 1986, he received a call from Alaska about an incident that occurred in U.S. airspace involving a Japanese airliner and a UFO. The pilot reported an object with a ring of lights four times the size of a 747. The craft shadowed the airliner, sometimes in front, sometimes behind, above and below. Both civilian and military radar were able to track the object in real time for over thirty minutes as the pilot reported its unconventional flight maneuvers.

Callahan investigated the incident. He was able to recreate the event on video using radar data and voice recordings, which he used to brief FAA Administrator, Admiral Engen, who in turn, arranged a briefing for President Reagan's scientific staff and their team, including the CIA and the FBI. Callahan said the FAA gave Reagan's team a "dog and pony show" then handed off the evidence. The CIA swore everyone to secrecy. The meeting never happened. The incident never happened. When Callahan asked why, assuming the UFO was secret U.S. aircraft of some sort, he was told this was the first time that extensive radar data of a UFO had ever been recorded and that the event had to be kept from the public in order to prevent panic.

Callahan could prove his story. He showed the press the actual voice tapes, computer readouts, videotape, reports, etc. and explained that because the FAA didn't have any protocols for dealing with UFOs the original data remained in his office until the day he retired when it was packed up by a staffer along with the rest of his belongings and sent home with him. He identified the case as UFO Incident Japan 1648, which happened on November 18, 1986. "I'm prepared to go to congress, to swear before congress, that everything I've told you people and everything that is here is the truth," said Callahan to applause as he left the podium.

LT. COL. CHARLES BROWN, U.S. AIR FORCE (RET)

Col. Brown flew bombers in Europe during World War II. He joined the newly formed Air Force Office of Special Investigations at Wright Field in Dayton Ohio after the war and was assigned to Project Grudge, the Air Force's first official program to investigate UFOs. Grudge was a precursor to the more commonly known Project Blue Book.

Brown's experiences led him to conclude that UFOs were real. He said UFO sightings had been confirmed by both radar and visual evidence, including ground visual and ground radar, as well as, airborne visual and airborne radar. "The individuals who made the sightings were everything from airline pilots, military pilots, police officers, some of the people that your lives depend upon on a daily basis. These are very reputable and credible people," said Brown, who concluded there was no good reason to doubt the reports. "These vehicles have been seen and confirmed all over the planet," he said, urging the media to believe the Disclosure Project witnesses that would follow him to the podium. He closed with a pledge to testify or sign a sworn statement and left the stage.

COMMANDER GRAHAM BETHUNE, U.S. NAVY (RET.)

Graham Bethune was the type of witness that convinced Brown UFOs were real. Bethune was a Navy pilot with a top-secret clearance. On February 10, 1951, he and his crew encountered a disk-shaped craft during a nighttime flight from Iceland to Newfoundland over the open ocean.

According to Bethune, he saw what looked like the glow of a city on the water in the distance. The glow turned out to be a huge circle of lights that suddenly went out as they approached. Something launched from the surface and a gigantic craft was on top of them in an instant. Bethune made a whooshing sound to describe its speed. In his full account published in the book *Disclosure* that Greer handed out at the press conference, Bethune said the object covered the distance from the ocean surface 15 miles out to their position at 10,000 feet in a "fraction of a second."[57] His natural instinct was to take evasive action, but before he could react the craft was on top of them. It was so large and close that he could see nothing out the cockpit window but the craft, which looked like a classic flying saucer. Onboard instruments began experiencing electromagnetic interference. After a brief but extremely close encounter, the flying disk assumed a stable course tracking the aircraft at a range of 1-5 miles at which point Bethune and others could clearly see the side of a domed craft about 300 feet in diameter bathed in what looked like some sort of color-shifting plasma. The craft paced the plane for an extended period time before zipping off. Radar technicians estimated its departure speed at approximately 1,800 miles an hour. All 31 passengers saw the flying disk, including a psychologist who refused to look at it because it was a career killer to believe in such things. Upon landing, Bethune and crew were interrogated by Air Force investigators. They were also required by Navy Intelligence to make individual reports. Bethune said, "The truth is here" and showed the media an 18-page official Navy/Air Force report on the incident found in the national archives. He added, "I will testify under oath before Congress that everything I have said is true."

DON PHILLIPS, LOCKHEED SKUNKWORKS, CIA CONTRACTOR

Don Phillips began his career as a design engineer for Lockheed Skunk Works and worked directly with aerospace legend, Kelly Johnson. He did a tour of duty in the Air Force and then returned to the aerospace industry as a civilian contractor for multiple U.S. intelligence agencies, including the CIA. His experience at the highest levels of the aerospace industries within the military-industrial complex included access to top-level information on UFOs and ETs. During his time at Skunk Works, he worked on the SR-71 Blackbird spy plane, which was instrumental in helping to end the cold war. According to Phillips, the Blackbird did more than just spy on the Soviets.

He said "a special model built for the CIA," was used to monitor traffic to and from planet Earth.

Phillips was also a first-hand witness to UFO activity. In 1966, he was stationed at Las Vegas Air Force Base near the Groom Lake flight test facility at Area 51 where prototype aircraft like the SR-71 Blackbird were put through their paces when he was awakened in the middle of the night by some sort of commotion. He went to investigate and found a group of men, including the chief of security, staring at something in the sky. Phillips looked up and saw six or seven bright objects zipping about at tremendous speed, which he estimated to be between 2,400 and 3,800 miles per hour. He said the objects were so fast it looked like they had tails much like a cursor does when moved quickly across a computer screen. What's more, they showed extreme maneuverability, coming to a dead stop from incredible speed and reversing field at an acute angle. The impromptu air show ended after the UFOs came together and formed a rotating circle and then disappeared. Radar technicians confirmed the sighting. Phillips' colleague, radar specialist Anthony Kasar told him, "We didn't give them clearance-the standing order was to let them fly through the radar beam. We documented six to seven UFOs." Whatever they were, they were solid objects under intelligent control. Phillips said, "I will testify under oath as to what I say is true and I will do so before Congress."

Due to the time constraints of the Disclosure Project press conference, Phillips was unable to fully describe the depth of his knowledge of the UFO phenomenon. His complete account laid out in the book *Disclosure* offered a glimpse of what Congress would hear in full and open hearings.[58]

Phillips had knowledge of the Roswell Incident.. He knew people who'd seen the craft and the bodies and could verify a lot of what Corso wrote about in *The Day After Roswell*. He knew and worked with people who had been involved in the projects Corso had written about.[59] What's more, during a stint as a contractor for the CIA, Phillips learned of a truly definitive UFO investigation made by NATO. During the early stages of the Cold War, tensions rose as both the U. S. and the Soviet Union accused each other of airspace violations, which nearly triggered a nuclear holocaust until both sides realized that something unusual was happening. The NATO investigation found there were 12 extraterrestrial races that had been here for hundreds, perhaps thousands of years. Phillips said the report was so rich in detail about the identity and the agenda of these extraterrestrial races that there had to have been contact. He also said that President Eisenhower had formal contact with at least one race and that the event had been documented on film.

CAPTAIN ROBERT SALAS, U.S. AIR FORCE

Captain Robert Salas was next to the podium. In March 1967, Salas served as a missile launch officer at Malmstrom Air Force Base in Montana. He was on duty under ground in the command center of a nuclear missile facility known as Oscar Flight when he received a call from the head security guard who said there was "a bright glowing red object hovering outside the front gate."

As Salas was briefing his boss Commander Fred Meiwald, missiles began dropping offline one by one into no-go mode. Six to eight missiles went offline within minutes of the UFO's appearance at the front gate. Then the glowing object left at high speed.

When he reported the incident to the command post, Salas was told that the same thing had happened that morning at another nuclear missile facility nearby called Echo Flight, which lost all ten of its missiles when a UFO appeared.

Salas said Commander Eric Carlson and Deputy Commander Walt Figel were witnesses that would corroborate his story. He held up documents for the cameras, including a summary of the Echo Flight incident obtained from the Air Force under FOIA that included references to UFOs, telexes from SAC headquarters and the complete report of a similar incident that happened at a nuclear missile site on Minot Air Force Base in North Dakota. Salas read aloud from one of the SAC telexes, "The fact that no apparent reason for the loss of ten missiles can be readily identified is cause for grave concern to this headquarters."

In the expanded version of his testimony available in *Disclosure*, he said despite the "grave concern" of SAC headquarters, the Air Force stopped an investigation of the incident midstream. According to Salas, Bob Kaminski, head of the investigative team, told him he was ordered to stop the investigation and forgo writing a final report.[60] Salas told the media the following Disclosure Project witness would elaborate on the investigation and that there are at least 12 witnesses who would substantiate various parts of the story. Salas wrapped up his statement with the familiar pledge; "I'm willing to testify to the truth of all these matters that I've spoken about in front of Congress under oath."

LT. COL. DWYNNE ARNESSON, U.S. AIR FORCE (RET.)

Following Salas, Col. Dwynne Arnesson introduced himself to the press. Arnesson served as a communications and electronics officer for the Air Force in locations all over the world. He held a SCI-TK clearance, which meant he was cleared above top secret. He retired a Col. at Wright-Patterson Air Force Base in 1986 after a 26-year career in which he had been the commander of three different units.

Arnesson corroborated Salas' testimony. In 1967, Arnesson, like Salas, was stationed at Malmstrom Air Force Base in Great Falls, Montana. He was the officer in charge of the communication center and the top-secret control officer for the division. He was trusted with distributing nuclear launch authenticators to SAC missile crews. "During that time, I can recall seeing a message come through that communication center which said, basically what Bob just got through talking about, is that a UFO was seen near the missile silos and the missiles were deactivated," said Arnesson, who went on to work as a computer systems analyst for Boeing after leaving the Air Force. At Boeing Arnesson's boss was Bob Kaminski, head of the team sent to investigate the missile failures at Malmstrom. Kaminsky and Arnesson became friends and talked about the incident many times over the years.[61] According to Arnesson, Kaminski, who has since passed away, told him "those missiles were perfectly clean." The investigation couldn't explain why they went offline.

Arnesson told the media about two other UFO-related experiences. While stationed at Caswell Air Force Base in Maine, he heard of another UFO/nuclear missile incident. Caswell was right next door to Loring Air Force Base where Arnesson had contacts in security that told him about UFOs hovering near the nuclear weapon storage area.

Earlier in his career, when he was a communications officer in charge of the cryptographic center at Ramstein Air Force Base in Germany in 1962, he saw a classified message about a UFO incident. The memo said a UFO had crashed on the island of Spitsbergen, Norway and a team of scientists had been dispatched to investigate. Arnesson signed off, "I'll be glad to testify to Congress that this is absolutely the truth."

HARLAND BENTLEY, U.S. ARMY

After a short stint in the Army, Harland Bentley went to college and pursued a career in nuclear engineering. He became a contractor for NASA, the Department of Energy and other electronics firms in Washington D.C. During his brief tenure in the Army as a radar operator, he witnessed a dramatic UFO incident. In 1958, Bentley was a Private First Class stationed north of Washington, D.C. on a Nike Ajax Missile Base. He was in his bunk when he heard a noise like a pulsating transformer. He looked outside and saw a disk-shaped craft crash to the ground, leaving behind debris as it somehow recovered and took off again. Bentley said there was more to the story but he was pressed for time and had to move on.

The rest of the story could be found in his testimony in *Disclosure*. Any member of the press interested in following up had access to details such as the description of the debris that the object left behind, which included a glowing white hot washing machine-sized piece, and the subsequent clean up operation that included the use of radiation suits.[62]

At the press conference, Bentley skipped ahead to the following night. He was on radar duty when he got a call from Gaithersburg missile base about 12 to 15 UFOs hovering 50-100 feet in the air. Bentley heard the same sound he'd heard the previous morning, except there was a lot more of it. He checked his radarscope and located the blip over Gaithersburg. Moments later, the squadron of UFOs took off. In one sweep of the radar beam the blip covered two thirds of his scope, which factored out to a constant speed of 17,000 miles an hour.

Bentley had another unusual UFO-related experience later in his career. He was working in California on an unrelated classified project when he heard a startling event unfold over a live astronaut communications link during one of the Apollo missions. His ears perked up when he heard the word "bogey," which was a term he understood to mean UFO. Apparently an object of some sort was on a collision course with the Lunar Module about to loop around the moon. The astronauts requested permission to take evasive action but before any maneuvers became necessary the object assumed a parallel course and began to pace the Apollo spacecraft. Again Bentley didn't have time to give the press details. If one checked the testimony he gave in *Disclosure* one would have found that the object was a disc-shaped craft with portholes and the astronauts, who never lost their cool despite the circumstances, could see figures moving around inside. They took pictures before the UFO took off in a flash. "There they go," Bentley heard, along with "Damn that was fast!" He left the podium with the familiar words, "I will testify before Congress if necessary and explain exactly what happened."

SERGEANT KARL WOLFE, U.S. AIR FORCE

Karl Wolfe was an Airman Second Class in the mid 60s when his technical expertise led him into highly-classified territory. It was a nuance he didn't have time for at the podium that could be found in his testimony in *Disclosure.*

Wolfe was a precision electronics photographic repairman for a photoreconnaissance operation run out of a brand new facility at Langley Air Force Base. His group processed film for top-secret spying programs, which included the U2 spy plane program as well as a spy satellite photography program, both completely unknown at the time. He had a Top Secret Crypto clearance. His duties required him to maintain equipment in some of the country's most sensitive facilities such as the war room at SAC.

In 1965, Wolfe was sent to repair some computerized contact printing equipment at an NSA facility that was a part of the Lunar Orbiter project at Langley Field. When he entered the installation, he was surprised to find an atmosphere of doom and gloom among a diverse staff that included many foreigners and their interpreters. The equipment he was sent to repair had to be removed from a darkroom. During the wait, a fellow airman explained that the Orbiter's mission was to scout potential landing sites for the 1969 moon mission. On each successive pass of the moon, the orbiter took photos, which are arranged in mosaics to create a picture of its surface. Then the Airman told him that they'd discovered a base on the backside of the moon. He laid out several pictures showing huge structures, including towers, spheres, mushroom-shaped buildings, domes, etc.

Wolfe said the architecture was similar to Earth's, only on a much larger scale and although the buildings were highly reflective like metal, it looked like they were made from some sort of fabricated stone. Some of these stone buildings were half a mile in size. It was immediately clear to Wolfe why such an atmosphere of dread pervaded the facility. "At that point I was very concerned because I knew we were working on compartmentalized security. He had breached security and I was actually frightened at that moment and I did not question any further. And a few moments later someone did come into the room," said Wolfe, who thought the airman was distressed and simply needed someone his own rank to talk with.

In *Disclosure*, he spoke about the system of compartmentalization that made him fear for his life.[63] Although his security clearance allowed him access to many highly classified areas, there were strict rules of conduct. He was briefed about his task and what he was allowed to discuss with another person. He was told to be cautious when off base and not to drink or take drugs and to be wary of people attempting to strike up a friendship. His whereabouts had to be known at all times and if he had to travel he would be accompanied by someone with a gun who had orders to kill him rather than let him fall into enemy hands. Wolfe understood that his life was in jeopardy at all times. He said that he would have loved to discuss the base further but was afraid for his life.

Wolfe closed with an anecdote about his naïveté in expecting to hear about the discovery on the nightly news. "Here it is more than thirty years later and I'm still waiting and I hope we hear about it tonight," Wolfe said to the assembled media and added, "and I will testify under oath before Congress that what I'm saying is the truth."

LARRY WARREN, U.S. AIR FORCE SECURITY OFFICER

Larry Warren was a security specialist at Bentwaters Air Force Base in England also known as RAF Bentwaters, a NATO Air Force facility and home to the 81st tactical fighter wing to which Warren was attached. He had a secret security clearance. It was his job to guard nuclear weapons stored in secret at the base. In December 1980, Warren witnessed a dramatic UFO event that has become known as the British Roswell incident. UFOs invaded the base and fired pencil-thin beams of light into the nuclear stockpile. "The objects were on the ground on two different nights. Potentially there was another life form seen- this is an unpopular truth. These events were of extreme defense significance to not only her majesty's government, but this government as well and they are still shrouded in secrecy," said Warren.

In his broader testimony given in *Disclosure*, the events seemed quite literally beyond words at times.[64] He did his best to describe the appearance of a basketball-sized red orb that exploded into blinding points of light in complete silence, revealing a large pyramid-shaped object and child-sized humanoid beings in cocoons of light. He explained that the craft, which was difficult to look at directly because of some sort of distortion effect, left trace evidence on the ground.

Warren was debriefed after the incident. He was told he'd experienced interaction with advanced civilizations, something that been going on for a very long time. Then he was shown film of UFO encounters from the days of propeller-driven aircraft on up through the space age. The footage showed astronauts pointing to structures on the moon as well as UFOs leaving its surface. Finally, he was ordered to sign a false statement, forget about the incident and get on with his life.

Warren told the media the events resulted in a memo written by Deputy Base Commander Lt. Colonel Charles Halt that looked like "science fiction" and that Halt had made an audiotape of the incident as it unfolded. Warren spoke to the press only of evidence in the public domain. In *Disclosure*, he explained that some of the events had been captured on film and video, which remain secret. After calling everyone heroes, including the press, Warren made the familiar pledge, "I will testify before Congress if asked."

SERGEANT CLIFFORD STONE, U.S. ARMY

Sergeant, first class Clifford Stone was a NBC (Nuclear/Biological /Chemical) specialist in the U.S. Army for more than 20 years. He had a secret clearance with carte blanche to do whatever was necessary during special operations that included the recovery of ET spacecraft. Stone said such occurrences were rare. He was involved in just 12 retrieval operations during his career. The first incident occurred in 1969 at Indian Town Gap, Pennsylvania while he was stationed in Fort Lee, Virginia. The retrieval team was told the craft was one of ours, but Stone discovered otherwise. He was the first person to see the bodies upon boarding.

Many of the crash retrieval operations in which he participated included ETs, both dead and alive. He said that as these operations were happening in secret the American people were told there was nothing to UFOs. "I know we're not alone in the universe. I know that absence of evidence is not evidence of absence- it's evidence that has been denied the

American people," he said to applause from an audience that had clearly become inspired by the witness testimony.

Stone told members of the media interested in hearing details to contact Greer who would arrange an interview. In *Disclosure*, he elaborated on his experiences and the history of secret UFO operations.[65] He said that an elite investigative unit founded as the 4602nd Air Intelligence Service Squadron was assigned to work with Project Blue Book but was actually part of a secret UFO operation. One of its missions was to retrieve unidentified crashed objects. It was the original ET crash retrieval operation, which was known as Operation Blue Fly, according to Stone. Blue Fly evolved into Operation Moon Dust, which expanded retrieval operations to include the spacecraft of other countries. Stone said that ET craft were handled like any other airplane accident or hazardous waste situation until an onsite analysis concluded that the craft was extraterrestrial. Once such a determination had been made, a special operations unit specifically trained to deal with the dangers posed by biological contamination and ET technology would assume control of the retrieval operation.

In the process of performing his duties, Stone experienced a form communication that ETs called "interfacing." Through this interface he was able to learn about extraterrestrial culture. "You will learn that ETs have a perception of God. You find they have families. You find they have cultures. You find that they have likes and dislikes," said Stone, who felt it was important to emphasize that ETs were not merely entities or creatures as we tend to think of them, but were "real people" who were perhaps more civilized than we are.

Sergeant Clifford Stone was clearly moved by his experiences and he said as much. In signing off, he vowed, "I stand before you today and my almighty God and I tell you this, if Congress calls me in and says will you testify in detail what you know- I stand here today prepared and ready to do just that."

MARK MCCANDLISH, U.S. AIR FORCE

Mark McCandlish introduced himself as aerospace illustrator with a secret security clearance who'd spent more than 20 years working as a conceptual artist for a variety of defense contractors including General Dynamics, Lockheed, Northrop, McDonald-Douglas, Boeing, Rockwell International,

Honeywell, and Allied Signet Corporation. He showed the media prints of his work, including an illustration of Rockwell's X-30 Aero-Space Plane. After displaying his work, McCandlish described several incidents involving flying discs, both theirs *and ours*.

The first incident took place in 1967 at Westover Air Force Base, where he saw a UFO hovering over a nuclear weapons storage facility. McCandlish said he watched the unknown craft for about ten minutes until it suddenly departed like a bullet shot from a rifle.

A UFO sighting at a nuclear missile facility was a common experience among Disclosure Project witnesses. What was not common was a man-made flying disk sighting in a hangar at an Air Force base. McCandlish said he had learned of a craft that had been back-engineered from extraterrestrial technology called the Alien Reproduction Vehicle (ARV).

The story began with a colleague who witnessed a special presentation for top military brass and select members of congress in a large hangar at Norton Air Force Base during an air show on Saturday, November 12, 1988. The secret exhibit featured three disk-shaped craft that hovered silently off the ground.

After hearing his friend's story, McCandlish contacted the office of Congressman George E. Brown, Jr., the representative of that district who was also the Chairman for the Congressional Committee on Space Science and Advanced Technology at the time. McCandlish correctly guessed that Brown's office must have coordinated the presentation at Norton Air Force Base along with the local Air Force Office of Public Affairs. A member of Brown's staff confirmed the exhibit and the fact that there were three disks on display known as the Alien Reproduction Vehicle. Greer held up a large detailed diagram of the ARV that McCandlish had drawn based in part on a rough sketch by his colleague.

Over the years, McCandlish heard stories from others who also had chance close encounters with the ARV. "Subsequently, I've done a lot of research on this product, this vehicle," said McCandlish, who discovered substantial documentary evidence supporting the clandestine development of an ARV-like craft. He held up several declassified documents for the press to see. One showed the Air Force and NASA both conducted extensive wind tunnel tests on disk-shaped craft. Another even more intriguing find was a Hercules Aerospace interoffice memo that described new concepts in science called zero-point energy and scalar waves, which he had come to understand was the basis for the antigravity propulsion system used by the ARV. What's more, the memo referred to meetings with the Defense Intelligence Agency (DIA) as well as a cooperative effort with the Russian scientific community to investigate what they called the *fundamental enabling technology* originally discovered by Tesla.

McCandlish's appearance on stage at the National Press Club was riveting. His deeper testimony in *Disclosure* was mind blowing.[66] The secret ARV exhibit seen by his colleague Brad Sorenson included videotape of the craft rising from a dry lakebed and shooting off out of sight in mere seconds. Beside the video was a cut-away illustration that showed the internal components of the ARV, including a control system, Tesla coil, central column vacuum chamber, camera-driven guidance system, oxygen tanks, robotic arm, etc., all linked by fiber optics. Three hovering ARVs completed the exhibit. The smallest of the craft had several panels removed, revealing details seen in the illustration.

McCandlish was able to gather enough information about the ARV to figure out what made it tick and how it was able to make light speed and beyond as a three-star General at Norton Air Force Base was alleged to have claimed during the presentation.

Einstein showed that as an object accelerates, its mass increases. As it approaches the speed of light it becomes so massive that it would take all the energy in the universe just to hit light speed. McCandlish said that the ARV was able to turn what would appear to be the ultimate barrier into a launch pad with its zero-point energy antigravity propulsion system also known as electrogravitic propulsion.

McCandlish explained that zero-point energy was what kept the electron in orbit around the nucleus of an atom. Anyone who knew how to tap the zero-point energy field would have access to the ultimate source of unlimited energy. He referenced physicist James Clerk Maxwell's estimate that a cubic yard of so-called empty space contained enough energy to boil all the oceans of the Earth. What's more, such tremendous potential, amazing in itself, was only half the story. The process of tapping the zero-point field came with an incredible benefit: the key to faster-than-light travel.

When energy is drawn from the zero-point, electrons in orbit around a nucleus slow down, reducing inertia, and in turn, mass. McCandlish explained that this "mass-canceled" state does not affect the atomic structure, which remains intact. Uranium is still uranium, just lighter.

Consequently, a craft able to use the zero-point energy field of its own local environment as its power source, i.e., the craft itself, would reduce its mass as it accelerates through space offsetting the increase anticipated by Einstein. McCandlish said, "In effect, the faster you go, the easier it becomes to go up to and exceed the speed of light."[67] This was the secret of the Roswell craft. McCandlish referred to Corso and *The Day After Roswell*, explaining that fiber optics was the key component in a zero-point energy antigravity drive spacecraft.

Corso wrote that German Paperclip scientist Hans Kohler told him the glass fibers conducted a beam of light like wires conducted electricity. He said the ETs used the glass wires to run the ship's communications and telemetry and that one day fiber optic cables would replace our antiquated phone system.[68] McCandlish explained that fiber optics was used for much more than just broadband communication by the ETs. In fact, fiber optics made the zero-point electrogravitic propulsion system viable.

As a spaceship and its entire atomic structure, including its electrons, became mass-canceled upon drawing energy from the zero-point field, its telemetry would go haywire and its guidance and control systems would fail. Imagine Han Solo putting the Millennium Falcon into hyperdrive only to have it fly off into hyperspace like a birthday party balloon losing air.

In order to avoid flying right through a star or bouncing too close to a supernova, a spacecraft with a zero-point antigravitic propulsion system, like the Roswell craft and the ARV, had to be wired with fiber optics because photons had no mass and would not be affected by the transition to a mass-canceled state. Fiber optics meant that if the Millennium Falcon had such a propulsion system it really could make .5 past light speed.

The Disclosure Project Press Conference at the National Press Club was not the proper forum for a technical discussion of the ARV's capacity to circumvent the cosmic speed limit and McCandlish appropriately kept to anecdotes about the craft and supporting documents. The proper venue would have been something akin to the symposium held by the House Science and Astronautics Committee in the wake of the Condon investigation in 1968. McCandlish stated his intent to testify before such a body. "I am prepared to testify in detail concerning these events and their truthfulness before Congress," he said.

DANIEL SHEEHAN, ATTORNEY

Attorney, Daniel Sheehan took the podium and introduced himself as general counsel to the Disclosure Project. Sheehan's resume spoke for itself. A graduate of Harvard Law School, he established a career as an advocate for the public interest. As general counsel for the *New York Times*, Sheehan argued before the Supreme Court for the Times' right to publish the Pentagon Papers. He served as legal counsel in other high-profile cases involving government covert operations including the Watergate, Iran-Contra, Three Mile Island and the Karen Silkwood affair. After Watergate, Sheehan went back to the Harvard Divinity School for his masters and PhD in the study of Judeo-Christian Social Ethics in Public Policy and went on to become the general counsel for the U.S. Jesuit Headquarters in Washington D.C.

In addition to his role of general counsel for the Disclosure Project, Sheehan was also a witness. His involvement with UFOs began in 1977 when President Carter's request for a briefing on the subject set in motion a series of events that soon had the phone ringing at the U.S. Jesuit Headquarters.

Sheehan received a call from the Director of the Science and Technology Division of the Congressional Research Service, Marcia Smith, who requested a meeting. "She informed me that President Carter, upon taking office in January of 1977, held a meeting with then the Director of Central Intelligence, who was George Bush Sr. and demanded that the director of Central Intelligence turn over to the president the classified information about unidentified flying objects and the information that was in the possession of the United States intelligence community concerning the existence of extraterrestrial intelligence. This information was refused to the president of the United States by the director of Central Intelligence, George Bush Sr. The director insisted that the president, in order to have access to this information, needed to have clearance," said Sheehan, explaining that Bush suspected Carter was preparing to disclose the truth to the American public. He told the president he'd have to go through official channels to have the information declassified. Smith was the official channel. The House Science and Technology Committee had asked her to make a thorough investigation of extraterrestrial intelligence and its relationship to the UFO phenomenon, which is why she sought Sheehan's help as general counsel for the Jesuits in the U.S. in gaining access to information about UFOs and ETs held in the Vatican Library. "I pursued that with the permission of Father William J. Davis, the director of the national office and we were refused access, as the United States Jesuit Order, to the information in the possession of the Vatican Library," said Sheehan, who later succeeded in gaining access to the classified portions of Project Blue Book on behalf of Smith.

In May 1977, months before the release of Steven Spielberg's classic *Close Encounters of the Third Kind*, Sheehan had a close encounter with classified evidence at the Madison Building of the U.S. Library of Congress in a basement office secured by three guards. Once his identification had been checked and verified, he was granted entry into the office that stored classified Blue Book files. Inside, he found a microfilm with a dozen unambiguous photos of an unidentified craft that had crashed, dug a furrow in a field of snow and become embedded in an embankment. Some pictures showed air force personnel surrounding the object. Others showed symbols on the side of the craft. Despite a dictum against note taking, Sheehan managed to smuggle out a copy of the symbols he made on the back of a legal pad.

When he returned to Jesuit Headquarters and reported his findings he was given the go-ahead to brief the National Council of Churches and to request that the entire 54 major religious denominations in the United States make a study of extraterrestrial intelligence. That recommendation was declined, he said.

Pressed for time, Sheehan put an exclamation point on his testimony with an eye-opening revelation that he had given a three-hour seminar for the top fifty scientists in the SETI program at the Jet Propulsion Lab in 1977. He offered to meet with members of the press to answer any questions and referred to the Iran-Contra scandal once again, which he said was related to the secret government that conceals UFO/ETI information from the American people.

Sheehan closed with the familiar oath, "I'm more than happy to testify under oath to these details to the United States Congress."

DR. CAROL ROSIN

Carol Rosin was the final Disclosure Project witness to the podium. She introduced herself as the spokesperson for the late Werner von Braun, the father of modern rocketry.

In *Disclosure,* Rosin said she made appearances for von Braun when he was too ill to speak.[69] With the press conference running late and the opportunity to take questions from the press dwindling, she had little time for backstory. Rosin explained that in 1974 she was introduced to von Braun, who was dying of cancer. During their first meeting, he insisted she help fight a plot to hoodwink the public into supporting space-based weapons. "There is a lie being told to everyone that the weaponization of space is now first being based upon the evil empire: the Russians. There are many enemies, he said, against whom we're going to build this space-based weapon system. The first of whom was the Russians. Then there would be terrorists. Then there would be third world countries. Now we call them rogue nations or nations of concern. Then there would be asteroids. And then he would repeat to me over and over, the last card... would be the extraterrestrial threat," said Rosin, who told the media that the great German rocket scientist rubbished spaced-based weapons as an untestable, unworkable, destabilizing boondoggle, useless against other weapons of mass destruction like suitcase bombs, biological and chemical weapons, etc.

Thanks to von Braun's influence, Rosin became a space and missile defense consultant and was the first female corporate manager in the aerospace industry. During her career, she witnessed the plot described by von Braun unfold. In 1977 she attended a meeting at Fairchild Industries in which plans were drawn to provoke the gulf war as a pretext to trigger the next phase of weapons development. She said the plan called for a terrorist threat in the gulf region when $25 billion had been spent in the effort to weaponize space. Rosin demanded to know why plans were being made to build spaced-based weapons against countries that weren't enemies. When her demands fell on deaf ears, she resigned and went on to found the *Institute for Security and Cooperation in Outer Space* based on von Braun's dream to transform the military-industrial complex into a "global cooperative space industry" that would develop solutions to the energy crisis and global-warming induced climate change.

Rosin became emotional in summarizing von Braun's vision, "We can have a whole planet now that lives in peace on Earth, with all the cultures on Earth, and with all the extraterrestrial cultures in space, and these are words that Wernher von Braun told me in 1974 and I will testify before the Congress under oath about everything I have said and more."

QUESTIONS FROM THE MEDIA

Greer reclaimed the podium and told the media it had seen a mere "snapshot" of Disclosure Project witness testimony. Each of the 400 hundred witnesses could have spoken for hours about their experiences. When the questions came it was clear that Big Media didn't like what it saw on the Polaroid and wanted no part of the bigger picture.

A UPI reporter asked Greer why the ARV would be on display at an air show and how he knew the secret craft was not simply a product of the defense industry. The irrational skepticism Greer warned against was palpable. He patiently explained that the ARV was the product of the defense industry; that it had been manufactured by Lockheed Martin, Northrop, SAIC and other aerospace corporations; that it got its name from the study of extraterrestrial craft and that the Disclosure Project had additional witnesses with documents who would be able to establish its existence before Congress.

Unfortunately Greer's explanation didn't seem to make much of an impact. The UPI reporter pressed for direct evidence that the ARV had its roots in extraterrestrial technology and asked how a rocket engine could translate into electricity. It was clear that the UPI had assigned a reporter whose work would be unlikely to appear in *Jane's Defense Weekly* or *Aviation Week.*

Greer did his best, but nuances like zero-point energy and antigravity propulsion were next to impossible to market to a press trained to obsess over a scandal with a stained blue dress. Nevertheless, Greer referred the members of the press to the briefing documents for a more detailed explanation of the ARV and its propulsion system, noting that it was a complex technical issue beyond the scope of the press conference.

More skepticism came from the publisher of a small newsletter about space reconnaissance and surveillance who asked Greer if he was suggesting that UFOs had been airbrushed out of over 35 million images of Earth taken from space since the launch of Landsat 1 in 1972. Greer answered back that there is a compartmented operation that sanitizes images that come from government satellites before they are released to the public. There were Disclosure Project witnesses who had knowledge of or had participated in these operations. He referenced the testimony of DIA intelligence analyst John Maynard and NASA contractor Donna Hare and said there were other Disclosure Project witnesses that hadn't testified at the press conference who also had been involved in projects in which UFOs were taken out of satellite images. Greer also said it was possible some had slipped through but the Disclosure Project didn't have the budget to search every image.

Although some questions from the press practically dripped with skepticism, others were far less contentious. When questioned about the vetting of the witnesses, Greer reassured the press that, although the Disclosure Project did not have the budget to do a fifty thousand dollar background check like the CIA, the witnesses had the documentation to prove who they were. Those who had served in the military had the forms to verify their service and establish the fact of their careers. What's more, Greer noted that Disclosure Project witnesses like himself, attorney's Daniel Sheehan, Stephen Lovekin, and others would lose their license to practice if they were to perpetrate a hoax upon the public.

Other questions suggested open-mindedness towards the Disclosure Project narrative, especially among international reporters. A British reporter asked retired sergeant Clifford Stone if he could describe what the ETs looked like. Stone said that he could but it might take awhile. By the time he retired they had catalogued fifty-seven different species. He said that some could literally pass for human while others were obviously alien, like the Grays. In general, extraterrestrials were bipedal and humanoid, which he said was a mystery that would have to be answered by science.

Another reporter from a Mexican newspaper asked Greer who was profiting from the suppression of ET technology that would solve the energy crisis. Greer said that Big Oil and related geopolitical and financial infrastructures were the big winners and that the National Security Council was afraid the loss of fossil fuel profits would be a multi-trillion dollar lightning bolt to the global financial system. He said, "What is more serious to the national security? Keeping the status quo or letting ourselves go into a global ecosystem collapse?"

TRAFFIC JAMMED

Government insiders first attempted to force Disclosure back in the 1960s at a time when the news media was not nearly as ubiquitous as it is today. Such efforts, which will be examined in the context of paradigm shift in the following chapter, were obviously unsuccessful. Simple denials were enough to carry the day.

Censorship in the twenty-first century isn't so simple, but it is doable. The Disclosure Project experienced electronic censorship in real time. The first hour of the press conference broadcast live on the Internet by Connect Live for the National Press Club was externally jammed, something that the webcast and Internet hosting company had never experienced before.

Greer and his team anticipated the NSA would take such actions and the webcast was restored by the second hour of testimony. Once the webcast was back online over half a million people logged on to watch it live and when all was said and done over three million viewed the event. At the time it was the most watched webcast in history.

Over the years, many more have undoubtedly seen the press conference, which is available on the Internet. Connect Live told Greer they had never seen such volume for a news webcast. Bandwidth was maxed out. There was no way to tell how many people tried to log on who couldn't. Actual viewership could have been much higher.

The National Press Club had also never seen anything like the Disclosure Project press conference. According to Greer, they were "stunned" by huge media turnout and the buzz about the "Real X-Files" in the corporate media. "They also told us it was the best attended press event at the National Press Club since Ronald Reagan had been in the building," said Greer, who expected there would be some coverage in the mainstream media.[70] Total media silence would make the cover-up obvious. Ultimately, Greer said the Disclosure Project story would "beta-test" the power of the shadow government. Would the story have legs or would the intelligence community succeed in breaking them?

BRAKING NEWS

"We've seen the photographs and heard the stories of what some say is evidence of UFOs. Now a group of scientists, former Air Force and FAA officials is lending its voice to the argument that we are not alone. Dr. Steven Greer heads up the Disclosure Project, a group that compiles information from people who say they've encountered extraterrestrial forms of life," reported Elaine Quijano on *CNN Headline news* from the Disclosure Project press conference in Washington D.C.

On the surface, the report seemed like any other, but the subtle signs of mainstream media bias against UFOs were readily apparent to the careful observer. Quijano reported that Commander Bethune "believes he saw a UFO fifty years ago while flying to Newfoundland." In fact, as the reader will recall, Bethune testified to a very dramatic up-close encounter with a domed craft that had launched from some sort of huge mothership sitting on the ocean's surface. Quijano used the word "believe" as if to imply that there was some doubt about what was seen. Bethune and his entire crew didn't "believe" they saw a UFO. They knew they'd seen one.

Believe is a word that the mainstream media attaches to UFOs in order to sow doubt about their existence. The word "believers" is routinely applied to those who think UFOs are real craft as if their existence is a matter of religious faith and not something that can be proved objectively true.

Such tepid semantics are indicative of the institutional skepticism of the establishment media. CNN's report exhibited all the telltale signs of simplified disinformation identified by COMETA. Quijano made no mention of the ARV, back-engineered ET technology or its potential as a solution to the energy and environmental crises. In the conclusion to her brief-but-toothless report, Quijana noted that the Disclosure Project sought open congressional hearings, which were not in the plans according to a spokesperson for the Senate Technology and Space Committee. End of story.

The Disclosure Project witnesses named names and provided a glut of checkable details for the press just as Corso had. What's more, they had official documents to back their testimony. They'd handed the media an unprecedented opportunity that would challenge an army of journalists. Yet there was no follow-up. Much like the UFOs that travel so fast they often disappear off a scope after a single sweep of the beam, the Disclosure Project story vanished from the media's radar screen after a single blip. Instead of hitting the gas to chase the biggest story of all time, the establishment media slammed on the brakes. The media's bizarre response to the Disclosure Project press conference prompted researcher Jonathan Kolber to write, "If the witnesses were neither lying or delusional, then the deafening media silence following May 9th *implies an intentional process of failure to explore and reveal the truth.* Said less politely, it implies censorship."[71] So much for the Journalist's Creed posted in bronze at the National Press Club. Walt Williams must have been spinning in his grave at such a betrayal of the public trust. Kolber noted the Disclosure Project witness testimony itself included a possible explanation for the willful failure of the media. "One of the witnesses reported how he became aware of 43 persons on the payroll of major media organs while in fact working for the U.S. government. Their job was to intercept ET-related stories and squelch, spin or ridicule. If we accept his testimony as factual, it provides a plausible explanation for the deafening silence following May 9th," wrote Kolber, who concluded, "Since an exposé of witness deceit or mass psychosis would itself have been a good, career-building story for some reporter, but no such story has appeared, I concluded that these witnesses are who they claim to be. If these witnesses are who they claim to be, then they presented testimony they believe truthful. Yet no *factual* detail of any of that testimony has since been disputed in the media. Half a year is enough time to do the research. I believe the testimony is true as presented."

SUMMARY AND CONCLUSIONS

A virtual army of government whistleblowers inspired by Col. Corso and *The Day After Roswell* formed a movement to disclose the truth about UFOs and extraterrestrials. Their efforts were further validated by the COMETA report. Led by Dr. Steven Greer, the group engaged the Clinton administration in an effort to achieve formal disclosure. In spite of Clinton's interest in the subject, such efforts were unsuccessful. Clinton was either unwilling or unable to disclose the truth about UFOs. He's alleged to have said there is a shadow government over which he has no control. Whatever the case, Greer, and not Clinton, made history in achieving public disclosure of the extraterrestrial presence at the National Press Club on May 9th 2001.

The mainstream media made a cursory announcement and promptly returned to regularly scheduled programming, something they would have been unable to do had the announcement come from the president. For this and other reasons it seems unlikely that any president will ever officially disclose the truth. There's just too much downside. Such a disclosure could lead to panic and social upheaval and a loss of confidence in the government and the military, putting the career of any political leader who opened such a can of worms at risk. There's also too much political pressure from special interests ranging from a fossil fuel industry trying to preserve the value of its assets to a military-industrial complex that enjoys an overwhelming geopolitical advantage because of its monopoly on superior technology as well as commercial interests in spin-offs worth billions in profits. COMETA concluded it was in the Pentagon's interest to maintain secrecy for as long as possible. Add all these factors together and Disclosure becomes a political impossibility for the president.

Clinton's response to Disclosure Project briefings proved COMETA's analysis was spot on. The president passed the buck on Disclosure to Greer, who was willing and able, but who didn't have the political gravitas to make it stick. And so UFO disclosure is stuck in a catch-22 double bind. Disclosure can only happen unofficially, but without the "official stamp" there can be no real Disclosure. As a result, even though Disclosure happened in 2001, the world goes on as if it hadn't. And the question remains as always: When will the government disclose the truth about UFOs? It won't. As COMETA showed, it has every incentive not to. But at some point government Disclosure is going to become moot.

Mark Twain said history doesn't repeat itself, but it does rhyme, which is why the tune played by the establishment sounds a lot like it did back in Galileo's day. When Galileo invented the telescope and showed that Earth wasn't the center of the universe the Catholic Church couldn't handle the truth any more than the U.S. government. The Church did its best to suppress and deny the truth just as the government does today. Of course, the relentless progress of science eventually forced the Catholic Church to cry uncle- in 1992. Although the Church backed down early in the 18th century, it never officially acknowledged Galileo until Pope John Paul IV apologized to the Galileo family four hundred years after his death.

If the past is precedent, perhaps Greer and the Disclosure Project witnesses will get an apology from whoever is president in the year 2350- if anyone is still around, which looks more and more unlikely all the time. Industrial civilization is trashing the planet and the exponential rate of technological advance is transforming civilization in ways we don't even understand.

Greer presented Disclosure as more than a matter of intellectual curiosity, but as an issue of vital importance to the future. It was important to get the truth out about UFOs because they didn't run on fossil fuels. By making disclosure a green cause, Greer may have unwittingly politicized the issue.

After three months of media silence following the Disclosure Project press conference, historian Richard Dolan argued that Greer had overreached. He criticized the decision to promote Disclosure as a "save the world" leftist agenda that only served to alienate the establishment. Dolan said a source told him that the Disclosure Project brain trust thought they needed to leverage the energy and environmental crises because UFOs alone wouldn't be enough to force the government to come clean.

While Dolan had a point, the unavoidable truth is that there is no winning strategy to force the government to make Disclosure official or to compel the media to investigate the story. The government demonstrated its control over the media as far back as 1947 when it threatened to revoke the license of a Roswell radio station if it broadcast an interview with rancher Mac Brazel. The Disclosure Project witness testimony is replete with such anecdotes, from the censoring of UFOs in satellite photos released to the public to the government assets within the news media working to kill UFO stories. What's more, the allegations are supported by a 1991 CIA document entitled, *Task Force Report on Greater CIA Openness* in which the CIA boasts about having achieved complete control over the media enabling it to "turn some intelligence failure stories into intelligence success stories."[72] There may be no better example of the CIA's control of the media than the recent film *Kill the Messenger* about the life and death of Pulitzer Prize winning journalist Gary Webb. When Webb reported on the CIA's complicity in cocaine trafficking in the *San Jose Mercury News* the mainstream media led by *The New York Times*, the *Los Angeles Times*, and the *Washington Post* viciously attacked Webb, debunking the story rather than follow up on it. Webb was discredited and driven to suicide. In its recent review of the film the *Times* finally admitted that Webb was right.[73]

The Disclosure Project is its own best example of the Big Media's role in the establishment agenda to resist the truth about UFOs. Beginning with the electronic jamming of its live webcast and the failure of the mainstream media to investigate the story, the Disclosure Project has been purposely stuffed down the memory hole on several glaring occasions.

In his autobiography, *Forbidden Knowledge – Hidden Truth,* Greer said that several prominent television producers planning an exposé on the Disclosure Project sought his help. Emmy award winning executive producer of *ABC News,* Ira Rosen, who'd been an investigator for Mike Wallace at *60 Minutes,* worked for a year preparing a story on the Disclosure Project. Greer wrote, "He wanted to do a very strong "Prime Time Live" and "20/20" piece, if not a series on this. But after this national press event, he called and said, "Well, it looks like I'm not going to be able to do this story." I asked, "Why not?" He says, "They won't let me put it on. They won't let me do this piece." I asked, "Who's they?" He said, "Well, Dr. Greer, you know who they are…""[74]

In 2004, television producers again approached Greer for access to the Disclosure Project evidence. Skeptical because he'd been down that road before, Greer nevertheless agreed to cooperate with Jordan Kronick and Mark Obenhaus, producers of the 2005 ABC News Special *UFOs: Seeing is Believing* hosted by Peter Jennings. Kronick told Greer that the Disclosure Project evidence was exactly what they were looking for, yet none of it made the final cut. Greer labeled the documentary a hoax and accused *ABC News* of defrauding the public. He said that Kronick and Obenhaus assured him they were making a serious documentary, but they were actually planning to make a disinformation piece all along. A blow-by-blow account of the affair can be found on the Disclosure Project website.[75] Anyone who doubts Greer's version of events has to account for the complete omission of the Disclosure Project in *UFOs: Seeing is Believing,* which never mentioned Greer or the press conference or any of it- not even in an attempt to debunk it. It was like a CIA wet dream, like it never happened at all. The Disclosure Project was simply ignored, omitted and censored. Skeptics and debunkers could perhaps cast doubt on one man no matter his track record as they had with Corso, but what could they do with four hundred Corsos? Unable to dismiss or debunk the Disclosure Project, the only remaining option was to ignore it as if it never happened. Such further episodes of censorship served to reinforce Kolber's argument that the deafening silence of the establishment represented de facto confirmation of the Disclosure Project testimony.

In such an atmosphere, it would seem unlikely that any disclosure strategy would prevail. The "tightly focused" limited hangout advocated by Dolan failed as well. On November 12, 2007 another disclosure press event was held at the National Press Club in Washington D.C. Independent journalist Leslie Kean and documentary filmmaker James Fox organized a panel that featured the same caliber of high-level military and government officials, pilots and aviation experts, including one of the original Disclosure Project witnesses, former FAA official John Callahan.

The message of this press conference was *UFOs are real objects of unknown origin and the government doesn't want to tell us*. The witness pool was much smaller than the Disclosure Project and more international in scope. Former Arizona Governor Fife Symington moderated the event. Symington, once an air force pilot, was a first hand witness to the Phoenix Lights UFO. He flatly rejected the Air Force's argument that the sighting was the result of flares and said he saw a huge craft that challenged his view of reality.

Like the Disclosure Project, the witnesses described dramatic close encounters with unknown craft. Government knowledge was implied and extraterrestrial visitation was suggested, but there was no testimony about ETs, no accounts of UFO crash retrievals or references to ARVs. The group simply said the UFO phenomenon was real.

In closing, Symington lobbied the government to stop perpetuating the myth that all UFOs can be explained in conventional terms and pointed to a recent UFO sighting at O'Hare Airport that made international headlines. He said that the FAA's explanation that a disc-shaped craft seen hovering over a hangar by airline employees was caused by the weather was the kind of foolishness that had to end and he called on the government to reopen its UFO investigation.[76]

The panel's conclusions echoed the COMETA report, which had only managed to penetrate the mainstream media's UFO firewall thanks to Kean and the *Boston Globe*. Unfortunately, the same couldn't be said of the press conference modeled after its conclusions. Once again the media issued a twitter-like sound-bite before washing its hands of the story.[77] Reuters published a report that exemplified mainstream media coverage. In fact, some media outlets simply re-published the Reuters story, which tied UFO disclosure to the upcoming presidential election – not because it was an important issue – but because Dennis Kucinich was laughed at for admitting he'd seen one.

Reuters made a straw man argument, noting the testimony of Symington, Callahan and their colleagues before closing with a boilerplate statement lifted from the Air Force website that nothing had occurred since the close of Project Blue Book that would warrant reopening an official UFO investigation. One can't help but wonder that if these events didn't warrant serious attention, what would? Perhaps the proverbial landing on the White House lawn? Or maybe a close encounter with Spielberg's ET mothership at the Super Bowl?

The absurdity of the Air Force's position made one wonder if reporters even bothered to ask for comment, perhaps opting instead for a simple cut and paste from the Air Force website for the only answer they knew they could publish. Coverage of the event appeared scripted. It looked as if a template had been distributed throughout the mainstream media. Just fill in the blank. Nothing has occurred since the close of Project Blue Book that would justify the Air Force reopening its UFO investigation, blah, blah, blah. No reason to follow up- back to your regularly scheduled programming.

If there was any remaining doubt that the media was in the tank with the National Security State, its treatment of yet another attempt at disclosure in 2010 put those doubts to rest. Researcher Robert Hastings, author of *UFOs and Nukes*, led a third group of witnesses to the podium at the National Press Club.

Hastings said he'd spent the past 37 years locating and interviewing former and retired military personnel about UFO incursions at nuclear weapons sites. The message of this witness pool, which included original Disclosure Project witnesses Robert Salas and Dwynne Arnessonn, was clear and the tone urgent. "I believe, these gentlemen believe, that this planet is being visited by beings from another world who, for whatever reason, have taken an interest in the nuclear arms race which began at the end of World War II. Regarding the missile shutdown incidents: my opinion, their opinion, is that whoever are aboard these craft are sending a signal to both Washington and Moscow, among others, that we are playing with fire; that the possession and threatened use of nuclear weapons potentially threatens the human race and the integrity of the planetary environment," said Hastings. What's more, the witnesses felt a sense of duty to speak out about what they believed to be a profoundly important message, he said, about what was obviously a matter of national security.

Bob Salas, who testified at the first Disclosure Project press conference about a UFO that knocked nuclear weapons offline at Malmstrom Air Force Base, held up a copy of the air force's policy on UFOs. "No UFO reported, investigated and evaluated by the air force was ever an indication of threat to our national security, said Salas, reading from the document. "That is clearly misleading. That is false based on our testimonies," he said, demanding the government explain the discrepancy between their experiences and its official policy. He asked the media to make a serious investigation, which he promised would yield documentary evidence that would confirm the testimony given at the press conference. Nevertheless, media coverage didn't change. Disclosure was a one-off affair with no follow-up.

CNN, MSNBC, FOX, *USA Today*, *The Daily Mail*, *The Daily Telegraph*, UPI, etc., didn't include a response from the Air Force in their reporting.[78] If one wanted to know what the Air Force thought about its former officer's testimony one had to find a copy of the *Air Force Times*, which said, "When asked to comment on the new assertions, an air force spokeswoman cited a 2005 fact sheet that said: "Since the termination of Project Blue Book, nothing has occurred that would support a resumption of UFO investigations."[79] This was the same document that said UFOs weren't a threat to national security that Salas called false at the press conference. In reality, what the Air Force did was use the very same document that Hastings' witnesses said was total bullshit to debunk the press conference. And no one called them on it.

It was pure Alice in Wonderland. Maybe the Air Force could blow-off Salas by simply quoting its policy back to him and get away with it, but the mainstream media couldn't. It had to abandon its template because Hasting's group utterly destroyed its premise. The mainstream media couldn't very well quote the Air Force that UFOs weren't *a threat to national security* or close its reports with the Air Force's boilerplate statement that *nothing had happened since the closing of Blue Book that justified reopening its UFO investigation* when that was the very policy challenged by Hastings, Salas and their colleagues.

The cognitive dissonance caused by the Hastings Disclosure press conference was perhaps best exemplified by the *Washington Post*, which posted a report that the Tucson Citizen rightly observed as "satirical" and "bizarre."[80] In an article entitled, *UFO visits? Hmmm. Cookies? Yummm*, reporter John Kelly made like Homer Simpson, showing greater interest in the cookies served at the National Press Club than the testimony about UFOs tampering with nuclear stockpiles.

No disclosure strategy can overcome such powerful institutional resistance. Greer's urgent call for Disclosure tied to the sustainability of civilization may have been a bridge too far, but the simple premise that *UFOs are real so let's reopen the air force's official UFO investigation* also flopped. Even Hastings' hair-raising warning about UFOs tampering with nuclear weapons failed to wake the media from its coma. Neither Greer, Kean, Fox nor Hastings had the title, and thus the juice, to pull it off. Only a sitting president, secretary of defense, secretary of state and such would force the media's hand. Disclosure is a classic Catch-22: One has to occupy high office in order to make Disclosure stick, but Disclosure is a political impossibility for those in high office. Such paradox has resulted in soft Disclosure, an unofficial announcement that advanced extraterrestrial cultures are present on Earth. The establishment and its gatekeepers in the mainstream media don't acknowledge this fact, but make no mistake-Disclosure has occurred. We are now in the early stages of a paradigm shift analogous to the Galileo episode. Greer, Hastings and the disclosure project witnesses have been met with institutional resistance just like Galileo. Nevertheless, the Disclosure movement has shown that the Fermi paradox is only for those without a need-to-know such as presidents Jimmy Carter, Bill Clinton and anyone else not involved in the compartmentalized process to harvest the exotic technology of advanced extraterrestrial cultures operating on Earth.

The Disclosure Project event at the National Press Club in Washington D.C. may be as close as we will ever get to an official admission of an extraterrestrial presence on Earth- absent an undeniable large-scale extraterrestrial event in broad daylight on live national television.

In the final analysis, the Disclosure Project and subsequent disclosure events have, for all intents and purposes, gone unchallenged. As Edgar Mitchell said of the COMETA report- all that's missing is the official stamp. Unfortunately, if the past is precedent, an official announcement isn't coming any time soon. Regardless, history shows that a paradigm shift of unprecedented magnitude is underway.

CHAPTER 4

PARADIGM

Science today is locked into paradigms. Every avenue is blocked by beliefs that are wrong, and if you try to get anything published by a journal today, you will run against a paradigm and the editors will turn it down.
— **Sir Fred Hoyle, 1996**

It is difficult to get a man to understand something when his salary depends upon his not understanding it.
— **Upton Sinclair**

IF A TREE FALLS IN THE FOREST

A year after its original press conference, the Disclosure Project was in the news again. Not because long-sought congressional hearings had finally been won, but because the mainstream media's failure to investigate had become the story.

In Britain, *The Sunday Express* sounded the death knell for Disclosure in an article with the headline: *After 50 Years The Cover-Up Conspiracy Goes On.* Reporter Hamish Mackenzie delivered the grim news that the media's initial excitement over the Disclosure Project press conference had devolved into the deafening silence first noted by Kolber. "But one year on, the Project seems nowhere nearer achieving its goal, despite positive feedback from US Senators and overwhelming interest from the public via their website," wrote Mackenzie, who reported that the Disclosure Project had amassed over 100 new witnesses and that Dr. Greer was looking to build a global grass roots network to push the media and thus the government to respond to the story. "We were disappointed, but not surprised by the limited coverage," Greer told Mackenzie.[1]

In the U.S. only *Florida Today's* Billy Cox noted the passing of disclosure's one-year anniversary. Cox's article, *National media sidestep UFOs*, said that the Disclosure Project had been designed to be so compelling that the media couldn't possibly "freeze it out," yet it happened anyway. Cox interviewed veteran UFO reporters, Patrick Huyghe and Terry Hansen, neither of which was surprised by the media's lack of response. Huyghe, author of *The Swamp Gas Times: My Two Decades on the UFO Beat*, said the day may come when the national media would be forced to cover the UFO phenomenon whether it wanted to or not. He pointed to a recent event in Carteret, New Jersey in July 2001 as an example. UFOs appeared over the turnpike causing commuters to pull over so they could watch the impromptu airshow. FOIA requests made by the National Institute of Discovery Science showed that FAA radar at the Newark International Airport tracked targets that had no transponders. Huyghe asked, "Now, imagine if something like that had happened over a major metropolitan area two months later, after 9/11, when we were all on a heightened state of alert."

Like Huyghe, Hansen wrote about the struggle to cover UFOs. The reader will recall that in his landmark work *The Missing Times: News Media Complicity in the UFO Cover-up,* Hansen revealed evidence that the CIA founded the *National Enquirer* for use as a psychological warfare tool in accordance with the 1953 Robertson panel recommendations that the government use the media to debunk UFOs. "The Disclosure Project was a remarkable story, with men at a high level breaking their security oaths. Local and regional media around the country treated it as a straightforward item, but the national networks, PBS, they virtually ignored it," said Hansen adding, "This story could be covered right now. '60 Minutes' could blow the lid off it by interviewing retired airline pilots who aren't afraid to talk about incidents and near misses. But the major media is waiting for the green light from the White House or the Pentagon."[2]

Of course, the Pentagon's interest in delaying disclosure for as long as possible – i.e. indefinitely - means there will never be a green light absent some unforeseeable urgent need to disclose like the occurrence of undeniable extraterrestrial incident.

The Phoenix Lights episode almost became such an event. Citizen's demanded answers from their local representatives. The phones rang all the way up to Senator John McCain's office. When the air force blew the whole thing off as nothing more than flares, the public got angry. Local news media reported the story, but it wasn't covered nationally for months. It appeared as if the mainstream news media only covered the event because it couldn't continue to ignore what had become a high profile kerfuffle. Three months after the incident, suddenly there it was. All four major networks, as well as *USA Today*, carried stories on the Phoenix Lights UFO *on the same day-* an unlikely coincidence.[3] Nevertheless, like all high-profile UFO events, the Phoenix Lights aircraft carrier-sized UFO incident faded from the media's radar screen and the public's consciousness just the same. Had it occurred in broad daylight and been broadcast on live local news like the occasional high-speed police car chase, the next great paradigm shift would have been upon us like the meteor in *Deep Impact*.

The UFO cover-up looked like it might unravel on more than one occasion. In the 1990s it was the Phoenix Lights UFO that almost flipped the script. In the 1960s it was the infamous swamp gas episode that prompted then-Michigan congressman Gerald Ford to call out the Air Force. Ever since the 1940s Roswell has been a threat to put an end to the charade.

One of the key defining characteristics of the government's UFO policy is how many times it almost failed. The cover-up was like a leaky dike. The air force and the media plugged the holes with simple authoritarian statements to stop the flow of information: *There is no evidence that UFOs are extraterrestrial spacecraft - UFOs are not a threat to national security - nothing has happened since the closing of Blue Book that justifies reopening the air force's UFO investigation…*

Once the excitement died down traditional belief systems resurfaced: It was a just a weather balloon - UFOs can't be extraterrestrial craft because interplanetary space travel is impossible - The government isn't hiding the truth about UFOs, etc. History shows that the dominant worldview is a strong underlying sociological force that favors the status quo.

RELIGION VS. SCIENCE VS. RELIGION

The way we view the world has changed radically over time. As observations mounted, our beliefs evolved. The first great shift in worldview came when the assumption that the Earth was flat gave way to the realization that it was, in fact, a sphere. In the third century B.C., the Greek scholar Eratosthenes, head librarian at the Library of Alexandria, calculated its circumference by measuring shadows at high noon on the summer solstice in two separate cities in Egypt. Eratosthenes calculations weren't perfect, but they were remarkably accurate, bringing the real world into sharper focus.

Another assumption - that the Earth was the center of the Universe - managed to stunt the advance of astronomy for more than a millennium. Greco-Roman mathematician and astronomer Claudius Ptolemy perfected the geocentric model of the Universe in the second century A.D. Ptolemy imagined a grand celestial machinery was responsible for the motion of celestial objects.[4] He thought this universal machine worked much like the gears and wheels of the little machines that were cutting edge technology back in his day. The Sun, Moon, planets and stars were attached to a series of nested crystal spheres with the Earth at the center. Ptolemy explained the retrograde motion of the planets by attaching them to a rotating wheel called an epicycle, which was in turn attached to a crystal sphere that revolved around the Earth. The stars, which appeared to be in fixed position, were attached to the outermost sphere. The whole Universe was thought to be not much bigger than the solar system. It was unknown at the time that the stars were other suns.

The system worked. Astronomers used it to make reasonably accurate predictions of planetary motion. Ptolemy's geocentric model of the Universe held up for over 1,500 years, but as observations mounted over time astronomers had to add more and more wheels, gears and other tweaks. The universal machine became increasingly complex and then it broke down. A tweak in one spot caused a glitch in another. Astronomy went into a crisis mode and the search for a solution was on.[5]

In the sixteenth century, Polish astronomer Nicolaus Copernicus found the answer. Earth was not the center of the Universe around which everything else revolved. Copernicus' heliocentric model put the Sun at the center. Earth and the other planets orbited the Sun. Copernicus didn't publish his thesis until he was on his deathbed for fear of ridicule. The idea that Earth wasn't in a fixed position and was actually in motion around the Sun was considered absurd at the time.[6]

Belief about mankind's place in the Universe was, and still is to a large degree, sacred. To argue against it was dangerous. In the year 1600, former Dominican Friar, mathematician and philosopher Giordano Bruno was burned at the stake by the Catholic Church for heresy, in part because he espoused the Copernican system and all its implications, including the plurality of worlds. Bruno was the first to realize that stars were other suns that had planets of their own. He thought the Universe was infinite, that there was no center. At his trial he was ordered to recant his beliefs. He refused and was sentenced to death.[7]

The Bruno episode foreshadowed the crisis that Western religion would face when Galileo pointed his newly invented telescope at the heavens, kicking off the modern era of astronomy. It wasn't long before he began writing about his discoveries, which included many more stars than could be seen with the naked eye, mountains and valleys on the Moon, and most significantly of all, four moons in orbit around Jupiter. The view through the telescope showed that not everything in the Universe revolved around the Earth. Jupiter's moons blew away an argument against Copernicanism that the Earth would leave the Moon behind if it were in motion. Galileo proclaimed confirmation of the Copernican model. It was also clear that Bruno was right. Stars weren't just lights attached to a crystal sphere like a colossal Christmas ornament. They were other stars.

The Catholic Church struck back. It banned Copernicus' book *De revolutionibus orbium coelestium* and ordered Galileo to stop writing about the subject. A decade afterward Galileo violated the Church's edict and the Inquisition ordered him to stand trial in Rome. Like Bruno, he was found guilty of heresy. He was forced to recant his belief in Copernican heliocentrism and sentenced to house arrest where he spent the rest of his days.

The crisis in astronomy had become a crisis in religion. The new model of the Universe opened up a can of worms for the Church. Some argued that belief in other inhabited worlds didn't conflict with scripture, but others saw the proverbial elephant in the room. Mathematician and astronomer Johannes Kepler, whose laws of planetary motion further validated the Copernican model and laid the foundation for Newton's theory of gravity, said "if there are globes in the heaven similar to our

Earth... Then how can all things be for man's sake? How can we be masters of God's handiwork?"[8]

Fortunately for the Church, the advance of astronomy showed that the local neighborhood looked like a barren, inhospitable, lifeless desert. The Pope didn't have to worry about an imminent scientific discovery of inhabitants on the Moon, Mars, Venus or any of the other planets. Our apparent solitude in the solar system kept alive for the Church, the possibility, no matter how infinitesimal, that we were still God's crowning achievement.

When science inevitably discovers ETs on a planet in another star system there will be what science philosopher Thomas Kuhn called a 'paradigm shift' of epic proportions. Kuhn introduced the concept of paradigms in his book, *The Structure of Scientific Revolutions*. He defined a paradigm as a constellation of beliefs, values, techniques, etc., that unite a community. Most scientists, he said, solve puzzles and work on problems in furtherance of the paradigm. They reject anomalies that don't fit out of hand. Others that Kuhn calls 'revolutionary scientists' begin looking for alternative theories when the outliers pile up. When a better theory emerges a scientific revolution occurs and one paradigm is abandoned for another. The transition from Ptolemy's geocentric model of the Universe to Copernicus' heliocentric model is the classic example.

Kuhn saw that change came about in science much like in politics. "Political revolutions are inaugurated by a growing sense, often restricted to a segment of the political community, that existing institutions have ceased adequately to meet the problems posed by an environment that they have in part created. In much the same way, scientific revolutions are inaugurated by a growing sense, again often restricted to a narrow subdivision of the scientific community, that an existing paradigm has ceased to function adequately in the exploration of an aspect of nature to which that paradigm itself had previously led the way. In both political and scientific development the sense of malfunction that can lead to crisis is prerequisite to revolution."[9]

When the Church faced a crisis paradigm shift wasn't an option. Instead came the Reformation, which splintered Christianity into various sects, each with its own constellation of beliefs. The triumph of science over religion made the scientific paradigm the dominant worldview. Western religion has struggled to come to terms with science ever since. Two centuries after Galileo, the Church suffered another gut-punch when

Charles Darwin published *The Origin of Species*. Darwin showed that all of nature, human beings included, evolved naturally through an algorithmic process he called natural selection. Attempts to reconcile Creationism with Darwin's Evolution, including rebranding it as *Intelligent Design*, have all failed. The geocentric paradigm, although greatly diminished, hasn't yet completely faded. Deeply ingrained beliefs die hard. About 20 percent of the population still think the Sun revolves around the Earth and, there remain to this day, about a thousand flat-earthers.

The advent of the scientific method led to the development of a technological civilization on Earth, but in supplanting the religious worldview, science itself became a religion of sorts. Ironically, future discoveries seem destined to threaten its core beliefs. Advanced ET civilization is one such discovery. So far, science hasn't had to confront much evidence. But when it has like it did in 1968 with the Condon investigation, scientists act more like the priests at Galileo's Inquisition than scientists.

In theory, Science is a self-correcting process. Observation. Reproducibility. Evidence. Proof. Science is authoritative. It's pronouncements come with the cold, hard weight of reality. As a result, scientists have become the new priests. And like the old priests, they're all too human. Science may be self-correcting, but human beings? Not so much. Greed, corruption, careerism, incompetence, etc., short-circuit the corrective process.

In 2011, scientific misconduct reached crisis levels. The Wall Street Journal reported a sharp rise in retractions of scientific papers in peer-reviewed scientific journals. A whopping twenty-six percent was due to fraud. Lancet editor Richard Horton called the big increase in fraud "a scar on the moral body of science."[10]

Unfortunately such egregious, unethical behavior stems from an all too common cause- the struggle to advance one's career. Scientists are just like anybody else. They want to be rock stars too. "A single paper in Lancet and you get your chair and you get your money. It's your passport to success," said Horton.

Overly ambitious doctors aren't the only reason that the medication in your medicine cabinet may not work as advertised. The Vioxx scandal showed how corporate profits also trump science. With the help of the FDA, pharmaceutical giant Merck distorted drug trials in order to hide evidence that Vioxx caused heart disease.[11] FDA scientists spoke out about an internal power struggle with top administrators intent on putting drugs on the market regardless of the risk to the public. In one instance, the FDA refused to allow one of its own scientists to testify about his study that showed antidepressants increased the risk of suicide in children.[12]

Science is clearly a tool that can be misused to produce fake results. What's more, fraudulent data is like a virus because it infects ongoing research, further retarding the corrective process. Greed is the driving force behind such scientific misconduct, which has on occasion short-circuited technological progress in key areas and put the future of human civilization at risk. The cold fusion scandal is an important example that hints at why UFOs are such a threat to the establishment.

In 1989, University of Utah electrochemists Stanley Pons and Martin Fleischmann stunned the world with the announcement that they'd achieved nuclear fusion, the long sought after Holy Grail of alternative energy.

Fusion would be a huge upgrade for our nuclear power plants, which use fission to generate energy. Fusing atoms instead of splitting them releases far more energy and far less radiation. And unlike fission, which requires heavier, much less common elements like uranium, fusion is done with hydrogen, the most common element in the universe, making it, for all intents and purposes, a limitless energy source. Just one cubic kilometer of ocean water could provide more energy than all the oil reserves on Earth. Just one gallon of water would be the equivalent of 300 gallons of gasoline.[13] The only catch was that it was much more difficult to fuse atoms than split them. Nuclear fusion required tremendous heat and pressure. Or so it was thought- until Pons and Fleischmann flipped the script, showing extreme heat wasn't necessary at all.

The news of room temperature nuclear fusion was especially threatening to scientists who'd based their models on the stars, which are nature's nuclear fusion reactors. Low energy nuclear fusion, as it's now called, was not on their radar screen. The implications of such a discovery are paradigm altering. Cold fusion had the potential to change the world. And that was the problem, especially for the hot fusion scientists who'd been blindsided by the discovery, not to mention the fossil fuel industry. Careers hung in the balance. Millions of dollars were on the line. A major scientific revolution was a lethal threat to the status quo. If cold fusion was real, a scientific revolution was inevitable.

Laboratories around the world attempted to reproduce Pons and Fleischmann's work with mixed results. The question of whether or not a new era of free energy was on the horizon made worldwide headlines. President George H.W. Bush ordered the Department of Energy (DOE) to conduct an investigation. When the verdict came back cold fusion was declared a mistake, or even worse, fraud. Once the DOE rendered its judgment, the media gave the subject of cold fusion the scorn and ridicule treatment normally reserved for UFOs. The only problem was the DOE was dead wrong. On purpose.

According to Eugene Mallove, MIT played a central role in the DOE's effort to tar and feather cold fusion as bad science. As the chief science writer at MIT, Mallove had a front row seat. In *Infinite Energy* magazine and in his book *Fire from Ice: Searching for the Truth Behind the Cold Fusion Furor*, he gave a blow-by-blow account that showed there was indeed bad science- on the part of MIT. "The story of cold fusion's reception at MIT is a story of egregious scientific fraud and the cover-up of scientific fraud and other misconduct—not by Fleischmann and Pons, as is occasionally alleged—but by researchers who in 1989 aimed to dismiss cold fusion as quickly as possible and who have received hundreds of millions of DOE research dollars since then for their hot fusion research, wrote Mallove, who said the hot fusion scientists at MIT's Plasma Fusion Center threw a party they called a 'wake' to celebrate the death of cold fusion- before they'd even looked at the final data. They didn't believe cold fusion was possible and didn't care what the data said. No theory could account for such low energy nuclear reactions. *It can't be; therefore it isn't.* Even if the data came back positive cold fusion couldn't be real.

Mallove saw firsthand that MIT did in fact reproduce Pons and Fleischmann's cold fusion effect, but the hot fusion scientists at the Plasma Fusion Center fudged the data to get rid of the positive result. What's more, MIT's hot fusioneers did their best to make sure that no real news about cold fusion reached the public. Professor Herman Feshbach prevented MIT's *Technology Review* from publishing an article about cold fusion written by Mallove. When Mallove confronted Feshbach, he refused to debate the facts and told Mallove he didn't want to see any more evidence for cold fusion because it wasn't possible.

Mallove accused the 'academic-government complex' of crimes against science. "The energy and environmental future of the world hung in the balance – and the MIT PFC people failed us. They preferred to get rid of a scientific claim in which they did not believe, and which threatened their federally-funded program, by playing politics with the media, trivializing their experiments, and ultimately foisting on the world highly flawed data."[14]

As a result of high-level scientific misconduct, research dollars for cold fusion dried up in the United States, Mallove resigned in protest, and Pons and Fleischmann left the country in search of funding in France. Since then, cold fusion research has continued in underground labs on meager funds.

Cold fusion was left for dead by the media. In the year 2000, at the British Association's Festival of Science, Arthur C. Clarke blasted editors and journalists for trashing the subject. "Over the last decade there have been literally hundreds of reports from all over the world from highly qualified people and distinguished institutions of anomalous sources of energy… Although there are a lot of crooks, cranks and cowboys in this field, I believe there is now enough published evidence to prove something strange is going on," said Clarke, who saw the fossil fuel era coming to an end and thought cold fusion might be the answer.[15]

Positive results kept piling up. In fact, by 2004 almost 15,000 cold fusion experiments had been performed. Success rates ranged between 83 and 100 percent.[16] Scientists like Pons, Fleischmann, Mallove and others were raising hell. Meanwhile, scientists like Hermann Feshbach flat-out refused to look at the data just like Catholic priests in Galileo's day. Feshbach even violated Clarke's Law: "When a distinguished scientist states that something is possible, he is almost certainly right. When he states that something is impossible, he is very probably wrong," Clarke famously declared in his essay *Hazards of Prophecy*.[17]

Despite Clarke's plea for sanity, mainstream media continued to give cold fusion the UFO treatment. Positive reports went ignored just like high-quality UFO sightings, while stories that ridiculed the field made the news. The belief that cold fusion was hot garbage went viral, generating enough cognitive inertia to counter mounting evidence to the contrary. Nevertheless, a major paradigm shift in physics is inevitable. In an interview with Steve Greer published in *Disclosure*, Mallove said cold fusion was "100 percent certain," comparing the controversy to both the Galileo and Wright Brothers episodes. What's more, he predicted commercial products would eventually come to market, thus destroying the ruse perpetrated by MIT. Mallove told Greer he'd seen other so-called over-unity devices that showed electromagnetic theory was in for "radical revision."

Today almost no one remembers that the Wright Brothers were ridiculed and debunked for years after their initial flight at Kitty Hawk. The scientific establishment sneered at the idea. Lord Kelvin, rock star physicist of his time, declared manned, heavier-than-air flight impossible.[18] Kelvin was a founding father of the theory of thermodynamics. His stature gave him great power and influence. His word was taken as received truth. Especially when others of his ilk, like Thomas Edison, also thought the airplane would never fly. As a result, the editors at *Scientific American* magazine dismissed the Wright Brothers story for five years. To them it was just a ridiculous hoax unworthy of acknowledgement or investigation.[19]

Just three decades later, the overlords of science were at it again. Astronomer Richard van der Riet Woolley famously declared spaceflight an impossibility, confidently dismissing heavier-than-air flight analogies in the process. "Space travel is utter bilge," he said upon his appointment to Astronomer Royal in England. Sputnik blasted into orbit the following year.

In the long run, science may be self-correcting, but the average scientist doesn't seem much different than the typical priest when their worldview is called into question. The big bang theory is regarded as scientific fact, but it's not, according to revolutionary scientists like Eugene Mallove, Paul LaViolette, Halton C. Arp, Sir Fred Hoyle, Tom Van Flandern, Fred Alan Wolf and Edwin Hubble, whose discovery that distant galaxies were 'red-shifted' led the astronomical community to conclude that the Universe was expanding. Hubble himself did not believe in the big bang, always referring to the 'apparent velocity' of the galaxies. Hubble thought it more likely that photons simply ran out of steam as they travelled through interstellar space, but this 'tired-light' concept violated the First Law of Thermodynamics, a sacred law of physics.

Astrophysicist Paul LaViolette also had doubts about the big bang after his subquantum kinetics theory predicted the stationary Universe tired-light model. When he began to investigate the big bang theory he found that astronomers compared their expansion predictions against just one set of cosmological test data and they routinely tweaked their models to fit the data, an act he said most scientists would consider "despicable," but was somehow acceptable in astronomy because the "ruling majority" believed the big bang theory was already "established fact."[20]

When LaViolette put the theory on trial he used multiple cosmological tests instead of just one. If corrections to a model made the data fit on one test, then those same adjustments should make the data fit on all others as well. Instead, LaViolette found adjustments that made the expanding Universe fit like a glove on one hand, made it fit like a shoe on another. Like Ptolemy's geocentric model after it broke down, tweaks that fixed something in one place threw things out of whack somewhere else. Therefore, LaViolette compared both the big bang and stationary universe tired-light models against multiple data sets without any tweaks or corrections at all. It was the first time such a cosmology testing technique had been tried. What he found was that the tired-light model more closely fit the data than the expanding Universe. In fact, LaViolette disproved the big bang theory in *The Astrophysics Journal* in 1986 with his paper: *Is the Universe really expanding?* It took him eight years to wear down the editors, who finally relented after exhausting all possible objections, giving him the opportunity to introduce a new model called continuous creation cosmology that arose from his subquantum kinetics field theory.

The big bang's demise got little media exposure, but LaViolette's paper did stir things up in the astronomical community. After its publication, he received congratulatory letters from notable astronomers and astrophysicists around the world, who were unhappy with the amount of fudging necessary to make the big bang theory work. In 2004, in an open letter to the scientific community published in *New Scientist magazine*, a group of astronomers and astrophysicists compared inflation, dark matter, and dark energy – concepts necessary to make the expanding Universe theory fit the data that have never been observed in nature and for which there is no evidence – to Ptolemy's epicycles.

Sir Fred Hoyle, founder of the Institute of Astronomy at Cambridge, said the big bang and its exotic concepts of inflation and dark matter was like "medieval theology." Perhaps in a thousand years the big bang will be just as fictional as Ptolemy's crystal spheres, but today it's regarded as fact by the scientific establishment. In an interview with science journalist John Horgan, Hoyle said, "Science today is locked into paradigms. Every avenue is blocked by beliefs that are wrong, and if you try to get anything published by a journal today, you will run against a paradigm and the editors will turn it down."[21]

Will the Big Bang go the way of Ptolemy's crystal spheres? Last time, astronomers needed a millennium to sort things out. It doesn't look like we have that much time this go around. Paradigm protectionism has become an existential threat. The fossil fuel paradigm is a primary example.

At this point, the concept of global warming/climate change is well known. Tesla may have been the first to realize the danger over a hundred years ago.[22] In general, scientists began warning about greenhouse gasses as early as the 1950s. But it wasn't until 1988, after James Hansen, director of NASA's Goddard Institute for Space Studies, went before congress to sound the alarm, that government took action.[23] The result was the United Nation's Intergovernmental Panel on Climate Change (IPCC).[24] Thousands of scientists from 195 countries contribute to the IPCC, which has issued several reports over the years, each one more alarming than the previous. The IPCC's conclusions are unequivocal. Human activity is the driving force behind global warming-induced climate change. No ifs, ands, or buts.

In a 2014 press release the IPCC stated the impacts would be "severe, pervasive and irreversible," but that it was still possible to avoid the worst-case scenario, which climate activist Bill McKibben likened to a 'zombie apocalypse.' Bottom line- industrial emissions have to be cut drastically and fast. The danger is such that the Pentagon declared climate change an immediate threat to national security.[25]

It's also a threat to every SUV-loving member of the fossil fuel community. For this group, reflexively engaging in paradigm protectionism, climate change is a hoax perpetrated by thousands of scientists presumably seeking to protect their nest egg and advance their careers much like MIT's hot fusioneers. But the IPCC isn't anything like the Plasma Fusion Center at MIT. The IPCC does no original research of its own and it doesn't monitor the temperature or any other aspect of the climate itself. It doesn't even pay its scientists. They contribute on a voluntary basis by reading peer reviewed journals and writing reports for the panel, which in turn, issues a grand summary representing the aggregate knowledge of climate scientists worldwide.

The possibility of such a hoax is, of course, highly unlikely. As the COMETA report showed in regards to UFOs, hoaxes are quickly exposed. Scientific misconduct, on the other hand, is another story. Climate change deniers claimed to have found evidence of data manipulation, but the claims didn't hold up. According to Naomi Klein, author of *This Changes Everything: Capitalism vs. the Climate*, so-called 'climategate' was a "manufactured scandal."[26]

There were some scientists who easily could have been accused of wrongdoing. Scientists hired by the oil industry. Big Oil funded lobbyists and think tanks willing to cast doubt on the science behind climate change and even went so far as to offer $10,000 dollars to individual scientists and economists to write articles that would undermine the global scientific consensus.[27] Aerospace engineer Wei-Hock "Willie" Soon received $1.2 million for attempting to show that an increase in solar activity, not human activity, was the cause of global warming.[28] The fossil fuel lobby then paid media mouthpieces to spread the views of its hired guns far and wide. It used its influence on the Bush administration to censor official reports about global warming and to resist regulations that would hinder future activities and potential profits.[29]

If there were any remaining doubts that Big Business mobilized to prevent the march of science from trampling its profits, it was swept away by the recent book, *Merchants of Doubt: How a Handful of Scientists Obscured the Truth on Issues from Tobacco Smoke to Global Warming*. Authors Naomi Oreskes and Erik M. Conway uncovered an operation led by a small cabal of scientists who were originally funded by the tobacco industry, then by foundations and think tanks, and eventually by the fossil fuel industry. The goal of these industry-sponsored scientists was to create the illusion of legitimate scientific doubt on issues where there really wasn't any. Issues such as the dangers of tobacco smoke, the viability of SDI, the causes of acid rain and the ozone hole, and finally, the reality of global warming induced climate change. These scientists conducted virtually no original research of their own; nevertheless, they challenged the data of the IPCC, disputed its evidence and smeared its scientists. Although only a tiny minority, this cabal was able to use its credentials and connections to gain media attention and spread misinformation about legitimate scientific results. "It is a story about a group of scientists who fought the scientific evidence and spread confusion on many of the most important issues of our time. It is a story about a pattern that continues today. A story about fighting facts, and merchandising doubt," wrote Oreskes and Conway.[30]

Thanks to this band of scientific saboteurs, we may never know if establishment figures like Big Bang proponent Neil Degrasse Tyson, Sagan's successor, will someday be forced to acknowledge that his beliefs are indeed equivalent to medieval theology as Hoyle said. The IPCC says the world will experience centuries of warming, increasingly volatile weather patterns, more violent storms, crushing drought and rising seas. Could they be wrong? Maybe. As we've seen throughout history, an overwhelming scientific consensus is not proof that scientists are right. But it doesn't seem too likely. The naysayers are not a band of revolutionary scientists with a sack full of anomalies that the establishment is ignoring. They are a collection of mercenaries with sacks full of oil industry cash. The IPCC could be wrong about how it all shakes out. Instead of steadily rising seas, sinking cities and hotter temperatures, maybe warmer seas will shut down the North Atlantic current, which will ultimately result in a new ice age like Whitley Strieber and Art Bell wrote about in *The Coming Global Superstorm*. Either way it's curtains for life as we know it.

To the rational-minded, the risk that the IPCC is wrong is simply too big a gamble to take, especially in light of the 'One Percent Doctrine' established by notorious Vice President Dick Cheney, who argued that if there's even a one percent chance an enemy is developing a nuclear weapon the U.S. has to respond as if they do have a nuclear weapon. Here we have 97 percent of the world's climate scientists saying they are 95 percent certain we're going to experience catastrophic climate change, yet there is still resistance from the corporate establishment, especially the energy industry. "Those who profit from the unconstrained pollution that is the primary cause of climate change are determined to block our perception of this reality. They have help from many sides: from the private sector, which is now free to make unlimited and secret campaign contributions; from politicians who have conflated their tenures in office with the pursuit of the people's best interests; and — tragically — from the press itself, which treats deception and falsehood on the same plane as scientific fact, and calls it objective reporting of alternative opinions," wrote Al Gore, who could have just as easily been speaking about the suppression of the truth about UFOs and the extraterrestrial presence.[31] In fact, UFOs are an even bigger threat to the status quo than cold fusion or climate change.

CLOSE ENCOUNTERS WITH THE EXORCIST

Extraterrestrial spacecraft are a problem for both religion and science. Neither worldview officially recognizes that such things exist. Neither knows what to do other than look the other way, but occasionally some brave soul within the power structure attempts to sort things out.

Within the Catholic Church, Monsignor Corrado Balducci was that guy. Balducci was an expert in parapsychology and demonology who served for years as the exorcist of the Archdiocese of Rome. He was widely recognized as one of the most respected Italian theologians and was known to have been close to Pope John Paul II. He was also a regular guest on Italian State TV where he said as a matter of plain fact that ET contact was real.[32]

In 1999 and again in 2001, The Monsignor published papers about UFOs, ETs and Catholicism. He had come to the only conclusion anyone familiar with the COMETA report, the Disclosure Project and 60 years of UFO history could. There are simply too many credible witnesses to ignore. "The general a priori-skepticism, the systematic, total denial, damages, even destroys the basic value of the human testimony with grave and incalculable consequences, since it is indeed the fundament of human society, if individual, social or religious. Of course there is always one or the other exemption, there are errors and lies, but generally all our life is based on what we learned from others. It is unthinkable to live without this basic confidence, unimaginable are the consequences of a general negation of the human experience on the individual, social and religious life. It would destroy the very fundament of any human society!" warned Balducci in *UFOs and Extraterrestrials… A problem for the Church?*[33]

In his writings, the Monsignor insisted the existence of ETs was consistent with Church doctrine and called attention to other prominent Church officials who'd made statements about the reality of extraterrestrials, including the recent example of Padre Pio, who was beatified by the Pope in 1999 and canonized in 2002. Balducci's advocacy for UFO eyewitnesses made him an important voice in the nascent disclosure movement. In 2000, the Monsignor gave an interview to Steve Greer that was subsequently published in the book *Disclosure* and distributed to the media at the Disclosure Project Press conference in Washington D.C. Given Balducci's stature within the world's largest religious community of over a billion Catholics, it was remarkable the mainstream press was able to ignore it.

In the interview, Balducci dispelled fundamentalist Christian fears that the UFO phenomenon was the work of the devil. He told Greer he thought ETs further evolved than us must also be more spiritually advanced. Humans were the bottom rung on the cosmic totem pole. There was no one below us. According to Balducci, the existence of intelligent ETs less spiritually evolved than humans was impossible.

The Church hasn't taken an official position on the extraterrestrial presence and the Monsignor was careful to add the disclaimer that he was only expressing his personal opinion. Nevertheless, it appears he had the tacit approval of the Church. According to Italian researcher Paola Harris, former assistant to Blue Book astronomer J. Allen Hynek and confidante of the Monsignor, the Church was aware of the Balducci's TV appearances and did nothing to silence or discourage him from speaking out. In fact, Balducci knew the Pope followed him on TV. "Balducci is known to us researchers as the 'unofficial' voice of the Vatican," wrote Harris.[34]

For all intents and purposes, it appeared as if the Church - perhaps having learned its lesson - was preparing itself for the next great paradigm shift. Ever since the days of Galileo, the Church has done its best to stay on top of all things astronomical. It has its own observatory, originally located in Italy, which now sits on Mount Graham, Arizona. It has it's own astronomers, whose mission is to show that science and religion are compatible. "To have a small group of priests doing science is important to show there is no conflict," said Father George Coyne, Director of the Vatican Observatory, who didn't hesitate to rebuke a Viennese cardinal who had spoken out against evolution.[35]

It was also important to make sure that modern day priests didn't get caught with their pants down again. In the aftermath of the Disclosure Project press conference in 2001, statements coming out of the Vatican's observatory reinforced the perception that the Church knew which way the wind was blowing and was trying to get out in front this time around. In the January 7, 2002 edition of the *Corriere della Sera*, a Milan newspaper, Father Coyne, said, "The universe is so vast that it would be madness to think that we're an exception," adding, "the more we study the stars, the more aware we become of our own ignorance."[36]

In 2008, after Benedict had replaced the late Pope John Paul and long after the Disclosure Project had disappeared down the memory hole, it still looked like the Church was hedging its bet on the new paradigm. Coyne's successor, Father Jose Gabriel Funes, did an interview with the Vatican newspaper, *L'Osservatore Romano*, on the subject of extraterrestrial life and its impact on the Church. Funes said aliens weren't a problem. "This is not in contrast with the faith, because we cannot place limits on the creative freedom of God," he said, referring to an alien being as an 'extraterrestrial brother.'[37] But by 2010, it was clear the wind was blowing the other way. Speaking at the British Science Festival, the 'Pope's astronomer,' Brother Guy Consolmagno, said the odds against finding intelligent extraterrestrials and being able to communicate with them made the question of alien contact impractical.[38]

The Pope's guy didn't acknowledge eyewitness accounts of alien contact that have already occurred. It was as if Balducci and the Disclosure Project episode had never happened. It would seem unimaginable aliens in the distance are much more palatable to the establishment than humanoid ETs in the here and now. Unfortunately, there was no one around to remind Brother Consolmagno about the fundamental importance of eyewitness testimony. Monsignor Balducci died in 2008.

Consolmagno's remarks showed the extraterrestrial presence was still a problem for the Church. Despite Balducci's efforts, to reconcile ETs with scripture, he was never able to answer Kepler's simple question. *How can everything be for man's sake? How can we be masters of God's handiwork?* At its core, Western religion is geocentric. Scripture reflected the knowledge of the times. It seems the Church has never fully come to terms with the Copernican revolution.

Balducci's claims notwithstanding, UFOs were still a big no-no, especially for the Jesuit astronomers, who sit at the nexus between science and religion. UFOs are heretical to their colleagues outside the Church. In 2010, the Queen's astronomer, Lord Martin Rees, president of the Royal Society, dismissed UFO believers as "cranks" despite having stated in the same speech that intelligent life may exist in forms we can't imagine and there may be aspects of reality beyond our ability to comprehend just as quantum physics is beyond a chimpanzee.[39]

It's not exactly clear why those who believe real UFOs are extraterrestrial craft must be cranks. The whole point of Fermi's paradox is *they should exist* and *they should be here*. The Hubble Deep Field images put an exclamation point on Fermi's epiphany. One would think the cranks would be those that ridicule and deny reports from credible witnesses that fulfill Fermi's expectations. In reality, there is no paradox, only the illusion of one thanks to establishment figures like Rees. The risk of being branded a heretic by an archbishop of astronomy is apparently enough to make Jesuit astronomers like Brother Consolmagno forget about Monsignor Balducci, the Disclosure project and his warning about the importance of such witness testimony.

UFOs make the nexus between science and religion a rock and a hard place for the Jesuit astronomers. A Brookings Institution study commissioned by NASA in 1960 called *Proposed Studies on the Implications of Peaceful Space Activities for Human Affairs* found that scientists and religious fundamentalists would be most threatened by the discovery of extraterrestrial life.[40] It's not surprising that Consolmagno, Rees and their colleagues do what Corso said the military did when confronted with a problem it couldn't solve. Can't prevent UFOs from violating our airspace? What UFOs? No UFOs- no problem.[41] At least the late Monsignor had the courage to face the new paradigm.

WEIRD SCIENCE

The UFO phenomenon has inspired more than its fair share of scientific misconduct. After the Roswell Incident, the real scientific investigation was conducted in the classified stratosphere of the military-industrial complex while the public was given pseudoscientific explanations and rigged scientific studies to support the UFO cover-up.

The secret UFO investigation used the system of compartmentalization developed by Vannevar Bush for the Manhattan Project, restricting information on a need-to-know basis. One only had access to information necessary to perform a task. This way a spy could only do so much damage. The worker bees only had a piece of the puzzle, not the big picture. According to Corso, only Majestic-12 knew the whole truth. But in order to carry out investigations and operations, others had a need-to-know certain facts about UFOs. When there was no need-to-know, then there were no UFOs. As one moved up through the lower classification levels and became involved in activities related to UFOs, one would learn they were real, but of unknown origin. Only at the highest levels would it be made known that real UFOs were extraterrestrial craft and only at the Majestic-12 level would it be known that the military-industrial complex was in possession of an actual ET vehicle and bodies.

Bush's compartmented system of information management gave rise to Escher-like constructions of reality. The secret memo from Twining to Schulgen is a prime example. Twining said flying disks were "something real and not visionary or fictitious" and described the classic metallic disc-shaped craft with a dome on top."[42] The memo, which wasn't declassified until 1967, made it known that UFOs were real- *but at the classification level of secret* they were said to be of unknown origin.[43]

The letter conspicuously noted an absence of hard evidence in the form of crash debris- a fact misused by skeptics to debunk the Roswell Incident.[44] The debunkers misinterpret the memo because they don't account for the compartmented system of information management used in military intelligence. In fact, just the opposite is true, but saucer debris only exists at the highest classification levels, according to UFO researcher Bruce Maccabee, whose interpretation is consistent with the Majestic-12 operation to gather intelligence on flying disk activity, which required it to be known at the compartmented level Secret that the phenomenon was real, but of unknown origin.[45]

An organization like Majestic-12 would operate unlike any traditional organization. Imagine you are overseeing such a highly compartmented operation. You might take an 8am briefing on the progress of the government's UFO investigation classified at the level of secret, in which it was said that UFOs were real objects of unknown origin. The project director might deliver a report about an internal debate over whether UFOs are interplanetary spaceships or simply the product of a terrestrial foreign power- perhaps one engaging in some sort of psy-op. Next, your 10 o'clock briefing might be with a Top Secret group cleared to know that UFOs were real and were extraterrestrial and whose primary task was to lead the previous lower level secret investigation away from concluding this to be true. Of course, a major theme of this group's efforts would be its emphasis on the lack of physical evidence- something this Top Secret group was not cleared to know about. Ironically, this group would have had a specific need-**not**-to-know. After lunch, having digested the first two briefings, you might have an afternoon meeting with the Above Top Secret science team under the leadership project administrator Vannevar Bush about the very evidence withheld from the second group. Bush's team, which previously confirmed the extraterrestrial origin of the vehicle by measuring its isotopic ratios, had an update on the effort to understand the propulsion system of the spacecraft.

Such machinations would naturally generate some confusion, especially for those on the outside looking in, which could only aid the purposes of the cover-up. In fact, at the onset of the UFO era, whenever a cover-up was alleged, simple bureaucratic mix-up was often offered as an alternative explanation. Confusion was cover for the cover-up. The system worked and the operation likely would have hummed along without a hiccup had UFOs not continued to violate U.S. airspace.

The Air Force was obligated to investigate, but the decision to deny the presence of ETs meant that the investigation would never be allowed to bear fruit publicly. Consequently, Air Force investigators like astronomer J. Allen Hynek, were forced to concoct mundane and transparently implausible explanations for highly anomalous, widely witnessed UFO incidents that, in the end, only served to erode the government's credibility. To astute observers, the picture presented by the Air Force appeared distorted and incongruent. As in the Escher illustration, *Relativity*, one could see the various stairways leading to different realities, but one had no access to those stairs. This culture of official suppression and disinformation inevitably gave rise to civilian UFO investigation.

The study of UFOs, or 'ufology' as it's known, is a difficult enterprise. Because the civilian UFO researcher has no access to the artifacts or classified information, the phenomenon can only be studied indirectly. This process consists of the evaluation of eyewitness testimony along with any additional evidence in the form of radar returns, photographs, video, and in some cases, physical trace evidence such as depressed grass and soil, broken or burned vegetation, radiation, etc., left behind by the craft. The Holy Grail of hard physical evidence is not available in the public domain. Given the example of the Roswell Incident, it's apparent that when extraterrestrial technology falls into human hands, it is confiscated and hidden.

Complicating matters, scientific misconduct committed during the early years of the government's official investigation convinced the scientific community that UFOs were nothing but myth, folklore, superstition and hokum. If a scientist engaged the subject, he or she risked facing the type of ridicule that could irreparably damage one's career. What's more, the emphasis on the lack of a smoking gun marginalized the existence of physical trace evidence.

Skeptics and debunkers insist that only extraterrestrial hardware that can be tested is acceptable as proof of an extraterrestrial presence. As Carl Sagan famously declared, "Extraordinary claims require extraordinary evidence." On the surface, it seems a reasonable suggestion. However, in the case of UFOs, where the government has every incentive to seize and then deny the existence of the hard evidence, Sagan's argument serves as a catch-22. Without a smoking gun in the form of hardware, civilian scientists can't confirm what the eyewitness testimony, radar returns, physical trace evidence, etc., strongly suggest- that some UFOs are extraterrestrial vehicles. In the final analysis, the extraordinary evidence that would satisfy the scientific community's ultimate burden of proof is shrouded in a compartmented veil of extraordinary secrecy.

Many scientists, including physicists and astronomers, have had UFO sightings and experiences, but because of the stigma that has been purposely cultivated, they have been effectively deterred from undertaking investigation or speaking out. When they've dared to buck the system, as did atmospheric physicist James McDonald, the damage to one's career and personal life is often catastrophic. Even the mavericks that are not easily deterred find that their hands tied. In a recent example, 1993 Nobel Prize winning biochemist Kary Mullis wrote about a bizarre experience that he attributed to a possible case of alien contact in his autobiography *Dancing Naked in the Mind Field*. Mullis stated that although he couldn't deny that the incident occurred, as a scientist, he couldn't write papers about it because he couldn't replicate the experience and there was nothing tangible on which he could perform experiments.[46]

Without direct access to the extraterrestrial hardware, there is little that civilian scientists can do to advance ufology beyond speculation. Given the circumstances, perhaps the most fruitful aspect of civilian UFO investigation has been research into the government's cover-up. Despite the government's denials, UFO activities over U.S. airspace elicit a response from the national security apparatus. This in turn generates a historical record that is difficult, if not impossible, to completely obscure. The study of this interaction through FOIA requests, declassified government documents and whistleblower testimony has revealed a great deal of information about the

ET presence including the readily apparent fact that the definitive hard physical evidence exists under lock and key. It is this facet of civilian UFO investigation that has also led to the discovery of improprieties committed in the name of science in order to mislead the public.

Ufology also raises sociological issues. Misguided skeptics wax poetic wondering why people believe in UFOs, but the more one investigates the phenomenon, the more one sees the question reversed. The question becomes, why are people, to borrow Greer's phrase, so "irrationally skeptical," about UFOs and what has led science to follow the path of religion in denying this reality?

It's fitting that the first prominent civilian UFO researcher reluctantly began his investigation as a skeptic. Former Navy pilot Donald Keyhoe began a writing career after retiring from active duty and became one of the nation's foremost aviation writers. He accompanied Charles Lindbergh on a nationwide tour and wrote a popular book about the experience called, *Flying With Lindbergh*.[47] He was a natural choice to cover the flying saucer story and was assigned the task by the editor of True magazine. Keyhoe expected to find evidence of American or Russian experimental craft, but upon investigation, discovered the Air Force was hiding a much bigger secret about the existence of ET spacecraft.[48]

Keyhoe became involved in an internal power struggle between those within the Air Force who wanted the truth made known and those who sought to hide it at all costs. The conflict fit the disclosure-by-cover-up scheme dreamt up by Majestic-12 and may have been manufactured somewhat like the hypothetical scenario above. Whatever the case, the ex-naval aviator exposed the cover-up, time and again. Keyhoe showed that the Air Force was lying about UFOs.[49] When his efforts threatened to succeed, those in charge turned to the scientific community to reinforce the status quo.

Over the course of his investigation, Keyhoe became a first hand witness to scientific misconduct at the highest levels. He saw how rigged science was used to convince the scientific community as well as the general public that UFOs were nothing but hokum. When it came to UFOs, the policy dictated the science instead of the science dictating the policy. If studies weren't rigged it caused big problems for those in charge of keeping the Big Secret. The cover-up crowd faced the constant threat of exposure, not just from UFO activities, which they couldn't control, but also from those within the lower classified ranks and from rival agencies in other countries. A declassified Top Secret Air Force memo found in the National Archives dated November 4, 1948 showed that Swedish air intelligence analysts thought UFOs were probably extraterrestrial craft. "Reliable and fully technically qualified people have reached the conclusion that 'these phenomena are obviously the result of a high technical skill which cannot be credited to any presently known culture on Earth.' They are therefore assuming that these objects originate from previously unknown or unidentified technology, possibly outside the Earth," read the memo.[50]

That same year, the lower ranks in the U.S. Air Force's official UFO investigation known at the time as Project Grudge, came to similar conclusions. According to director Ed Ruppelt, Project Grudge issued a report called *Estimate of the Situation* that made its way up the chain of command without dissent until it reached the office of Air Force Chief of Staff, Hoyt Vandenberg, who shot it down because it because it lacked "proof." [51] Keyhoe discussed the report with Ruppelt at length. He concluded Vandenberg intentionally set the bar at Saganesque heights to prevent the lower classified levels from blundering into highly classified territory.

The authors of *The Estimate* concluded that ETs were in observation mode and that an attack wasn't on the horizon. The Air Force must have been confident in its conclusion. The military reinforced the cover-up by silencing pilots. Regulations were put in place that prevented both military *and civilian* pilots from talking publicly about their UFO sightings.[52] As historian Richard Dolan noted, it was in the air that we most often came into contact with the extraterrestrial presence. Although ground observers also saw UFOs, the primary theater for contact was in the skies and pilots made the most reliable witnesses.

Analysis by both the Swedish and U.S. Air Force showed that if scientists had access to pilot's reports they might reach the same conclusions. From the perspective of those behind the cover-up what was needed was a way to prevent the civilian scientific community from investigating UFOs. Scientists are naturally skeptical. Given that interstellar travel was inconceivable at the time, almost any other explanation seemed more likely. The stage was set for Harvard Astronomer, Donald Menzel, who was more than willing to reprise the roll of Lord Kelvin- with a twist.

THE PIED PIPER

Don Menzel was the most fanatical UFO debunker of his time. He laughed-off the very idea of ET visitors, gave pseudoscientific explanations for every major UFO sighting and assured his peers that UFOs were pure nonsense- a collection of illusions caused by natural phenomena.

As a prominent astronomer known the world over, Menzel's claims, like Lord Kelvin's, were received wisdom for the public and his peers. As far as the establishment was concerned, he was Moses returning from Mount Ararat with the Ten Commandments. His word was The Word.

Also like Kelvin, his statements suggested absolute, unfettered certainty, yet his methods for arriving at such conclusions were anything but scientific. Even the Air Force, which tried its best to diffuse the situation by finding prosaic explanations for UFO sightings, did not accept Menzel's analysis. In fact, Project Blue Book staffers told Keyhoe, that Menzel never looked at their files before rendering judgment even though they were made available to him. Keyhoe was flummoxed, unable to understand how Menzel could offer such simple solutions without examining the Air Force reports, which included hundreds of high-quality, unexplained sightings. There were reports of high-speed intercept attempts of structured craft by top-notch Air Force pilots complete with radar returns and multiple witnesses, and yet Menzel wrote them off as if they were just lights in the distance. He even had the audacity to claim that a UFO sighting made by fellow astronomer Clyde Tombaugh was an atmospheric illusion- a claim that Tombaugh flatly rejected. It was clear to all who did their homework that Menzel tailored the facts to fit his opinion. But why?

On the surface, Menzel seemed like just another bloviating elitist, but there was more to the famed astronomer than met the eye, a fact that was unknown until his name appeared in the Majestic Documents. Ufologist Stanton Friedman thought it likely meant that the documents would turn out to be fake, but upon investigation the Harvard professor's presence on the Majestic-12 roster served to enhance the document's authenticity.

Friedman found that Menzel lived a double life unmentioned in various biographies. He held a Top Secret Ultra clearance and did clandestine work for a number of intelligence agencies, including the NSA. His specialties were radio wave propagation and cryptography, which he used to break Japanese code during the war. It was a skill set that would have been invaluable in an attempt to decipher symbols found in the alien craft recovered at Roswell. And Menzel would have also have been a key cog in the camouflage scheme described by Corso. As an authority figure in astronomy, his statements about UFOs would be convincing.[53] If Keyhoe had seen the Majestic Documents he would've understood Menzel's claims for what they were- anti-UFO propaganda.

The Washington National sightings of 1952 are a perfect example.[54] The Air Force attempted to intercept UFOs when as many as 15 were seen both visually and on radar over the White House and Capitol Hill on consecutive weekends in July.[55] The UFOs seemed to play a game of cat and mouse, taking off and disappearing at a fantastic speed whenever fighter jets were sent after them and reappearing after the jets returned to their bases. The story made front-page headlines. There was such a feeding frenzy in the media that the Air Force was forced to call the largest press conference since WWII.[56]

At the presser, Director of Air Force Intelligence, Major General John Samford gave an explanation cooked up by Don Menzel, who said that most UFO sightings were atmospheric mirages caused by ice crystals, refraction and temperature inversions.[57] It was theoretical snake oil that couldn't possibly explain the Washington National sightings. Not a single radar operator at the airports involved thought that temperature inversions explained what they saw on their scopes and, in some cases, with their eyes. Neither did the three officers sent by the Pentagon who were also in the radar room during the sightings. But the media never heard about their experiences and opinions because none of those involved in the actual investigation were made available at the press conference.

If the press had heard from the witnesses it would have learned there was a mild inversion layer in D.C. at the time of the sightings, but it was completely inadequate to explain what was seen on radar, and totally ludicrous in terms of the visual sightings and the photos taken of the bright objects seen over the capitol building. In fact, Keyhoe got an Air Force spokesman to admit that temperature inversions couldn't possibly explain the Washington National sightings.[58] The temperature inversion theory was permanently laid to rest in 1969 when the Air Force published a report called *Quantitative Aspects of Mirages*, but the damage was done.[59] The bogus answer served its purpose just like the Roswell weather balloon cover story. The public forgot all about UFOs in the nation's capital.

In the final analysis, Menzel used pure pseudoscience to debunk UFOs. He used his position as an authority figure to lead his colleagues away from highly classified truth like the pied piper used his pipe to lead the children out of town in the famous legend. Menzel turned the natural skepticism within the scientific establishment about interplanetary visitors into an a priori bias against flying saucer reports. As a result, the scientific community ignored the phenomenon and ridiculed anyone within its ranks who took it seriously.

Although scientists like to accuse ufologists of pseudoscience, history shows that the pseudoscientific shoe is often on the other foot. UFO history is replete with such examples.

THE VENUS EXPLANATION

In 1948, fighter pilot Captain Thomas Mantell was killed while attempting to intercept a UFO in Kentucky. Thousands saw the strange round craft, including state policemen. According to witnesses, it was moving at a "pretty good clip" before coming to a hover over Godman Air Force Base in broad daylight.

Military personnel watched the UFO through binoculars for over an hour before ordering Mantell, a World War II fighter pilot, to attempt an intercept. "It appears to be a metallic object... tremendous in size... directly ahead and slightly above... I am trying to close for a better look," reported back Mantell just before he crashed and died.

The Air Force claimed Mantell flew his fighter, an F-51 not equipped with oxygen, up to 20,000 feet where he blacked out and plunged to his death. And what was Mantell chasing? The planet Venus.[60] The press bought the story, which was more than a little farfetched. Don Menzel pooh-poohed the incident as a simple misidentification of a sundog, a reflection of the sun off ice particles in clouds.[61] It was difficult to tell which explanation was less plausible. Sundogs disappear when aircraft change altitude due to the change in reflection angle. And a sundog didn't explain sightings made from the ground. Or the Godman tower. Venus, on the other hand, was for all intents and purposes, invisible in the bright daylight sky.[62]

The Air Force eventually dumped the Venus explanation for a Navy Skyhook balloon, although no records corresponding to the date and time of the incident could be found to support the claim.[63] The Mantell Incident is one of the most significant events in UFO history. It changed the minds of many high-ranking officers within the Air Force who thought flying saucers were a joke and it drew perhaps the most important UFO investigator in history, Don Keyhoe, into the fray.

Keyhoe was a skeptic until True Magazine asked him to investigate the Mantell case. As a former navy pilot, he thought the Venus explanation was ludicrous. He'd never heard of a pilot mistaking Venus for an aircraft, even at night. He also thought the suggestion that Mantell's "huge metallic object" was just a hallucination caused by an oxygen-starved brain was bunk. Mantell was an experienced wartime fighter pilot well aware of his limits. He told Godman tower that he would break off pursuit at 20,000 feet and his observations, which were consistent with other eyewitness accounts, were made before he flew into thin air. A friend who'd flown with Mantell for years who considered him one of the most cautious pilots he'd ever known said, "The only thing I can think was that he was after something that he believed to be more important than his life or his family." Keyhoe also knew that Mantell wasn't chasing any kind of balloon. His background as a pilot included experience in flying balloons. He knew hurricane force winds would've been necessary for such a simple object to lead a fighter pilot and his wingmen on a thirty-minute chase. If the UFO was a balloon they would've have overtaken it within seconds. Colonel Hix and the others in Godman tower would've easily identified a balloon. Keyhoe couldn't find a conventional explanation. Even J. Allen Hynek, whose job it was to provide prosaic explanations for UFO sightings, found it difficult to conceive of a man-made object large enough to be seen simultaneously from as far as 175 miles apart as eyewitnesses had reported. Hynek also rejected the Venus explanation.[64]

Keyhoe was the first to make the case in public that the Swedish and the U.S. Air Force made in secret. If flying saucers were real – and they were – they could only be one of two things: secret military craft or extraterrestrial spacecraft. Keyhoe dismissed the first possibility. The flying discs were obviously not the next step in modern rocketry. They were a quantum leap beyond anything anybody had and it made no sense to test such technology over the general population or over another country where it could fall into enemy hands. "During the wave of 1947, several classified documents expressed the belief that the objects were a secret American, or possibly Soviet, technology. Yet the group assigned to the problem in 1948, Project

Sign, rejected both explanations. If Soviet, why fly these things over the American heartland? If American, why fly them over cities, where everyone could see them, or over sensitive installations, where they were harassed by our own aircraft? Add on top of this the amazing production levels that would have been necessary to fly so many of these objects, which were seen all over the world," wrote historian Richard Dolan.[65]

Obviously, the Air Force couldn't blame UFOs on secret craft even if it were true. But its policy of secrecy benefited from media speculation about such things in the wake of ridiculous answers like the Venus explanation. Time and again, the Air Force said UFOs were caused by the planet Venus. So much so, that Keyhoe recognized it as the standard, go-to explanation whenever there wasn't one.

The Air Force's tortured response convinced Keyhoe that it was doing its best to hide the presence of alien spacecraft. He was such an astute investigator that he not only showed that flying saucers were real, he also laid bare much of the Majestic-12 public relations campaign revealed almost 50 years later by Corso. 'Project 'Saucer' [Project Grudge] was set up to investigate and at the same time conceal from the public the truth about the saucers," wrote Keyhoe, who was spot-on in describing the plan to use the official investigation to both explain away flying saucers and gather intelligence on their activities. What's more, he cracked the code of the MJ12 public acclimation program. "On top-level orders, it was decided to let the facts gradually leak out in order to prepare the American people," said Keyhoe about the Air Force's schizophrenic game plan to let Schrodinger's cat out of the bag. In fact, *True Magazine* editor Ken Purdy thought the government was using Keyhoe's exposé as a trial balloon because the Air Force made no effort to stop its publication.

In January 1950 *True* published Keyhoe's *The Flying Saucers are Real*, touching off a firestorm. Phones rang off the hook in the Pentagon and in *True's* offices. The public wasn't panicked. It was excited. Everyone wanted to know more. Instead, it was the Air Force that seemed to panic. They denied everything, issued a report explaining away all sightings in conventional terms and closed Project 'Saucer.' Behind the scenes, all the Air Force did was rebrand its UFO investigation as Project Blue Book.[66] In the process, it stashed as much of its UFO data as it could.

Corso used to an old story he'd been told to illustrate how UFO secrecy works. "A group of men were trying to protect their deepest secrets from the rest of the world. They took their secrets and hid them in a shack whose very location was a secret. But the secret location was soon discovered and in it was discovered the secrets that the group was hiding. But before every secret could be revealed, the men quickly built a second shack where they stored those secrets they still kept to themselves… This process repeated itself over and over until anyone wanting to find out what the secrets were had to start at the first shack and work their way from shack to shack until they came to where they could go no further because they didn't know the location of the next shack," wrote Corso, attempting to explain the ins and outs of UFO secrecy. According to the Colonel, in the real world this meant that if one discovered a Roswell shack, "you would find code-named project after code-named project, each with its own file, security classification, military or government administration, oversight mechanism, some form of budget, and even reports of highly classified documents. All of these projects were started to accomplish part of the same task: manage our ongoing relationship with the alien visitors we discovered at Roswell. However, at each level, once the security had been breeched for whatever reason – even by design – part of the secret was disclosed through declassification while the rest was dragged into a new classified project or moved to an existing one that had not been compromised." Project Grudge was one of those shacks and Project Twinkle was one of its secrets. In 1949, the Air Force set up Twinkle in attempt to get a handle on the 'green fireball' UFOs seen in New Mexico. Multiple observation posts were equipped with a theodolite movie camera system, which was designed to capture the altitude, size and speed of the objects through triangulation on film.

It wasn't long before Twinkle bore fruit. The project ceased operations before its second anniversary. Officially, the Air Force declared Project Twinkle a failure, but documents found in the national archives show otherwise.[67] At White Sands Proving Ground, Twinkle's cameras caught four objects thirty feet in diameter traveling at a high rate of speed at an altitude of 150,000 feet- higher than any manmade object could reach at the time. Keyhoe never saw the film, but his sources told him that a theodolite had tracked the objects at over 15 thousand miles an hour.[68] Despite its mission, it appears Twinkle was never meant to be such a rousing success, at least for the lower classification levels. Project Twinkle's final report omitted the film and subsequent analyses.[69] As a result, Twinkle's closing led one away from the Top Secret truth and the White Sands UFO film disappeared into another of Corso's shacks.

It was clear that real science took place behind the scenes while lies and pseudoscientific gibberish were called The Truth and served to the public. Given the government's official position that flying saucers were illusions caused by mundane objects and events, it's no surprise the Air Force would suppress evidence that confirmed the existence of real UFOs that couldn't be laughed off with the Venus explanation. Skyhook balloons, weather balloons, sundogs, ice crystals, temperature inversions, the planet Venus, etc., were the only answers the Air Force would give for UFO sightings after its original investigation Project Sign became Project Grudge. The *Estimate of the Situation* led Vandenberg to blow up Sign, reassign its personnel, and reform the investigation as Project Grudge. It was the first time the Air Force rearranged its shacks. Under Sign, a UFO sighting might lead investigators to suggest Venus or a balloon as a possibility, but if it didn't check out, the official explanation was listed as unknown. Under Grudge, Venus *was the answer* or a Skyhook balloon *was the answer*, regardless of whether the explanation fit because designating a sighting as unknown was no longer an option and the Extraterrestrial hypothesis was strictly taboo. "The anti-UFO policy was set for all time," said Project Blue Book astronomer, J. Allen Hynek, about UFO investigation under Project Grudge.[70]

From a public relations standpoint, Grudge was nothing more than a debunking operation, which was an internal problem for the Air Force. The rank and file that had been exposed to UFOs, but had been left out of the loop, rebelled against the anti-UFO policy. A power struggle developed that played out in public in the reporting of Keyhoe and others. Keyhoe gave a blow-by-blow account of the clash between what he called the "censor-fighters" and the "silence group." According to Keyhoe, the censor-fighters knew UFOs were real and thought secrecy was dangerous. They pushed to get the truth out. But the silence group was fearful that chaos and panic would follow Disclosure so they fought for a policy of denial in order to avoid a crisis with which they didn't know how to cope. As Corso said, no aliens meant no military responsibility to deal with the problem.

Things came to a head shortly after the Washington National sightings, igniting a battle over UFO policy that became a serious threat to put an end to the cover-up.[71] Keyhoe's so-called silence group called on the CIA to torpedo the censor-fighters. With the help of Nobel-caliber scientists known to be biased against UFOs, the CIA arranged a rigged scientific study to quash the pro-UFO uprising within the military and intelligence communities and once again put the UFO genie back in the bottle. In January 1953, physicist H. P. Robertson chaired a panel that met over a four-day period. Officially, the Robertson Panel was supposed to study UFOs in order to recommend policy, but in reality it was nothing more than theater used to justify a policy that was already in place.[72]

Fake scientific studies feature the telltale signs of scientific misconduct and the Robertson Panel was no exception. In this case the preferred method was selection bias. According to Ruppelt, Major Dewey Fournet and other Blue Book insiders involved with the study, the panel chose to review 15 select cases out of hundreds of verified UFO reports. The strongest cases were left out. What's more, alleged Majestic-12 member, Lloyd Berkner was s Robertson panelist, at least in some capacity. Berkner arrived as the "study" was wrapping up, yet he reviewed and approved a rough draft of the final report before anyone else on the panel had seen it. Given such circumstances, one could argue that Berkner was there to guarantee the desired outcome, perhaps delivering the final report written by Majestic-12 to be rubber-stamped by Robertson and the panel. Whether or not it's true that Majestic-12 actually wrote the report before the panel even met, it seems someone did. "The final day was spent primarily in reworking the draft (evidently, *some* of the report had to reflect the week's work)," wrote Richard Dolan.

Whatever its genesis, the Robertson Panel report claimed UFOs were not a threat to national security and most sightings could be reasonably explained if more data was available. The panel did see a danger though. Not from the UFOs themselves, which it said were ephemeral whatzits of no consequence, but from the reports about them. The panel warned that if the Air Force was obligated to investigate every weird light in the sky it could make the country vulnerable by overwhelming vital defense resources. On the pretext that UFO investigation itself was dangerous, the panel directed the national security agencies to "take immediate steps to strip the Unidentified Flying Objects of the special status they have been given and the aura of mystery they have unfortunately acquired."[73] In short, the panel called for the government to debunk UFOs. According to the report, "The 'debunking' aim would result in reduction in public interest in 'flying saucers' which today evokes a strong emotional reaction. This education could be accomplished by mass media such as television, motion pictures, and popular articles."

The implications of the Robertson Panel "education" program were immediately obvious to Keyhoe's censor-fighters within the military. An intelligence officer told Keyhoe they'd been double-crossed by the CIA, which didn't want to prepare the public and was instead trying to bury the subject. Ruppelt and Air Force Public Relations Officer Albert Chop, who had been preparing for Disclosure, were ordered to stop. Chop said, "They [CIA] killed the whole program. We've been ordered to work up a national debunking campaign, planting articles in magazines and arranging broadcasts to make UFO reports seem like poppycock." Ruppelt told Keyhoe, "We're ordered to hide sightings when possible, but if a strong report does get out we have to publish a fast explanation– make something up to kill the report in a hurry, and also ridicule the witness, especially if we can't figure out a plausible answer. We even have to discredit our own pilots. It's a raw deal, but we can't buck the CIA. The whole thing makes me sick– I'm thinking of putting in for inactive." [74]

Keyhoe's censor fighters made it clear the Robertson panel recommendations had been put into policy. What's more, there's hard evidence that Big Media gave the intelligence community the big stage for its educational program. Thanks to a letter written by Robertson panel scientist Thornton Page, there's no doubt the 1966 CBS documentary *UFOs: Friend, Foe or Fantasy* hosted by Walter Cronkite was one of those TV shows designed to strip UFOs of their "special status." In the letter, found in the Smithsonian Institution archives by researcher Michael Swords, Page flatly stated the documentary was based on the panel's conclusions. [75] The Cronkite documentary was just one example of how the intelligence community went about implementing the policy.

It wasn't difficult for the intelligence community to get the news media in the U.S. to play ball. The media had been cooperating with the government on matters of national security since WWII, which enabled the CIA to develop assets it could call upon when needed. A CIA memo called *Task Force Report on Greater CIA Openness* written by the Public Affairs Office to the Director of Central Intelligence shows that by 1991, the agency had a stranglehold on the news media. "PAO now has relationships with reporters from every major wire service, newspaper, news weekly, and television network in the nation. This has helped us turn some 'intelligence failure' stories into 'intelligence success' stories... In many instances, we have persuaded reporters to postpone, change, hold or even scrap stories that could have adversely affected national security interests or jeopardized sources and methods."[76]

The 2001 Disclosure Project press conference was one of those instances when the intelligence community flexed its muscles, calling on its cronies to force senior producers at two Big Media networks to scrap major exposés. When Greer asked why the projects had been canceled he was told *they* wouldn't allow it. When he asked who *they* were he was told, "you know who *they* are." Greer and White House correspondent Sarah McClendon had presented dozens of credible, Top Secret witnesses ranging from Brig. General to Col. to FAA administrator. No anonymous sources. All on the record. Yet the Big Media did next to nothing. No follow-up or any further investigation of any kind.

The CIA didn't just control the media. Sometimes it *was* the media. Journalist Terry Hansen, author of *The Missing Times: News Media Complicity in the UFO Cover-up* found circumstantial evidence that the CIA created the *National Enquirer* in order to make UFOs into a laughingstock. Hansen thought it was no coincidence that CIA psychological warfare agent Gene Pope founded the newspaper – which regularly reported on UFOs - around the time of the Robertson Panel. "The stories were true, for the most part, but they mixed them in with celebrity stories, and trashy sensationalistic topics so that anyone who saw these stories in the National Enquirer would make the mental connection between UFOs and rather dubious sensationalistic reporting. So, it cast the whole subject in disrepute. And of course that's what psychological warfare people do. They use these ploys to muddy the waters and confuse people about what's really going on," said Hansen.[77]

What was really going on was a debunking campaign justified by fake science. Critics pointed out how ridiculous it was to call a four-day review a scientific study. Authors Barry Greenwood and Lawrence Fawcett found the science behind the Robertson Panel lacking. For comparison, they looked at a case involving a film of bright objects shot by a Naval officer in Utah investigated by both the Navy and the Robertson Panel. The panel, which spent all of 12 hours reviewing 15 pre-selected cases, debunked the film as a flock of seagulls despite two months of analysis and 1,000 man-hours by

Navy photographic experts who concluded that the film showed self-luminous, unknown objects operating under intelligent control.

Then there was the baffling ignorance of panel scientist Thornton Page, who rejected the possibility that UFOs might be extraterrestrial in part because sightings wouldn't be limited to one continent. Not only was it known from the outset of the UFO era that the phenomenon was global, but Robertson himself, along with panelist Louis Alvarez had been involved with the investigation of the so-called foo fighters encountered by both allied and enemy forces in the skies over Germany during WWII. In a serious UFO investigation, such a misstatement like Page's isn't possible. Page's ignorance of the most basic facts led Richard Dolan to write, "one is forced to ask: just where is the science in this scientific study?"

At the time, there was real science being done on UFOs, just not by the Robertson panel, which relied upon the star power of its scientists, whose conclusions were accepted as a matter of fact, much like Lord Kelvin and others before. The real science was done in secret at the Battelle Memorial Institute, which produced a study that flatly contradicted the Robertson panel claim that all UFO reports could be explained if more data was available.[78] Although the Battelle report, *Project Blue Book Special Report 14*, was made to appear to agree with the Robertson Panel conclusions, the actual data included in the study did not. The data showed when more information was available UFO reports become *less* explainable. What's more, Battelle found the probability of 'unknowns' being missed 'knowns' was less than one percent.[79] Despite Battelle's attempt to harmonize its study with the Robertson Panel by what Hynek later characterized as a "shamefully biased interpretation of statistics to support a preconceived notion," *Project Blue Book Special Report 14* had real scientific value because, unlike the Robertson Panel Report, this study contained actual data and showed a significantly higher unexplained rate of 22 percent.

Jacques Vallee discovered evidence that proved the Robertson Panel conclusions were, in fact, preordained, uncovering another one of Corso's shacks in the process. While reorganizing Hynek's files, Vallee found a classified memo he called the 'Pentacle Memorandum.'[80] The memo referred to a secret UFO investigation code named Project Stork that had the power to limit the scope of the evidence put before the Robertson Panel. Specifically, Project Stork claimed authority over "what can and what cannot be discussed" at the Robertson Panel meetings. The memo led Vallee to suspect there was a plot to persuade a naturally skeptical scientific community that UFOs were nonsense. In his diary, he wrote, "…[W]hat this document shows is that the scientific community has been led down a primrose path, beginning with the Robertson Panel and its group of prestigious physicists."

It would be more accurate to say that the effort to lead the scientific community astray began with Donald Menzel at the onset of the UFO era, but Vallee was essentially correct. The Robertson Panel served to formalize the process of pseudoscientific deception begun by Menzel.

Other clues in the Pentacle memo showed that a well-planned scientific UFO investigation was taking place in secret. The implications led Vallee to further speculate about the role of the Robertson Panel in such an operation. He wrote, "The intelligence agencies have determined that unknown objects are flying over the United States. If these are controlled machines they are far beyond anything we have. Public opinion demands some action. What could be simpler than assembling a panel of scientists? Perhaps not the best informed, but the most prestigious. They are shown a sample of reports, pre-selected by the Air Force. They find no reason, of course, to revise the current edifice of science on the basis of what little they are shown. And once the panel has been disbanded and public opinion quieted, what a wonderful opportunity for the military to resume its research in secret, with its own scientists, its own laboratories…"[81] Like Keyhoe, Vallee was an astute investigator able to intuit the basic modus operandi of the Majestic-12 operation. In fact, this was exactly how Twining's plan was supposed to work, according to Corso. Under the cover of explaining away the UFO phenomenon, the government would be free to investigate UFOs in secret.

WAR OF THE WORLDVIEWS

The Robertson Panel helped the silence group win the battle, but the war waged on. Keyhoe went on to found the National Investigative Committee for Aerial Phenomena (NICAP), a civilian UFO research organization that pushed hard for congressional hearings. Many of the censor fighters within the military joined NICAP, including Major Dewey Fournet, who confirmed the existence of the *Estimate of the Situation* in an affidavit. All the while the cover-up crowd did everything in its power to thwart the Disclosure advocates.

Not long after the Robertson Panel made its recommendations the Air Force issued order AFR 200-2, which funneled real UFO reports to Air Force Intelligence while directing the hoax's, mistakes and misidentifications to Blue Book and eventually the media. A violation of AFR 200-2 was punishable by court-martial. Another military order known as JANAP (Joint-Army-Navy-Air-Publication) 146(b) also channeled real UFO reports to "other appropriate agencies" including Air Defense Command, the Secretary of Defense and the CIA. Richard Dolan thought one such agency might have been Majestic-12 or a group like it based on comments Ruppelt made about a meeting with the Director of Air Force Intelligence that included the representative of a group of "scientists and industrialists" who were involved with UFOs and that the 'tone' of the discussion contradicted the official press releases. Whatever the case, JANAP 146(b) also made the unauthorized release of UFO information a crime punishable under the Espionage Act of 1934. A pilot could face up to ten years in prison or a $10,000 fine for violating the order, which extended to anyone who knew of its existence including merchant marines, commercial airline pilots, etc.[82]

These two orders cut off the flow of real UFO reports to the public and made Project Blue Book into a clearinghouse for explainable UFO reports. COMETA called the orders an "impressive repressive arsenal" used to keep news about real UFO incidents from reaching the public.[83] The system worked. Although genuine UFO reports managed to slip through on occasion, the number dropped significantly. The mainstream media delivered the message crafted by the Robertson Panel and UFOs did indeed lose their special status and fade from the public sphere.

In the beginning the battle between the Disclosure advocates and the cover-up crowd was stage-managed by Majestic-12 as part of its acclimation program. According to Corso, the *disclosure-by-cover-up* scheme was meant to prepare the public for an eventual confrontation with hostile extraterrestrial forces. Such was the immediate military response to the discovery of ETs and their far superior technology. But the urgency to prepare the public for the possibility of interstellar war likely faded as scientists working on the secret investigation began to understand the scope of the situation. ETs weren't just a little more advanced than us. They were far more advanced. And they weren't just visiting or sending an occasional probe to check us out like we do with Mars and Venus. This was something altogether different. If ETs really wanted to take the planet nothing could stop them. Human resistance would be like 300 Spartans raising their shields against the Death Star. Imagine our own colonial army with muskets and horses up against its modern descendants with tanks, fighter jets and drones, not to mention the nuclear bomb. Just a couple hundred years of technological advancement is an overwhelming and decisive advantage. If spacefaring ETs wanted to kill us off it would be a simple matter. All they would need to do is direct an asteroid at the Earth like the one that wiped out the dinosaurs. No, Ruppelt's group of scientists and industrialists likely realized fairly early in the investigation that the ETs present on Earth were not the advance scouts of an invading army. Certainly this assessment had been made by the time of the Robertson Panel, which convened six months after UFOs buzzed the nation's capitol.

The Washington National sightings were an ideal opportunity to allow the *disclosure-by-cover-up* plan to mature – especially in the wake of the Mantell Incident – if Majestic-12 thought it was a necessity to prepare the public for an alien invasion. But this didn't happen. In fact, it's possible the Washington National sightings played a role in the conclusion that UFOs were not a threat to national security. By playing cat and mouse with the Air Force on consecutive weekends in 1952, the extraterrestrial presence demonstrated both its superior capabilities and its aversion to military confrontation. If that was the message, it seems it was received. So the UFOs in Washington D.C. were explained away as temperature inversions giving Majestic-12 the opportunity to further investigate the alien presence in secret.

Ironically, the group was undone by the very secrecy upon which it depended. According to Corso, absolute secrecy prevented Majestic-12 from drawing on the resources of the government like any other committee. Consequently, narrowly defined sub-committees with lower classification levels were used to obtain funding. As the lower level committees absorbed its functions, a power struggle developed within the top-level group. Various factions began fighting each other for a bigger chunk of the black budget. Within five years, the operation became an unmanageable mess just as Truman feared.

"For all intents and purposes, the original scheme to perpetrate a camouflage was defunct by the late 1950s. Its functions were now being managed by series of individual groups within the military and civilian intelligence agencies, all still sharing limited information with each other, each pursuing its own individual research and investigation, and each – astonishingly – still acting as if some super intelligence group was still in command. But, like the Wizard of Oz, there was no super intelligence group. Its functions had been absorbed by the groups beneath it. But nobody bothered to tell anyone because a super group was never supposed to exist officially in the first place. That which did not exist officially could not go out of existence officially. Hence, right through the next forty years, the remnants of what was once a super group went through the motions, but the real activities were carried out by individual agencies that believed on blind faith that they were being managed by higher-ups," wrote Corso, whose boss, General Trudeau, concluded there was no one in charge[84]

Disclosure Project witness, Brigadier General Stephen Lovekin, who had an Above Top Secret clearance that included briefings on Roswell, backed Corso's claim that the government lost control of its UFO operations. Lovekin served under President Eisenhower on the staff of the White House Army Signaling Agency. He made it a point to note he was at the Pentagon at the same time as Corso. Lovekin said Eisenhower had been sold out and was worried that UFO policy had fallen into the wrong hands.[85]

If the original Majestic-12 operation was indeed defunct and there was no longer a top-level group coordinating its various sub-committees then these programs would've been free to pursue their own agenda just like Trudeau and Corso had. A cover-up and an acclimation program could still be in existence, running independently, no longer a part of a larger operation. What's more, if the military-industrial complex hijacked the government's secret UFO operations as Eisenhower is said to have alluded to in his infamous farewell address, according to Lovekin, then it was simply business as usual, just as it was for Corso and Trudeau. In the same way that they'd slipped ET technology into existing weapons development programs, the military-industrial complex threw ETs into the hopper as another potential enemy for the war machine to build weapons against.

After the corporate coup d'état of the Majestic-12 operation, the fruits of investigations like Project Twinkle and *Project Blue Book Special Reports 1-13* (which presumably exist, but have yet to surface) likely ended up in company shacks that Steven Greer spoke out about called Unacknowledged Special Access Programs. Within these programs, Science is used to exploit ET technology for the military-industrial complex, but not for the world at large. According to Lovekin, this technology is the primary reason perpetuating the cover-up. It seems ETs themselves are not a direct threat, but their technology is a threat to national *economic* security.

The inevitability that advanced alien technology will completely transform civilization as we know it scares the hell out of the corporate world, especially the oil industry. "I think the secrecy has been enforced because what would be revealed would totally destroy an economy that was designed by certain capitalists in this country a long, long time ago to maintain them and their corporations from here to eternity. I think oil has a special interest in seeing that it maintains its position where it is, regardless of what kind of pollution or disastrous side effects may have occurred or continue to occur," said Lovekin in his statement to the Disclosure Project, calling out corporations and governments as especially terrified of free energy that can't be monetized. Hence, free energy is strictly prohibited, just as it has been since J.P. Morgan blackballed Tesla and his wireless free energy system. "And from everyone I have talked to who knows something about this subject matter, they do believe the sources of energy that keep these vehicles in propulsion are sources of energy that are just as free as free can be. They don't cause any harm to the environment. They don't cause any footprints to be left anywhere..." said Lovekin.[86]

Given the example set by Corso and Trudeau, the disruptive potential of ET technology is a primary factor in the decision to develop and deploy such technology. In the process of making plans to exploit the Army's Roswell artifacts, Corso sold Trudeau on his plan to make fiber optic technology developed from the Roswell spacecraft available to replace the nation's antiquated telephone system on the promise that the undertaking "would not be seen by any company as an unwarranted intrusion."[87] Apparently, the same can't be said about free energy. As far as Big Oil is concerned, extraterrestrial electrics really is a War-of-the-Worlds-style existential threat.

At some point, as the intelligence flowed and the secret investigations and special reports piled up, the contours of the extraterrestrial presence must've come into focus. There must've been a Top Level Magestic-12 version of the *Estimate of the Situation* or an assessment of some kind.

Whatever the case, a decision was made to scrap the original plan in favor of pure cover-up and denial. Whether it was that ETs were benign or that their technology would kill the economy or some other unfathomable combination of reasons, plans to inform the public were abandoned. The Robertson panel ushered in the new policy and the cover-up became institutionalized. By the next time UFO sightings brought about another opportunity for the disclosure-by-cover-up plan to mature it was defunct. In the 1960s, a series of dramatic UFO sightings that included encounters with humanoid beings led to a crisis for the Air Force and its anti-UFO policy.

In 1964, in Socorro, New Mexico, police sergeant Lonnie Zamora responded to what he thought was some sort of accident, but instead was shocked by the sight of two child-sized humanoids tending to an egg-shaped craft that had apparently crash-landed in a gully. According to Zamora, when *they* saw him they rushed into the craft and took off in a flash.[88] The report ignited a firestorm. Army and Air Force Intelligence, Blue Book, FBI, CIA, NICAP and other civilian investigators all dove into the case, which became a landmark in UFO history. Zamora was a rock solid witness whose testimony was backed by trace physical evidence left behind by the craft. The scorched earth and deep indentations in the hard desert floor made his story impossible to dismiss out of hand. Project Blue Book investigators charged with providing simple solutions for UFO sightings were foiled. Pat answers like weather balloons, sundogs and the Venus explanation wouldn't fly. Despite its edict that every sighting be explained in conventional terms, the Zamora incident was left unexplained. Debunkers tried to dismiss the physical evidence as merely coincidental, but when Zamora-like cases began to accumulate, their argument fell apart. Hynek associate Ted Phillips specialized in the investigation of such cases. He founded the Center for Physical Trace Research and became the world's leading expert. Phillips went on to investigate hundreds of such cases over a thirty-year period. Contrary to the debunker's claims, the evidence was consistent to the point that researchers were able to make deductions about the physical characteristics of certain types of UFOs. For example, compression tests showed the egg-shaped objects weighed 14-18 tons, while the classic disc-shaped craft went 8-10 tons.[89] This was precisely the type of intelligence that Blue Book field hands were expected to produce as they explained-away UFOs.

Zamora was just the tip of the iceberg. The 1960s saw a tremendous UFO sightings wave. Reports came in from all quarters including NASA, astronomers, scientists, astronauts, policemen, weathermen, civilians, and, of course, pilots.[90] Increasingly, cases involved landings that included both humanoid sightings and trace physical evidence. The Zamora case was said to have transformed Hynek, who understood the significance of the trace evidence. If, in fact, it did make him go pro-UFO, it didn't stop him from continuing in his role as a debunker for Project Blue Book. As the great UFO flap unfolded throughout 1965 and into 1966, Hynek and the Blue Book debunking system were quickly overwhelmed by sightings they couldn't explain. What's more, UFO sightings occurred in association with power blackouts across the country and the world. UFOs were seen over sensitive Air Force bases, photographed, and tracked on both civilian and military radar and, complicating matters, the possibility of abduction by UFO emerged. The first so-called alien abduction report became public in 1965.

Like attempting to bail water out of a sinking boat with a bucket, the Air Force began dismissing UFO sightings with the usual pat answers, one after the other, sometimes without even going through the motions of an investigation. Quickly, the Blue Book boat began to sink. The Air Force's flimsy answers woke the press. On July 15, 1965, the Charleston Evening Post wrote, "Confronted by a UFO report, the service immediately begins to crank out of the wild blue yonder the same pre-recorded announcement it has been playing for 20 years: 'Scratch, scratch, the Air Force has no evidence, scratch, scratch, the Air Force has no evidence, scratch, scratch...'" The Seattle Times quipped, "Do you ever get the feeling that... the Air Force makes its denials six months in advance." Radio host Frank Edwards, said, "You'd do a lot better, gentlemen, if you'd draw your answers out of a hat."

After a major UFO event in the Midwest, it seems the Air Force did just that. Over several summer nights, UFOs were seen flying in formation over nine states, from South Dakota to the Mexican border. Reports came in from astronomers, state police, journalists and citizens. The objects were tracked on both civil and military radar and publicly confirmed by Air Force bases in Texas and Oklahoma in violation of AFR-200-2. In the absence of trace evidence, Blue Book tried to explain it all away as Jupiter and several of the stars in the Orion constellation. The problem was these stars were only visible in the Southern hemisphere at the time and couldn't be seen in the

North for several months.[91] Director of the Oklahoma Science Foundation Planetarium, Robert Risser said, "This is as far from the truth as you can get."

The Air Force's dunking policy had clearly jumped the shark, but the show wasn't cancelled until after one final performance, its grand finale. In Michigan, during a weeklong stretch in March 1966, strange craft were seen at close range on nearly a daily basis. Many of the reports came from police officers. A local Air Force Base also tracked UFOs on radar, but the sighting that got national attention was made by a local government official who saw strange lights maneuvering near a swamp. The incident became a lightning rod for the cover-up and brought the Air Force's UFO problem to a head on the national stage.[92] Hynek was sent to Michigan to put out the fire. Upon arrival, he held a press conference and suggested that "swamp gas" from decaying vegetation might have been the cause of lights seen near the ground. It was a stretch to say the least. Perhaps Hynek and the Air Force thought that swamp gas would work just as well as weather balloons had in Roswell or temperature inversions in Washington D.C. If so, they were wrong. The swamp gas explanation backfired.

Judgment in the court of public opinion was swift and harsh. The South Bend Tribune summed-up public sentiment with the headline, *Air Force Insults Public With Swamp Gas Theory*. Instead of dousing the fire, Hynek had inadvertently fanned the flames. The controversy spilled over into pop culture. On *The Tonight Show*, Johnny Carson interviewed a professor from Cal Tech who trashed the swamp gas theory. Project Blue Book lost whatever remaining credibility it had and became an embarrassment and a liability for the Air Force. Pressure built over the negative publicity and soon there were calls for Congress to take action.[93]

Future President Gerald Ford, then a congressman from Michigan and the House Minority Leader, demanded a formal congressional investigation. In a letter to the Armed Services Committee Chairman, he expressed disappointment with official efforts to explain the phenomenon. Ford wrote, "I think there may be substance in some of these reports and because I believe the American people are entitled to a more thorough explanation than has been given them by the Air Force to date… I think we owe it to the people to establish the credibility regarding UFOs and to produce the greatest possible enlightenment on this subject."

Incredible as it may seem, the Air Force managed to use the crisis as an opportunity to rid itself of its responsibility to investigate UFOs for the public. Despite the posturing, no one really wanted to deal with the hot potato that was the UFO problem. Ford's call for a congressional investigation resulted in a one-day hearing by the House Armed Services Committee. Congress invited just three witnesses. All from the Air Force. The committee agreed to hear only from Air Force Secretary Harold Brown, Blue Book head Hector Quintanilla and Hynek. The pilots, military personnel, astronomers, scientists, radar operators and civilians who'd actually seen UFOs weren't invited. NICAP, which had been pushing for congressional hearings for a decade, was left out in the cold. Keyhoe called the hearings a farce.[94]

With no one present who could object, the Air Force claimed it had no evidence UFOs were even real, much less extraterrestrial craft. The Air Force had nothing to hide, they said, and as if to prove the point, they recommended a new independent, civilian UFO investigation. On the face of it, the proposal seemed appropriate, but according to Jacques Vallee, there were rumors circulating in Europe that the Air Force was looking for a reason to justify an end to its UFO investigation and was shopping for a university willing to endorse a negative conclusion after a perfunctory study.[95] In other words, the government was looking to rerun the Robertson Panel playbook on a grand scale. Vallee noted that the rumors were taken so seriously in certain circles that a budding French study was scuttled as a result. After an unsuccessful attempt to persuade the Ivy League schools to take on the project, the Air Force reached an agreement with the University of Colorado. In October 1966, physicist, Edward U. Condon was named Director of the new UFO investigation, assisted by University of Colorado Administrator Robert Low.

According to Keyhoe, the announcement took the heat off the Air Force. As if by magic, all the lies were absolved with the assumption that a new civilian study would be an honest quest for the truth. But this was pure naiveté. The investigation that unfolded under the direction of Condon and Low was a virtual blueprint for how to commit scientific misconduct.[96] In fact, staff scientist David Saunders found an actual blueprint in the project archives. The memo, written by Low, showed how the study would be rigged.

Our study would be conducted almost exclusively by non-believers, who, although they couldn't possibly prove a negative result, could and probably would add an impressive body of evidence that there is no reality to the observations. The trick would be, I think, to describe the project so that, to the public, it would appear a totally objective study, but to the scientific community would present the image of a group of nonbelievers trying their best to be objective but having an almost zero expectation of finding a saucer. One way to do this would be to stress investigation, not of the physical phenomena, but rather the people who do the observing- the psychology and sociology of persons or groups who report seeing UFOs.[97]

It was clear right from the start that this was the strategy used by Condon and Low. Within a day of the Air Force announcement that Condon would head the new civilian UFO study, he was quoted in the *New York Times*. "It's highly improbable they exist," said Condon, adding, "The view that UFOs are hallucinatory will be a subject of our investigation, to discover what it is that makes people imagine they see things." What's more, Condon appeared to be as comically uninformed about UFOs as Robertson panelist Thornton Page. He told reporters that astronomers, FAA operators and satellite trackers hadn't seen UFOs. This simply wasn't true. The sightings wave that led directly to his contract with the Air Force included radar cases and reports by astronomers. In fact, NICAP's files contained hundreds of reports by veteran pilots, scientists, satellite trackers, FAA tower and radar operators, aerospace engineers and other highly credible witnesses, yet Condon chose not to investigate any of them, including the ones with explanations that were as far from the truth as you could get that caused the uproar in the first place. He didn't have to. The contract given to him by the Air Force gave Condon the right to pick and choose which cases to investigate.[98]

In accordance with the damning memo, Condon and Low designed their study with zero expectation of finding a saucer. In doing so, they made use of selection bias, one of the most common tools in the scientific misconduct toolbox. Condon and Low decided to investigate only current UFO sightings, which enabled them to ignore the great bulk of UFO evidence, including some of NICAP's strongest cases. Focusing on such a narrow window not only reduced their chances of "finding a saucer," it prevented them, as Hynek observed, from stumbling over any pesky patterns in worldwide UFO sightings over a twenty-year period.[99]

Despite Condon and Low's best efforts to guide the study to its desired conclusions, their staff scientists did indeed find a saucer. The Condon Investigation window was only open from November 15, 1966 to January 1968, but UFOs flew into it. As fate would have it, one of the most extraordinary UFO events of all occurred during this time period.

On October 4, 1967, Roswell-like event happened at Shag Harbor in Nova Scotia, Canada. A huge, bright orange, rectangular object with a trailing string of lights was seen lurching about in the sky in distress before tilting at a 45 degree angle and gliding into the harbor about a half mile offshore. Citizens, fisherman, mounted police and airline pilots all witnessed the incident. After the crash, a white light was visible bobbing on the water's surface slowly drifting out to sea, along with thick yellow foam and other debris. Although there were no flights in the area or missing planes, it was assumed to be some sort of plane crash. The Royal Canadian Navy conducted recovery operations, but according to the big brass, divers found nothing. The government would admit that something unknown had crashed in the harbor, but gave no further explanation.[100] The incident was reported both locally and around the world, but like UFOs themselves, it was gone in a flash and forgotten.

Decades later, researchers Don Ledger and first-hand eyewitness Chris Stiles conducted what is arguably the most successful and important civilian UFO investigation. The duo managed to obtain several government documents that plainly state that the object that plunged into Shag Harbor was a UFO, making it the world's only government-documented UFO crash. Thanks to the witnesses, especially Navy divers, Ledger and Stiles were able to piece together what happened to the object after it sunk. It was immediately clear to the divers it was "nothing from this earth." A flotilla of U.S. and Canadian Navy ships was dispatched to the area above the submerged object, which maneuvered its way towards a secret NATO sonar facility. Divers witnessed a second UFO join the first to assist with repairs. After a week, the objects moved out to sea took off up out of the water and zoomed off. The military monitored the entire operation but didn't interfere.

The Condon investigation was pressured to investigate the incident by NICAP and APRO (Aerial Phenomena Research Organization), another civilian UFO investigation that received dozens of letters from eyewitnesses. Staff scientist Norman Levine drew the assignment. It's not known what level of access Levine was given or whether he was shown any of the debris that was recovered, but he was upset with Condon for ordering him to list the sighting as unknown, according to Ledger and Stiles.[101] It's possible this incident had something to do with the fact that, as Administrative assistant Mary Louise Armstrong noted, Condon's staff scientists "came to a radically different conclusion" about UFOs than Condon had.[102]

When staff scientist David Saunders found the Low memo it had a toxic effect on the staff. Suddenly, the strange attitudes and behaviors of the project leaders became clear. It explained why Condon rejected NICAP's UFO reports, why he didn't interview a single credible witness and why he chose to focus on contactees who were totally lacking in credibility. The Low memo made clear to the staff scientists that they were participating in a charade. Some quit immediately, others began plotting against Condon and Low. Saunders leaked the memo to Keyhoe, which set off a chain reaction that blew up the project.[103] Condon fired Saunders and Levine when he discovered the memo found its way to James McDonald, a senior physicist at the Institute for Atmospheric Physics and a Professor at the University of Arizona Department of Meteorology. He was the worst possible nightmare for those behind the cover-up- a world-class scientist who took UFOs seriously.[104]

As an atmospheric physicist, McDonald was uniquely qualified to evaluate reports of unknown artificial objects operating in the atmosphere just as astronomer and meteoritics specialist Lincoln La Paz was the go-to guy for the green fireball UFOs in New Mexico. Unless UFOs were seen out in space, astronomers like Hynek and Menzel were really out of their field. When they offered explanations for UFOs seen in the atmosphere they were on McDonald's turf. And when those explanations were clearly bogus, McDonald took no prisoners. He'd seen a UFO himself and was upset by the swamp gas-type explanations offered up by Hynek and the Air Force. He knew Blue Book was a farce. Two years before, in the midst of the great UFO wave that led to the Condon investigation, McDonald had been granted access to Project Blue Book by the National Academy of Sciences Committee on the Atmospheric Sciences.[105] Once inside, he dove into the files. Jacques Vallee, who was at Blue Book at the time, wrote, "He began by requesting to be shown all cases of 'globular lightning.' He was amazed and horrified by what he saw: case after case that obviously had nothing to do with electrical discharges in the air. So he asked to see more and started reading the general files, getting increasingly upset as he kept on reading. McDonald moved very fast once he realized, as he told us very bluntly, 'that the explanations were pure bullshit.' So he bypassed the Major and went straight to the General who heads up the base, to tell him exactly what he thought of Blue Book. After forty-five minutes, which is much longer than Hynek ever spent with the General, they were talking about the humanoid occupants!"[106]

It was immediately clear why Blue Book's files were steeped in nonsense to McDonald when he found a copy of the Robertson Panel report in the Blue Book archives. Despite great professional risk, McDonald went public. He accused the CIA of ordering the Air Force to debunk UFOs and said Blue Book's official explanations were often "almost absurdly erroneous." In a subsequent interview, McDonald ripped Menzel for his pseudoscientific explanations for UFOs and said that there was "no sensible alternative" to the Extraterrestrial hypothesis.[107]

Fallout from the scandal spread quickly. In a devastating exposé, *Look magazine* called the Condon investigation a half-million dollar fiasco. *Look* published a blow-by-blow account of what it called a "near-mutiny" by staff scientists after discovery of the Low memo. As a result, support for hearings gathered momentum on Capitol Hill.[108] It looked like the opportunity to break the UFO cover-up had finally come when the House Science and Astronautics Committee scheduled open hearings for July 29, 1968. McDonald and Hynek were both invited to testify. But optimism at NICAP and throughout the UFO community was short lived. Criticism of the Air Force and the Condon investigation was strictly prohibited and the hearings were labeled a "UFO symposium," which Keyhoe called a euphemism for another non-investigation. What's more, NICAP was not allowed to present evidence. Keyhoe could only attend in silence and hope for the best.

The deck was stacked against him, but James McDonald went all-in anyway. "I have become convinced that the scientific community, not only in this country but throughout the world, has been casually ignoring as nonsense a matter of extraordinary scientific importance," said McDonald, who submitted 30 pages of confirmed UFO reports and the fake explanations assigned to them by the Air Force and others like well-known debunkers, Philip Klass and Donald Menzel. In the aftermath of the Low memo scandal, it became apparent that Condon and Menzel had been acting in concert. In her resignation letter, Mary Armstrong railed against Condon and Low for having her send confidential case material to Menzel, hinting that "outside forces" were guiding the study. McDonald did his best to neutralize those forces. He thoroughly destroyed the electrical plasma theories argued by Klass, a mere electrical engineer clearly out of his league, and the temperature inversion hypothesis proclaimed by Menzel, a leading astronomer who was, nevertheless, out of his field. He told the committee that astronomers would've given up trying to study the stars by looking at them through the atmosphere a long time ago if temperature inversions could cause such optical illusions.[109] McDonald made sure the committee understood that natural phenomena like the weather could not possibly explain multiple-witness, close-range, radar/visual sightings of an extended duration of luminous objects or machine-like objects described as cigar or disk-shaped, domed craft. He rejected the official explanation for the Washington National sightings in 1952, which he called "the most famous single radar-visual sighting on record." McDonald concluded, "My own present opinion, based on two years of careful study, is that UFOs are probably extraterrestrial devices... I now regard the [extraterrestrial hypothesis] as the one most likely to prove correct."

McDonald couldn't have made a much more powerful statement, but it still wasn't enough to overcome media bias/censorship to make headlines. The decision to ban criticism of the Air Force and the Condon investigation stripped McDonald's statement of its proper context. Prohibiting discussion of the cover-up for which the Low memo was smoking gun evidence made McDonald's statement seem like one man's opinion about some transient ephemeral phenomena instead of what the Air Force was hiding. Keyhoe's suspicions that the "symposium" was just another charade were confirmed when congressman William F. Ryan made the logical, yet verboten, suggestion that the committee investigate the Condon study, prompting chairman George Miller to make it known that they had no such authority to do so, which was bizarre considering the Low memo and the "near mutiny" that followed was the catalyst for the hearings/symposium in the first place.[110] It was clear the whole episode was just more theater, yet another head fake in a long line of head fakes, but with the help of Big Media it worked.

Having weathered the scandal, Condon gave the Air Force what it paid for on Halloween in 1968 when he delivered his final report called *Scientific Study of Unidentified Flying Objects*.[111] According to Condon, studying UFOs was a waste of time and money. By his decree, there were no unidentified flying objects; therefore nothing further needed to be done about them. The media reported Condon's conclusions and recommendations as if he were on the up and up, as if the Low memo scandal hadn't exposed the investigation as a fraud, and as if the fake hearings labeled a symposium somehow negated that fact. What Big Media did was give Condon a platform to deny the UFO cover-up even as he was in the process of perpetuating it.

What Big Media didn't tell its audience was that both he and Low were longtime assets of the national security state. Low was an intelligence officer during WWII and Condon worked on the Manhattan Project.[112] What Big Media also didn't report was that Condon's summary and conclusions weren't supported by the evidence in the body of the report. Some thought it was the dynamics of paradigm protectionism that led Condon to commit such egregious scientific misconduct. He simply did what was necessary to perpetuate his belief systems and the structures of the current paradigm. Or it could've been that the powers-that-be had the goods on him. During the investigation, Condon brushed off statements regarding a "worldwide blanket of secrecy" about UFOs made by Greek UFO researcher Paul Santorini. After Condon died in 1974, Dr. Santorini wrote, "It is a pity that an eminent scientist of his level blindly executed orders to back with his name a 'Report' that constitutes a scientific shame. But, I understand this was done to please some authorities unhappy with his 'securities' affairs."[113]

After the Condon report was released to the public in January 1969, Saunders, Keyhoe, and McDonald held a press conference to denounce the study.[114] Hynek, who was let go after twenty years of carrying water for the Air Force, blasted the report as trivial and irrelevant. Saunders published his insider account of the Condon Investigation called *UFOs? Yes! Where the Condon Committee Went Wrong* to coincide with the release of the Condon report. Saunders wrote that Condon and Low were anti-ET from the start and never intended to consider otherwise. If the committee had somehow concluded in favor of ETI despite all the guidance, Condon would've taken the whole thing classified. McDonald went for the jugular. He wanted Condon's files so he could reinvestigate several of the project cases, but

Condon had them torched. "One would think that they belonged to the scientific fraternity or to the public domain, since American taxpayers paid for the 'research,'" said Jacques Vallee. "Not so. When the project wrote its report the files were locked up by the University of Colorado in Boulder. They were later transferred to a private home and were burned shortly thereafter."

The evidence was destroyed. The scene of the crime wiped clean. The game was over. Once Condon gave the Air Force and the CIA the necessary pretext, all that was left was the wait for the other shoe to drop. In December 1969, the Air Force announced that Project Blue Book had been terminated, ending the government's official, public involvement with UFOs. The closing of Project Blue Book also brought with it the end of Keyhoe's reign as NICAP's director. Despite all his successes in forcing the truth out into the open by exposing the Air Force cover-up, UFOs had been officially debunked. He won many battles, but ultimately lost the war, which led to his ouster from NICAP at 72 years of age. Without Keyhoe, NICAP stopped challenging the Air Force, lost its edge and faded from relevancy until it went defunct. McDonald wound up with a bullet in his head, allegedly by his own hand. Some believe he had been 'suicided' as others have been who were threats to the UFO cover-up, including journalist Dorothy Kilgallen and Marilyn Monroe, who was planning to call a press conference to tell the world what JFK had told her about the recovery of an ET spaceship in Roswell just two days before she was found dead, according to Top Secret documents acquired by Steven Greer.[115]

It was the end of an era for those who fought against the tyranny of Air Force dogma about UFOs, which have since been relegated to the status of urban myth.

NOTHING HAS OCCURRED

Nevertheless, UFOs continued to be seen and reported regardless of the fact that they'd been written off by Condon and the Air Force. The first major post-Blue Book era UFO sightings wave happened in 1973 and there have been major UFO incidents in every decade since the closure of Blue Book continuing up to the present.

In 1975, several UFO incidents occurred over nuclear missile silos at strategic air command bases across the Midwest including Malmstrom Air

Force Base, which had experienced similar events in the past. In 1967, Disclosure Project witness Captain Bob Salas was involved in an event at Malmstrom in which nuclear warheads went off-line as a UFO hovered over the base. This incident occurred during the wave of sightings that eventually led to the Condon investigation.[116]

In 1980, another incident occurred at a nuclear installation. This time at NATO bases, RAF Bentwaters and RAF Woodbridge, which border Rendlesham Forest in England. The event was of such significance that it has become known as the 'British Roswell.' On two nights in late December, UFOs appeared in Rendlesham Forest. On the first night, base personnel investigating what they thought was likely a plane crash came face to face with a UFO that had landed. They took pictures and even managed to touch the craft before it took off and disappeared in a flash, leaving behind trace evidence in the form of indentations in the ground and high levels of radiation. UFOs returned just a day later, performing incomprehensible maneuvers. This time humanoid beings came out of the craft and interacted with military personnel. UFOs were also seen on RAF Woodbridge firing beams into nuclear weapons storage units that "adversely affected the ordinance," according to witnesses, many of which were U.S. military. The Rendlesham Forest incident is substantiated by military documentation and many of the witnesses have gone public including Deputy Base Commander Lt. Charles Halt, Airman First Class John Burroughs, Staff Sergeant James Penniston and Disclosure Project witness USAF security officer Larry Warren.[117]

In 1986, a Japan airlines flight near anchorage Alaska was shadowed for half an hour by a large object that was tracked on radar by the FAA, according to former FAA Division Chief and Disclosure Project witness John Callahan.[118]

In Belgium in 1989 through 1990, thousands saw huge triangle-shaped UFOs, which were tracked by both airborne and ground radar. The Royal Belgian Air Force worked with a civilian UFO organization called the Belgian Society for the Study of Space Phenomena (SOBEPS) to investigate the wave of sightings, which remain unexplained.[119]

In 1997, the Phoenix Lights episode caused a sensation in Arizona. Thousands saw a gigantic craft blocking out the stars as it crossed the sky. Governor Fife Symington, who kept his own sighting of the craft a secret for ten years, said he called the commander at Luke Air Force Base, a general of the Arizona National Guard and others seeking an explanation. He never got one.[120]

In July 2002, on the 50-year anniversary of the 1952 Washington National sightings, a UFO again appeared over the nation's capital. The mysterious craft did not respond to radio contact triggering calls to NORAD. In the post-9/11 climate, armed fighters were on 24-hour alert. NORAD scrambled two F-16 jets out of Andrews Air Force base to investigate. Civilians reported seeing an F-16 chase a bright blue UFO, which left the jet "in the dust." Air Force officials later admitted to scrambling jets, but denied there was an attempt to intercept a UFO.[121]

In 2007, at O'Hare International Airport in Chicago, mechanics, pilots and other airline personnel saw a classic flying disc hovering silently over a United Airlines terminal on an overcast afternoon. After several minutes, the disc shot up at fantastic speed through the cloud cover creating a hole in which blue sky could be seen. According to journalist Leslie Kean, The FAA and United Airlines initially denied any knowledge of the incident, but both were forced to admit that it did happen when a tape of United's UFO report to the air traffic control tower was released. The Chicago Tribune broke the story, which went on to become national news.[122] On the hot seat for an explanation, the FAA said the sightings were caused by a "weather phenomenon," an impossibility given the conditions at O'Hare that day, according to climatologists and other atmospheric experts. The incident has never been officially investigated.[123]

In January 2008, an enormous UFO blew into Stephenville, Texas at fantastic speed, coming to a hover not far from President Bush's home in Crawford. Eyewitnesses saw F-16 fighter jets make a futile attempt to chase the mile-long craft, which was tracked by FAA radar.[124]

The Air Force initially denied the presence of the jets, but later reversed course. They said F-16s seen by 50 eyewitnesses were simply on a routine training mission, ignoring the elephant-in-the-room UFO. But MUFON (Mutual UFO Network), a civilian UFO investigative organization, found that FAA radar records showed that an aircraft without a transponder did indeed breach restricted airspace over Bush's so-called 'Western White House.' In contrast, the Air Force said it couldn't find its own radar records for the night of the sighting and refused to release uncensored flight logs. According to journalist Billy Cox, the Air Force was able to get away with the runaround because the mainstream media never follows-up on UFO stories. The Air Force was never held to account. There was no one in Big Media like Keyhoe or McDonald to call bullshit. Nevertheless, news of the non-event became an international phenomenon.[125]

These are just a few examples. There've been thousands of real UFO reports since the close of project Blue Book in 1969. None of them have ever been publicly investigated by the Air Force or any other government agency. Local officials may offer some speculation on a case-by-case basis if pressed by media or a politician, as they did with the Phoenix Lights and O'Hare Airport episodes, but the institution of the Air Force will not comment officially and there is never a question of a new Air Force investigation no matter how compelling the circumstances of a UFO incident. Air Force policy is that it no longer investigates UFOs. The official website of the United States Air Force presents a fact sheet spelling out its UFO policy. The fact sheet flatly states that the decision to discontinue its UFO investigation was based on the Condon Report, which it presents as the final word on UFOs. Consequently, the Air Force has concluded:

No UFO reported, investigated or evaluated by the Air Force was ever an indication of threat to our national security;

There was no evidence submitted to or discovered by the Air Force that sightings categorized as "unidentified" represented technological developments or principles beyond the range of modern scientific knowledge; and

There was no evidence indicating that sightings categorized as "unidentified" were extraterrestrial vehicles.

The fact sheet goes on to say, "Since the termination of Project Blue Book, nothing has occurred that would support a resumption of UFO investigations by the Air Force."[126] Nothing could be further from the truth, but it is official reality nonetheless. Unreality has taken hold. During his investigation of the Mantell Incident, Keyhoe interviewed an Air Force officer who said, "I've been told it's all bunk, but you get the feeling they're trying to convince themselves. They act like people near a haunted house. They'll swear it isn't haunted- but they won't go near it."[127] The same could be said of scientists like Condon and the institution of science in general.

They'll swear there are no UFOs- but they won't go near the evidence. They act more like priests clinging to doctrine. In 1968 at a reception for astronomers in Victoria, British Columbia attended by Hynek, word began to circulate that there were UFOs outside performing odd maneuvers. Hynek noted that his colleagues made jokes and had a good laugh, but not one went out to have a look.[128]

According to a Brookings Institute report commissioned by NASA, scientists are afraid of the truth. "It has been speculated that of all groups, scientists and engineers might be the most devastated by the discovery of relatively superior creatures, since these professions are most clearly associated with the mastery of nature, rather than the understanding and expression of man. Advanced understanding of nature might vitiate all our theories at the very least, if not also require a culture and perhaps a brain inaccessible to Earth scientists," warned Brookings.[129]

Whatever the case, the collapse of anti-UFO scientific dogma is inevitable. Visionary founder of the Northrup Aircraft Company, John Northrup, trashed science's cornerstone investigation into UFOs as "one of the most deliberate cover-ups ever perpetrated on the public." Northrup quipped, "The 21st Century will die laughing at the Condon Report."[130]

SUMMARY AND CONCLUSIONS – PART ONE

UFOs are real. Disclosure has happened. Only politics and the inertia of the present worldview have prevented a profound paradigm shift. "Bloody hell, this is amazing- bloody hell," a cameraman was heard to say during the Disclosure Project press conference in Washington D.C. in 2001. A year later, British Journalist Hamish Mackenzie observed that, despite the fact that no one has disputed any of the witness testimony, it remained ignored by Big Media. [131] Over 150 journalists from television stations and newspapers worldwide had attended the press conference, yet the mainstream media didn't report on the UFO disclosure event at the Washington Press Club. There were no front-page headlines and no lead stories on the six o'clock news. What little coverage the event received was never followed up on and the subject was dropped and subsequently forgotten. It seems as if some sort of collective neurosis is at the root of such strange circumstances. Astronomer Chandra Wickramasinghe flatly stated that the discovery of extraterrestrial life has been suppressed because of "political and sociological considerations" referring to the type of paradigm dynamics written about by Thomas Kuhn. The instinct to deny reality when it conflicts with our assumptions about the world is a powerful force. Millennia ago common sense told us the Earth was a flat stationary object around which the Sun, Moon and everything else in the universe revolved. Stars were just pretty points of light, not other suns with worlds of their own. All these assumptions were proved false over time as the Universe came into focus through the lens of the telescope. The last remaining assumption of the geocentric era that we cling to is the belief that we are the crowning achievement of all creation. The reason the policy of cover-up and denial has prevailed to this point despite all its lapses and failures is that ET UFOs violate this last remaining assumption about Earth and our place in the heavens, which pervades all our institutions and power structures. The Hubble Deep Field images show that it is utterly statistically impossible madness to think we might be It. The images underscore Fermi's premise that we should see evidence of advanced extraterrestrial civilization because we're surely not the first to come this far. In this context, the UFO cover-up, the Condon affair, the unchallenged testimony of the Disclosure Project witnesses, etc., are definitive evidence that this last assumption is also false. Disclosure has happened, but paradigm shift hasn't yet. The will to preserve this system is so strong that the paradigm guardians are even willing to risk accidental nuclear war. During the Condon investigation, when it became clear to Keyhoe that Condon didn't take UFOs seriously, he submitted a secret report NICAP made to Congress about UFO sightings that almost triggered nuclear war. More than once, SAC scrambled H-bombers when UFOs were mistaken for incoming Soviet ICBMs.[132] One of those episodes occurred during the Condon investigation when a UFO crashed into Shag Harbor. Sources told investigators that fighters were scrambled when NORAD tracked an incoming object from the direction of Russia descending at Mach 10 from high altitude heading for the U.S. East Coast.[133] If the object hadn't stopped and hovered for a few moments before plunging into the harbor, nuclear holocaust might've become a reality. Such are the dangers of paradigm protectionism and the weak assumptions of the lesser mortals who came before us.

Science is supposed to transcend belief. Science is supposed to be self-correcting, but those who put self-interest before scientific fact can corrupt and delay the process. When we look at how science has been applied to

UFOs we find evidence of such corruption. Blue Book gave pseudoscientific answers for UFO reports. The Robertson Panel wasn't a real scientific study and neither was the Condon investigation. Both projects relied upon the stature of their leading scientists rather than actual science to make the case against UFOs. In spite of herculean efforts to limit the scope of official UFO investigations, the signal still managed to rise above the noise. Properly analyzed, the data behind Battelle's *Project Blue Book Special Report 14* showed that UFOs were real. And despite selection bias employed by Condon and Low, much of their staff reached the same conclusion.

Only the inertia of centuries of naïve assumptions about our world and sheer authoritarianism has enabled the establishment to perpetuate the status quo. But science isn't going to be able resist forever. Soon astronomers will have the ability to detect life on extrasolar planets. Exoplanets are too dim to be seen, but their presence can be detected in tiny fluctuations of starlight. Planets will affect the motion of a star, causing it to wobble as they orbit a common center of gravity. Exoplanets can also be detected when they pass in front of a star, causing its light to dim ever so slightly. To acquire such data, NASA has deployed the most sensitive telescopes ever designed, including the Keck, Spitzer and Kepler telescopes.[134] So far over 1,900 exoplanets have been found. Spectral analysis of starlight has enabled us to determine the basic elemental composition of these distant worlds. For the first time, astronomers have detected the chemical signatures of water and methane, two elements closely associated with life, on a large gas giant 63 light years away.[135] Although a significant milestone, the Jupiter-like planet is insanely inhospitable due to its close proximity to its sun.

Astronomers eagerly anticipate the day when they will be able to analyze the atmospheres of smaller Earth-like planets. When an exoplanet like Earth is found in orbit around sun-like star within the habitable zone and spectral analysis of this far-flung world reveals the presence of an atmosphere, water and methane, the process of declaring extraterrestrial life an empirical fact will begin. In fact, a prominent Russian astronomer has set a timetable for this exact scenario. "The genesis of life is as inevitable as the formation of atoms ... Life exists on other planets and we will find it within 20 years," said Andrei Finkelstein, director of the Russian Academy of Sciences' Applied Astronomy Institute in a speech at an international forum on the search for extraterrestrial life in 2011.[136] What's more, such a discovery may have already been made. An Earth-sized exoplanet only 20 light years away called Gliese581g led one scientist to make such a claim. Gliese581g is thought to be a rocky planet with an atmosphere located well within the habitable zone of its star, a red dwarf. "Personally, given the ubiquity and propensity of life to flourish wherever it can, I would say, my own personal feeling is that the chances of life on this planet are 100 percent. I have almost no doubt about it," said astronomer Steven Vogt.[137]

Exoplanet researchers estimate that there are approximately two billion Earth-like planets in our galaxy. The numbers are such that they expect to find not only life, but intelligent life. And that's just our galaxy. There are at least fifty billion other galaxies.[138] As technology continues to advance at exponential rates, the day will come when astronomers will have the ability to directly detect extraterrestrial civilization. And when they do UFO deniability will be a thing of the past. It's only a matter of time.

There never was a Fermi paradox. UFOs are, in fact, the extraterrestrial craft that Fermi expected. However, we're not merely being visited. Earth is a part of a vibrant intergalactic civilization. We're like the aboriginal tribes we watch on TV or on YouTube that live like primitives in the midst of an advanced culture they can't begin to comprehend. Hynek once called the body of UFO evidence an "embarrassment of riches" in making an argument against the Extraterrestrial hypothesis.[139] There were simply too many good UFO reports, he argued. Thousands and thousands every year. So much so that it was clear we weren't being visited like we visit Mars or Venus with an occasional probe. And Hynek was right. The high volume of real UFO, or ETV (Extraterrestrial Vehicle) sightings, as they should be known, isn't evidence of extraterrestrial visitation, it's evidence that the Galaxy has been colonized as Fermi paradox theorists expect.

PART TWO

POST-SINGULARITY EXTRATERRESTRIAL TRANSMIGRATION HYPOTHESIS

When the long awaited solution to the UFO problem comes, I believe it will prove to be not merely the next small step in the march of science but a mighty and totally unexpected quantum jump.
— J. Allen Hynek, 1972

We might well be part of a much larger and older supercivilization that has reasons of its own not to explain itself to us, or perhaps cannot explain itself to us, in the same sense that we could never, without massive and fundamental re-education, explain radio to an ancient Roman.
— Whitley Strieber, 2010

Violence is the last refuge of the incompetent.
— Isaac Asimov, Foundation

CHAPTER 5

ASTROENGINEERING

Aliens might communicate over interstellar distances, he said, by manipulating "a very small movable shield" above the surface of a local pulsar, in order to regulate its pulses (just as people once communicated by moving blankets in front of fires)... The stellar gods may "astroengineer" the galaxy as easily as we build a bridge or an overpass.
— Biographer Keay Davidson on Sagan statement made at first major international SETI conference in 1971

It is often said that one's first hunch is the right one... If they had known then what we now know about pulsars, perhaps they would not have rejected the ETI communication scenario as readily as they did.
— Physicist Paul LaViolette, 2000

A NEW WORLD IF YOU CAN TAKE IT

Col. Philip J. Corso died not long after publishing *The Day After Roswell.* Although he didn't live to participate in the Disclosure Project press conference in 2001, Greer included his testimony in the briefing materials. Also included was an interview with Corso's son, Philip Corso, Jr., who said his father told him about an encounter he had in 1957 with a "creature," which was a common term at the time for the beings recovered at Roswell.

According to Corso Jr., his father told him he encountered a being in a cave that he used to escape from the heat in a remote location out in the New Mexico desert near White Sands. The alien entity asked him to turn off his radar systems for 15 minutes.

Corso was shocked, not only by the presence of an otherworldly being, but that its request came telepathically and that this entity somehow knew he was the only person who could give such a command. He asked why he should do it and what was in it for him. And the being answered, "a new world if you can take it."[1]

Corso left the cave and gave the order to shut down the radar, but the message didn't resonate until much later in life. Corso, Jr. thought it meant we had a chance to create a new world, but we had to seize it. They weren't going to give it to us. It was an existential challenge. Unfortunately, it's seems to be a challenge we haven't been able to meet.

The first time we were gifted with the opportunity to live in the world of the galactic super-civilization was over a hundred years ago. Famed inventor Nikola Tesla almost brought it about singlehandedly.

Tesla studied physics, mathematics and engineering and became the world's greatest inventor. He invented the induction motor, fluorescent lights, neon lights, wireless communication, remote control and robotics. He laid the groundwork for radar, cryogenics, the use of X-rays and the understanding of cosmic rays. It was he, not Marconi who invented radio. And it was he, not Thomas Edison who electrified the world.

Tesla briefly worked for Edison before they became bitter rivals. Edison developed a method of electricity distribution known as direct current. It was inefficient and it lost power rapidly, but it could light an incandescent light bulb at a range of a couple miles. And so DC power took hold in wealthy metropolitan areas like New York City.

Tesla came along and blew DC out of the water. His method of alternating current allowed for long distance energy transmission at much higher voltages, much more efficiently than DC. Marc Seifer, author of *Wizard: The Life and Times of Nikola Tesla*, said Tesla's AC made Edison's DC look like a horse and buggy next to a jet airplane. Tesla was a quantum leap ahead.[2]

The age of electricity had begun. Tesla's AC turned Niagara Falls into a hydro-electric power plant able to supply electricity for the entire northeast. George Westinghouse, J. P. Morgan and others all cashed in on Tesla's brilliance, although the great inventor himself never really did. And he didn't really care. For Tesla the work itself, which he described as a state of "continuous rapture," was its own reward. What he did care about was building a better world for all mankind. AC was just the beginning. Tesla had much bigger dreams. His ultimate goal was to build a wireless free energy system that would power the entire world.

In 1899, Tesla set up an experimental lab in Colorado Springs capable of unleashing several million volts of lightning. He had already invented wireless radio on a small scale, famously using it to demonstrate the first remote controlled object, a model boat, at an Electrical Exposition held at Madison Square Garden in 1898. It was technology so advanced for the convention goers of the time as to seem like magic.[3] But Tesla was just getting started. He had much, much bigger tricks up his sleeve. His experiment in the wireless transmission of energy was a resounding success. When his assistant flipped the switch on the giant transmitter bolts of lightning leapt from the antenna turning the cold lamps that Tesla had placed in the ground into wireless torches as he watched from a knoll near a lake a mile away. Although unsubstantiated, it's been reported that he succeeded in demonstrating the wireless transmission of energy at a range of 26 miles.[4]

In 1901, Tesla convinced Wall Street's biggest wolf, J. P. Morgan, to invest $150,000 to build a worldwide radio transmitter. But he didn't tell the famous financier that the project was just the first step in his plan to electrify the world with the wireless transmission of free energy. If Tesla had been enabled to pursue his vision, anyone with a receiver, just like with radio, would be able to receive unmetered energy.[5] It would be the ultimate free lunch. It was, quite literally, a new world.

Tesla took Morgan's investment and instead of building the radio tower as contractually obligated, he began construction of a wireless energy transmitter that he called Wardenclyffe Tower. When Morgan discovered Tesla's ultimate intentions he cut off funding and made sure the father of wireless technology would fail to realize his dream.

Morgan, Westinghouse and other Wall Streeters were reaping huge profits from Tesla's AC power system and they weren't about to fund their own demise. Wall Street mogul Bernard Baruch is alleged to have told Morgan that Tesla was crazy for wanting to provide the world with free energy. He said they'd all go broke if they kept supporting him. So the bankers cut Tesla off and his vision never materialized.[6]

It was a victory for the monopolists of Wall Street and a tragedy for the human race. Tesla was inventing a world in which energy derived from "the very wheelwork of nature," in his words, would be transmitted wirelessly across the globe from tower to tower, station to station. All electrical devices would simply work. All the time. In perpetuity. What's more, Tesla envisioned a future that included an all-robot labor force, wingless antigravity craft, teleportation and time travel.[7] His ability to visualize such a fantastic future was extraordinary and unprecedented.

As a boy, Tesla was tormented by bright flashes of light and strange visions. A mere word spoken to him would summon an image of the object to which it referred so strongly that it looked tangible. He endured such intense eidetic imagery that he sometimes had one of his sisters help him sort what was real from what was hallucination. "To give an idea of my distress, suppose that I had witnessed a funeral or some such nerve wracking spectacle. Then, inevitably, in the stillness of night, a vivid picture of the scene would thrust itself before my eyes and persist despite all my efforts to banish it from my innermost being," said Tesla.[8]

Attempts to cope with this phenomenon led him to develop extraordinary mental capabilities. He never needed drawings, models or experiments. He was able to design and perfect inventions completely in his head much like Mozart was said to have written music already composed in his mind. He also experienced otherworldly visions causing him to feel as if a cosmic mind was exposing him to ideas it hoped to manifest in the real world. It was during one of these bright flash episodes that Tesla got the idea for his AC motor. He could see it clear as day in his head as if it already existed.[9]

Some think that ETs were the source of Tesla's visions. Tesla himself publicly declared he'd made contact with extraterrestrials during his experiments in Colorado Springs. In 1901, Collier's Weekly published an article by Tesla called *Talking with the Planets* in which the great inventor announced that he had detected what he came to believe were intelligent signals that could only be extraterrestrial in nature.[10]

Tesla's announcement was met with derision. Adversaries used his claims to smear him as a mad scientist, thus the scientific establishment distanced itself from him. In 1915, the *New York Times* announced that Tesla was to be awarded the Nobel Prize in physics for the invention of wireless energy, but it never happened.[11] The Nobel snub was a clear sign that the powers-that-be had decided that Tesla and his ambitions were to be shunned by official history.

Despite such a monumental slight and relentless ridicule, Tesla never backed down about the existence of extraterrestrials. In fact, it seems his public comments were just the proverbial tip of the iceberg. In 1931 in an interview in Time magazine celebrating his 75th birthday, Tesla said nothing was more important than establishing contact with ETs and that when we did we would discover there are other beings out in the universe much like us.[12] Tesla added that interplanetary contact would have a magical effect on humankind, apparently speaking from experience according to friends and associates who said he'd made contact with beings on other worlds on multiple occasions.

Longtime apprentice Arthur H. Mathews said that Tesla told him that extraterrestrials had probably been on Earth for thousands of years and that human beings were the test subjects of an experiment of extremely long duration.

Some believe Tesla himself was from another world. Author Margaret Storm wrote in her book *Return of the Dove* that Tesla was brought to Earth in a spaceship by extraterrestrials to be raised by "earth parents." He was an avatar whose raison d'etre was to bring about a New Age through the invention of advanced technology. And, although he is said to have become exasperated by others' belief that he was not a normal red-blooded human being like everyone else, Tesla once told an assistant that he often felt like a "stranger to this world."[13]

Whatever the source of Tesla's singular brilliance, the FBI seized his papers moments after his death in 1943 as a matter of national security. Officially, the government declared that nothing of significance was discovered in his technological treasure trove, but that certainly wasn't true. In his latter years Tesla announced he'd invented what he called a "Death Ray." In an attempt to make warfare obsolete, he developed a method for projecting a concentrated beam of energy that could destroy an entire armada of fighter jets at a range of 250 miles.[14] Tesla believed that if every country had such a weapon there would be no more wars.

Tesla's work was also of great scientific value to Majestic-12. After the FBI confiscated his life's work, copies that were transferred to the AMC at Wright Field under the command of alleged Majestic-12 member Gen. Nathan Twining eventually turned up in Col. Corso's files at the Army R&D's Foreign Technology desk in 1961.[15] According to Corso, the Majestic-12 group realized that the Tesla's work was the Rosetta stone for understanding extraterrestrial technology.

"For me the irony has always been the confluence between the historic work of Nikola Tesla and the technology that was ascertained the extraterrestrials had developed from evaluation of the Roswell wreckage. Tesla experimented with wireless transmission of energy, and the extraterrestrials seemed to have employed a type of wireless transmission of energy for navigational and defensive purposes. Tesla wrote about the theories behind the distortion or manipulation of a gravitational field through the propagation of electromagnetic waves, and the extraterrestrials seemed to have employed just this kind of technology for a propulsion system," wrote Corso, who literally had Tesla's blueprints for the New World land on his desk.[16]

FUTURE SHOCK

Ironically, in March 1895, Tesla survived an accident in his lab that would have won him a Darwin Award. During an experiment he was hit with 3.5 million volts. Had his assistant not cut the power he might have been killed.[17] Upon contact, he had what could be called an out-of-space/time experience. Paralyzed inside the electromagnetic field, Tesla could see the past, present and future all at once. It would have been a mind-blowing experience for anyone, but it was especially so for the great inventor who had the ability to remember an image down to the smallest detail as if he were simply replaying streaming video in his head.

After his near-death experience Tesla began to theorize that electromagnetic power could warp space/time, opening the door to teleportation and time travel. His ability to recall imagery as if he were looking at a hologram in his mind meant that he could see and understand what technology of the future looked like.

According to Corso, it looked a lot like the technology found in the Roswell wreckage, which would seem to make plausible the belief that Tesla received his mysterious visions from extraterrestrials and that maybe it was true that he was put on Earth to invent the infrastructure of galactic civilization. He is reported to have said about his adversaries such as Marconi, "The present is theirs, the future, for which I really worked, is mine."[18]

For the rest of us mere mortals the future is impossible to know. It's been said that the best way to predict the future is to invent it, but with the exception of Tesla, even those who have, like mathematician John von Neumann, inevitably fail to accurately imagine it.

Von Neumann was a legend who made major contributions to a number of fields. He made a huge impact on both theoretical and applied physics. He was a principal member of the Manhattan Project and the founding father of game theory and the concept of nuclear deterrence. He played the central role in developing the modern digital computer.[19] His colleagues often referred to him as the 'cleverest man in the world,' yet he was dead wrong about the future of his own invention. Von Neumann predicted that computers would always be expensive, cumbersome devices useful only in the development of nuclear bombs and weather control. He couldn't foresee a world in which computers would become cheap and ubiquitous.

It seems even those who are a driving force in shaping the future are unable to imagine it. The best that we can say is that our collective knowledge allows us to make educated guesses about what the future might look like, but there are sure to be many unforeseen twists and turns. Michio Kaku explained that the difference in the way in which we think, which is linear, and the rate of progress, which is exponential, made it impossible to predict the future. Kaku said the steady progress of science made short-term forecasts the safer bet, where projections decades into the future were subject to unexpected leaps and bounds.[20] It's difficult, if not impossible, to predict how our own technology will evolve, much less ET technology. Despite such formidable obstacles facing any futurist, many of our best and brightest minds, including Carl Sagan, Russian astrophysicist Nikolai Kardashev and theoretical physicist Freeman Dyson, took on the challenge of attempting to predict how advanced extraterrestrial civilizations might evolve.

Kardashev and Dyson developed a system of classification for extraterrestrial civilizations (ETCs) based on the production and consumption of energy. They labeled hypothetical ETCs as Type I, II and III.[21]

Under the system first proposed by Kardashev, a Type I Civilization would be able to harness the energy resources of its entire planet, engineering its weather and preventing natural disasters in the process. A civilization wouldn't become Type II until it had the ability to mine the energy of its star. Dyson imagined that such a civilization would construct a gigantic sphere around its sun that would absorb all its energy. A Type II civilization capable of building a Dyson Sphere would also be able to colonize star systems in its local neighborhood, and eventually the galaxy. A

Type III Civilization would utilize the energy of an entire galaxy and would be able to manipulate space-time itself, essentially becoming a galactic empire of sorts for all intents and purposes.

Here on Earth we have yet to neutralize hurricanes or draw energy from earthquakes, consequently we are a Type 0 civilization that gets its energy from dead plants. More precisely, we are a .7 civilization according to Carl Sagan, who predicted we would reach Type I status in about 100 years.

Kaku foresaw an even more transcendent civilization that he labeled Type IV. This civilization would be able to transcend the power of a single galaxy by tapping dark energy, which is thought to make up around 73 percent of everything in the universe. Kaku likened the power of such a civilization to that of the Q, the godlike character of the Start Trek Next Generation TV series.

In theory, the time it takes to transition from one civilization level to the next can be forecast by economic growth. A civilization with a GDP growth rate averaging 1 percent per year would need around 2,500 years to transition from one level of civilization to the next. Of course, such progress is not guaranteed. If the global economy is indeed a Ponzi scheme as some have charged, Sagan's estimate might represent our high point.[22]

Financial shenanigans are just one problem. The march towards Type I civilization is fraught with danger. The same innovations that spur progress also threaten it. Without computers, the climb up the Kardashev scale would be a long, slow grind if possible at all. With them, upward mobility will put the heat on civilization, literally.

Sagan saw the digital computing revolution as a game changer that warranted a new system of classification based on the amount of data a civilization could process. In Sagan's alphabetical system, a Type A civilization processes about a million pieces of information, which is the equivalent of a civilization that has a spoken language but not a written one. Ancient Greece, with its rich written language, would've been a Type C civilization, adding up to about a billion bits of information. By comparison, present-day Earth is difficult to gauge. A rough estimate puts us at Type H, making us a Type .7 H civilization under the Kardashev/Sagan system. A Type .7 H civilization with aspirations for Type 1 and beyond faces a serious challenge.

The energy and technology necessary for progress will produce a lethal amount of pollution and waste heat, possibly enough to destroy a Type I or

II civilization. The scale of the problem is difficult to imagine. "A Type II civilization, for example, consumes all the energy that is produced by a star. Let us say that its engines are 50 percent efficient, meaning that half the waste it produces is in the form of heat. This is potentially disastrous, because it means the temperature of the planet will rise until it melts! Think of billions of coal plants on such a planet, belching huge amounts of heat and gasses that heat the planet to the point that life is impossible," wrote Kaku.[23]

The problem of waste heat was such that Freeman Dyson suggested astronomers search for objects that emit infrared radiation rather than X-rays or visible light because a Type II civilization hidden by a Dyson Sphere would produce enough to glow infrared. So far none have been found. The implications for our smog-enshrouded Type .7 H Civilization are not pretty. We already have a problem with excess heat and it's only going to get worse. By the time Sagan estimated we'd make Type I civilization, the Earth will have become uninhabitable except for the poles because of runaway global warming-induced climate change, according to environmental scientist James Lovelock.[24] Attempting to achieve Type I on fossil fuels seems futile, especially in light of our pitiful energy efficiency. Currently, two thirds of all the energy consumed in the United States is dissipated as waste heat.[25] There are technologies in use in other countries that are much more efficient, but there's no sense of urgency to implement them.[26] Kaku warned that any civilization that let its energy grow out of control might commit suicide.

Unfortunately, ours appears to be one of those civilizations destined to overheat. Corporations that lack an existential purpose beyond generating profits for shareholders have neutralized our ability to govern ourselves. What's more, the Supreme Court of the United States legitimized the corporate coup d'état with its ruling in the Citizen's United case.[27] "If Exxon wants to spend $1 million (a bar tab for Big Oil) defeating an environmentalist running for city council, it can now do so. If Goldman Sachs wants to pay the entire cost of every congressional campaign in the U.S., the law of the land now allows it," wrote Newsweek's Jonathan Alter, who criticized the Citizen's United ruling as "the most serious threat to American democracy in a generation."[28]

No one is minding the store. Industries that profit from plundering the environment have succeeded in defeating government regulations.

Corporate interests systematically bludgeon the Environmental Protection Agency by way of the revolving door between government regulators and the industry they oversee.[29] Profit trumps everything. Such a civilization lacks not only self-awareness, but a vision for its future. We might very well melt the planet long before we harvest the full spectrum of the sun's energy.

Putting our house in order is a tall order. It will likely take a leader in the mold of John F. Kennedy to set a goal of achieving the type of advanced civilization imagined by Kardashev and Sagan. This means phasing out fossil fuels, eliminating greenhouse gasses, cleaning up the environment, increasing the energy efficiency of our infrastructure and developing the technology necessary to harvest the energy of the sun- all while somehow reversing global warming-induced climate change by the turn of the century.

Things don't look good, but not all hope is lost. As compelling as the projections of our best scientists are, they're still the product of linear thinking incapable of anticipating exponential progress. Just as computer scientists in 1947 couldn't imagine the development of the transistor would lead to the Internet, virtual reality and social media, it's very probable that ETCs don't exist as our best and brightest minds have imagined them.

In fact, the failure to detect the heat signature of an ETC is a sign that advanced civilizations develop differently than we expect. They have no need to build a Dyson Sphere. They've got something much more powerful.

THE SINGULARITY

The future is inherently unpredictable, but there's an event on the horizon so unimaginable that is literally defined by its absolute unpredictability. Exponential technological progress, which greatly exceeds the capacity of our linear imagination, leads to what futurists call the Singularity, a point in the not-too-distant future when artificially intelligent computers surpass human intelligence and become the driving force of civilization.

No one knows what happens next. Will artificially intelligent robots be our servants or our masters? Will they turn on the human race? Will we merge with this technology and become the AI robots? Or is there some other impossible-to-imagine outcome? Like the singularity in a black hole, it's difficult to predict what happens after you hit it. Hence, the name.

Ironically, the idea that human civilization will eventually be overwhelmed by technological progress was first proposed by John von Neumann who said, "the ever-accelerating progress of technology... gives the appearance of approaching some essential singularity in the history of the race beyond which human affairs, as we know them, could not continue."[30] Von Neumann may have missed on the world's demand for computers but his prediction about a technological Singularity looks spot on.

There is no better example of exponential technological progress than the computer chip. In the mid 1970s, former Intel chief Gordon Moore noticed it was possible to cram twice as many transistors on a chip every two years, thus doubling computing power. This trend became known as Moore's Law. Google Director of Engineering Ray Kurzweil, who has become the face of the Singularity within the scientific community, calls this runaway exponential growth the Law of Accelerating Returns. He says even Moore's Law is inadequate to describe the fantastically rapid change coming our way.

Despite such unimaginable progress and the limits of linear-thinking, Kurzweil has a clear vision of the post-Singularity world, which he believes will ultimately result in a merger between man and machine that will transform our civilization in ways beyond imagination.[31] "That merging is the essence of the Singularity, an era in which our intelligence will become increasingly non-biological and trillions of times more powerful than it is today—the dawning of a new civilization that will enable us to transcend our biological limitations and amplify our creativity. In this new world, there will be no clear distinction between human and machine, real reality and virtual reality. We will be able to assume different bodies and take on a range of personae at will. In practical terms, human aging and illness will be reversed; pollution will be stopped; world hunger and poverty will be solved. Nanotechnology will make it possible to create virtually any physical product using inexpensive information processes and will ultimately turn even death into a soluble problem," wrote Kurzweil about the implication of the Singularity, which looks like a fast track to Type IV civilization and the godlike powers of the Q.[32] Even Kaku's vision of the year 2100 casts us as gods who live in a world in which simply wishing for things is all it takes to get them.[33]

A post-Singularity civilization would be even more likely to colonize the galaxy and it would do so much more quickly and efficiently. Even Fermi paradox theorists consider it a possible solution. "Not every ETC will blow itself up, or choose not to engage in spaceflight, or whatever. But we can argue reasonably that every technological civilization will develop computing; and if computing inevitably leads to a Singularity, then presumably all ETCs will inevitably vanish in a Singularity. The ETCs are there, but in a form fundamentally incomprehensible to non-super-intelligent mortals like us," wrote Fermi paradox theorist Stephen Webb, who ironically reiterated Fermi's original question – "Where are the super-intelligences?" – in mistakenly concluding that the Singularity exacerbates rather than resolves Fermi's paradox.[34] In fact, the Singularity is the key to understanding the extraterrestrial presence on Earth and UFOs are the key to understanding the Singularity.

According to Kurzweil, a post-Singularity civilization will expand out into the galaxy as fast as it can, which is at least the speed of light and probably greater, using "exquisite and vast technology" to manipulate gravity and other cosmological forces in the process of engineering the universe as it sees fit.[35]

It's a safe bet a post-Singularity civilization will develop an energy source that makes a Dyson Sphere look like a fading campfire. In fact, it's a sure thing according to military-industrial complex insider witnesses who've testified about the development of Zero-Point Energy, the ocean of electromagnetic energy in which atoms swim that was once thought to be nothing more than empty space.

Physicist Hal Puthoff gave testimony to the Disclosure Project about his work to find a way to tap the zero point as Director at the Institute for Advanced Studies. Puthoff had extensive experience within the military-industrial complex, including stints at the National Security Agency, General Electric, Sperry, Stanford University and SRI International. He holds patents in various fields, including lasers, communications and energy and has published over forty papers on lasers, electron-beam devices, and quantum zero-point energy effects.

Puthoff said empty space wasn't really empty at all. In fact, atoms swim in a sea of energy, which physicists call the zero-point because if you could freeze all motion in the universe down to zero this energy would persist. ZPE is the fundamental energy in the universe, he explained, riffing on Clerk

Maxwell, "there's enough energy in the bottom of a coffee cup to evaporate all the world's oceans."

A Dyson sphere would likely be obsolete long before it ever rolled off the 3D-printer assembly line. A post-Singularity civilization that figured out how to harvest ZPE would have all the energy it could ever need. "The grand outcome would be that you could use it to power everything from electric toothbrushes, to aircraft carriers, to automobiles, to homes, to spaceflight," said Puthoff, who further explained that ZPE also made it possible to travel faster than the speed of light.[36] In theory, a craft that drew its energy from the zero-point energy field would also remove it as a barrier making it possible to accelerate up to and past the speed of light. It would be like a jet that was able to suck in the outside air and convert it into fuel.

The testimony of other military-industrial complex whistleblowers shows that the zero-point energy propulsion system described by Puthoff is not merely theoretical- it's fact. Disclosure project witnesses including Brigadier General Stephen Lovekin, Paul Czysz, Lieutenant Colonel Thomas Bearden, Eugene Mallove, aerospace illustrator Mark McCandlish and Paul LaViolette have all crossed paths with such technology in the course of their careers.[37]

LaViolette began researching Navy physicist T. Townsend Brown's work in electrogravitics in 1985 after his Subquantum Kinetics theory predicted the coupling of electricity and gravitation. At the Library of Congress, he discovered a report written in 1956 called *Electrogravitics Systems* that called for a "Manhattan-style" project to develop antigravity propulsion based on Brown's work. The report was available in only one other library in the country: the Wright-Patterson Air Force Base Technical Library. LaViolette connected the report to the Roswell Incident and to a leak about the B2-Bomber made to *Aviation Week and Space Technology* magazine in 1992 as evidence of the secret development of antigravity technology. Anonymous black project engineers attempting to force classified technology out into the open told *Aviation Week* that the B2-Bomber electrostatically charged both its exhaust and the leading edge of its winglike body. According to LaViolette, for anyone familiar with Brown's work this was "tantamount to stating that the B-2 is able to function as an antigravity aircraft."[38]

The so-called stealth bomber, officially revealed to the world in 1988, likely represents an incremental step in the effort to reverse-engineer ET technology. LaViolette believes we have craft that can easily navigate the solar system and we likely have bases on the Moon and Mars. Disclosure Project witness Mark McCandlish's testimony about the Alien Reproduction Vehicle shows that an ET craft has been fully and completely reverse-engineered.[39] In fact, thanks to whistleblowers from the aerospace wing of the military-industrial complex we don't have to guess at what a post-Singularity civilization will do or what it will develop. Zero-Point Energy/Antigravity Propulsion is, as the Hercules Aerospace memo quoted by McCandlish stated, the *fundamental enabling technology*.

The development of zero-point energy represents more than just a small step for mankind- or even several giant leaps. "And from everyone that I have talked to who knows something about this subject matter, they do believe that the sources of energy that keep these vehicles in propulsion are sources of energy that are just as free as free could be. They don't cause any harm to the environment. They don't cause any footprints to be left anywhere," said Stephen Lovekin,[40] who'd personally seen debris recovered from the Roswell spacecraft.

A civilization in possession of such technology wouldn't need to build a Dyson Sphere and so there's no need to look for one. Much like SETI's inability to detect ET radio signals, the failure to find the heat signature of a Dyson Sphere creates an illusion of negative evidence, which in turn, reinforces establishment beliefs about the absence of advanced extraterrestrial civilizations. Such circumstances make it difficult to recognize evidence that we don't expect to find- evidence that is certain to exist as a result of exponential technological progress. And like the belief that one is out of ketchup can prevent one from seeing the ketchup bottle in the refrigerator, a happenstance that psychologists call a negative hallucination, the belief that there are no post-Singularity ETCs might be preventing us from seeing evidence hiding in plain sight.

RADIO DAYS

The belief that the speed of light is an absolute goes hand in hand with the bias against UFOs. Puthoff argues that the emergence of Zero-Point Energy science shows that faster-than-light-speed travel is possible, interstellar travel is feasible and extraterrestrial visitation is plausible. Therefore, science should reconsider the UFO phenomenon, especially in light of the

Disclosure Project witnesses, including Col. Corso, whom he endorsed.[41] According to LaViolette, science also needs to reconsider /s as extraterrestrial radio signals.

LaViolette is the type of scientist that philosopher Thomas Kuhn called revolutionary. To Kuhn, there were two types of scientists. The first were caretakers. Technicians who go about refining a pre-existing "constellation of beliefs," that Kuhn called a paradigm. These bean counters ignored anomalies that didn't fit the paradigm. Most scientists fall into this category. The other kind saw the accumulation of anomalies as a flaw worthy of investigation. Kuhn showed that it was these scientists, and not the so-called "steady progress of science," that triggered scientific revolutions he called "paradigm shift."

LaViolette's research into pulsars makes him one of Kuhn's revolutionary scientists. A physicist with a PhD in Systems Science and Astronomy, LaViolette has published original papers in physics, astronomy, climatology and systems theory and has written several books including *Genesis of the Cosmos, Secrets of Antigravity Propulsion, Subquantum Kinetics, Earth Under Fire* and *Decoding the Message of the Pulsars.* He has also been a consultant to the United Nations on solar energy as well as numerous Fortune 500 companies on methods of stimulating innovation.[42]

LaViolette left no doubt about what type of scientist he intended to be when he founded a non-profit research institute called The Starburst Foundation. On the institute's website is a mission statement that could have been written by Kuhn himself. "History has shown that the most significant scientific breakthroughs were not deduced from the existing theoretical framework, but rather arose as marked departures from conventional thinking. Generally such new views challenged long-cherished assumptions espoused by the established paradigm and were therefore actively resisted by the old guard," wrote LaViolette,[43] who further explained that the peer review process was biased in favor of traditional research with the end result that innovative ideas went unfunded. He had seen such bias first hand during the year he spent at the U.S. Patent Office. Regardless of whether a device worked, patents were routinely denied on the basis that they violated the laws of physics. If one somehow slipped through, there were repercussions, he said, citing a patent submitted for a faster-than-light communications system that resulted in a public controversy. "The Patent Office, in its current approach, is actually breaking the law. It is trying to make happy the physicists who are with the American Physical Society — to keep them in power with their ideas, you might say, and withhold from public use good inventions that could solve our problems, like the energy crisis. There is a whole pattern of this going on at the Patent Office," said LaViolette, who recognized the need to establish The Starburst Foundation in order to pursue the unfunded, revolutionary ideas that had captured his imagination.[44] One such idea was that radio wave emitting neutron stars called pulsars might actually be a network of extraterrestrial beacons.

When the first pulsar was discovered in 1967, researchers Jocelyn Bell and astronomy professor Anthony Hewish thought they had discovered a radio signal from another world. In fact, they labeled the source of the precisely timed radio pulses LGM-1, which stood for Little Green Men.[45]

Although they held off on publishing their theory for fear of ridicule, excitement built in the astronomical community. At a press event held prior to the premiere of *2001: A Space Odyssey,* Arthur C. Clarke spoke about the discovery. "In the last few weeks there's been this tremendous excitement among the astronomers over the extraordinarily precise and rhythmic radio pulses coming from the direction of a point between Vega and Altair, which may yet turn out to have a natural explanation, but its periodicity and characteristics are so extraordinary that no explanation has yet- seems very feasible,' said Clarke,[46] who called the film an effort to educate the public about the inevitable discovery of extraterrestrial intelligence and the subsequent Galileo-like paradigm shift. But the excitement was short-lived.

Astronomers began to look for a natural explanation after another pulsar was discovered thousands of light years away from the first. They assumed that such signals must come from two different ETCs and concluded it was highly unlikely that both would be sending similar signals our way at the same point in time. Of course, pulsar discoveries didn't stop at two, but it wasn't just the multiplicity of pulsars that caused astronomers to abandon ideas about interstellar communication, it was also the nature of the signal itself, which was detectable across a vast spectrum of frequencies.

At the time, conventional wisdom was that an ETC likely wouldn't be able to broadcast a broadband signal because of the enormous power requirements. Astronomers assumed such a civilization would have to concentrate all its resources on a single channel likely to be discovered by another intelligent civilization. But the assumption hasn't held up. According to LaViolette, the development of particle beam weaponry gives us the capability to build a broadband ET communications system.[47] Back in the 1960s, Bell and Hewish weren't able to anticipate such wondrous technology. They suggested that white dwarf stars or neutron stars could be the source of the radio signals when they finally went public with their discovery. Eventually astronomers settled on what has become known as the Neutron Star Lighthouse model.

When a star of the right size goes supernova a neutron star is created. The forces of such a massive explosion are so great that a stellar core with a mass two or three times that of our sun is smashed into a city-sized neutron ball. "The result is theorized to be a state of matter so dense that all the star's nuclear particles have been transformed into neutrons and packed tightly together with the same density that exists in the nucleus of an atom," wrote LaViolette. To say that its matter is dense and its properties are strange is an understatement. Just one cubic centimeter of neutron star would weigh between 25 million and one trillion tons on Earth. A pulsar is stranger still. Astronomers think a pulsar is a rapidly rotating neutron star emitting radio signals from its poles that sweep by us like the revolving searchlight of a lighthouse.[48] The pulses, which sometimes number in the hundreds per second, show that the star is rotating so fast that centrifugal force must flatten it into the shape of a pancake. To date, astronomers have discovered over 1,500 pulsars.

Despite the astronomical community's acceptance of the Neutron Star Lighthouse Model and observations of binary pulsars' gravitational effects that showed the signals were indeed coming from massive celestial bodies, some continued to consider the possibility that pulsar pulses might be a product of extraterrestrial intelligence.

In 1971, at the first major international SETI conference that featured rock stars such as Russian astronomers Nicolai Kardashev and Iosif Shklovsky, SETI founder Frank Drake and physicist Freeman Dyson among others, Carl Sagan suggested that ETs might embed a message within a pulsar signal by manipulating "a very small movable shield" near the star's surface, which would be much like waving a blanket in front of a fire to make smoke signals. What's more, Sagan said ETCs might 'astroengineer' the galaxy as easily as we build a highway or a bridge and that certain astronomical phenomena such as fluctuating X-ray sources might actually be caused by ET technology.[49]

Sagan wasn't alone. The *New York Post* quoted MIT radio astronomy professor Alan Barrett, who wondered if pulsars "might be part of a vast interstellar communications network which we have stumbled upon."[50] But the scientific establishment wasn't interested in rethinking pulsars. Science had become dogma. Reputations were at stake. Careers were at risk. "We think of science as being based on observation and being open to change, but as you learn more about it and about the scientists themselves, you realize how much it is a religion," said LaViolette, who noted that even pulsar theorists were aware that the pulsar model was broken beyond repair. Yet there doesn't seem to be a would-be Copernicus among them. At least not when the best alternative explanation is extraterrestrial communication. It takes a true maverick to tackle such a problem. It takes someone like Paul LaViolette, whose career goal was to use systems theory to revolutionize physics; something he said had been done in other fields.[51]

Systems science is a paradigm shift in its own right. Systems thinking turns the reductionist model on its head, according to theoretical physicist and international bestselling author Fritjof Capra, whose classic bestseller, *The Tao of Physics*, showed how modern physics ignited this paradigm shift in worldview. In his acclaimed follow-up *The Web of Life*, Capra explained, "In the shift from mechanistic thinking to systems thinking, the relationship between the parts and the whole has been reversed. Cartesian science believed that in any complex system the behavior of the whole could be analyzed in terms of the properties of its parts. Systems science shows that living systems cannot be understood by analysis. The properties of the parts are not intrinsic properties but can only be understood in the context of the larger whole." What's more, Capra said that quantum mechanics showed there were really no parts at all, that "what we call a part is merely a pattern in an inseparable web of relationships."[52] It was this complex, roundabout "web of relationships" that led LaViolette to focus on pulsars.

As he set about using systems science to reinvent physics, LaViolette's research took an unexpected turn after a series of startling discoveries. He was developing a new cosmology based on his theory of subquantum kinetics when he discovered that the galactic core explodes periodically, sending a superwave of deadly cosmic rays that sweep the entire galaxy.[53] He found that such explosions have had dire consequences for the Earth in the past. Evidence found in polar ice cores led LaViolette to connect ancient legends about worldwide floods with the arrival of a superwave at the end of the last ice age. He also found that ancient knowledge of this event had been encoded in zodiac constellations in an attempt to warn future generations. What's even more fantastic, he found a warning about the galactic superwave in pulsars, which are massive stellar bodies used by ETs as a power source to beam a broadband radio signal.

According to LaViolette, when the galactic core enters its active phase enormous explosions generate an immense tsunami of cosmic ray particles and electromagnetic radiation that washes over the entire galaxy to the farthest reaches of its spiral arms and beyond. Such galactic superwaves, which occur every 13,000 to 26,000 years, represent a serious threat to life. A sufficiently intense superwave lasting several centuries would push enough cosmic dust and gas into the Sun to cause violent flaring activity endangering life on Earth. Even in the absence of the deadly flares, an influx of interstellar dust can cause climate change. Depending on circumstances, the superwave could induce either warming or cooling. In his book *Earth Under Fire*, LaViolette documented significant evidence that the end of the last ice age coincided with the arrival of a superwave around 13,000 to 16,000 years ago. The event triggered a tremendous coronal mass ejection that struck the Earth and Moon with deadly force causing the worst extinction event in millions of years. "This prolonged disaster may have spawned myths and legends describing celestial phenomena wherein a previously darkened Sun violently erupts to singe the Earth and trigger the release of vast deluges that wash over the land, events that are said to have nearly extinguished the human race," wrote LaViolette.[54] As terrifying as such devastation is to contemplate, the superwave poses an even greater danger. It could cause the Sun to go supernova.

The story told by LaViolette is utterly fantastic. The mind balks, but the evidence is impossible to ignore. And of all the puzzle pieces, pulsars are both the strangest and the most important. Although astronomers treat the neutron star lighthouse model as empirical fact, the theory is fundamentally flawed. When pulsars were first discovered, astronomers were only able to study the average number of pulses during a given time period. It was in this *time-averaged pulse profile* that they found such extreme precision.[55] Naturally, they assumed the pulses occurred at regular intervals. As the lighthouse metaphor implies, individual pulsar radio beeps should be regular and steady. In fact, they're not. Instead, they vary from one pulse to the next. They vary in such a way that adjustments had to be made to the basic model that beget further adjustments and so on. In short, the neutron star lighthouse model looks as imaginary as Ptolemy's epicycles. "Indeed, *the complexity of pulsar signal ordering far surpasses that of any other known astronomical phenomenon.* Even when the lighthouse model is made absurdly complex, it still falls short of satisfactorily explaining pulsar behavior, a shortcoming that today is widely recognized among pulsar theorists," wrote LaViolette.[56] This basic flaw in the neutron star lighthouse model makes all the other pulsar anomalies that much more significant.

Almost everything about pulsars is strange, including their location in the sky. If they were completely natural objects they would be distributed throughout the galaxy along with the supernovae that birthed them. But they're not. Instead, pulsars are found to cluster around an astronomically significant location known as the *one-radian point*. In geometry, a radian is a standard unit of angular measure that uses the radius of a circle as a yardstick to measure its angles. According to LaViolette, it's just the type of mathematical symbolism one would expect from an ETC attempting to communicate with other advanced civilizations.

Pulsar's become scarce after the point on the galactic equator that lays one radian of arc from the galactic core. Supernova remnants don't.[57] In fact, there's almost no evidence of a connection between pulsars and supernovas. It's a problem that torments pulsar astronomers and another strike against the neutron star lighthouse model.[58] It's also a sign of extraterrestrial intelligence. "It is the radian measure that we would choose if we were to design an ET communication message because we could be assured that it would be known to scientists of other advanced civilizations in the galaxy who were able to receive our signals," wrote LaViolette about the implications of the pulsar cluster around the one radian point.[59] What's even more amazing is that pulsar location phenomenon has an even deeper layer of complexity. The location of very unique pulsars is also very much anomalous. The Millisecond Pulsar is a prime example. Millisecond pulsars have periods shorter than 10 milliseconds, which means they pump out over 100 pulses per second. Out of 1,533 pulsars only 90 are millisecond pulsars. Of those 90, there is one that stands out above all the others- it is officially known as *the* Millisecond Pulsar because it's the fastest pulsar in the sky. It pulses 642 times a second with a precision that exceeds the best-known atomic clocks. Rapid pulse rate and extreme precision are but two of the Millisecond Pulsar's many unique attributes. It isn't just the fastest pulsar.

It's also the brightest, the most intense and the most fixed-position pulsar in the sky. It also emits visible flashes of light as well as giant powerful pulses. What's more, the Millisecond Pulsar is positioned almost exactly at the galaxy's northern one-radian point, closer than any other pulsar.

The odds that any pulsar would mark this spot are about one in 14,300, but the odds that this pulsar would also be the Millisecond pulsar are beyond imagination. There are only four other pulsars that emit visible light, therefore the odds that this one-radian pulsar would also be one that can be seen with an optical telescope is five out of 1,533 or about one in 300. There are only ten pulsars that emit giant pulses, so the odds that the one-radian pulsar would also belt out these intense blasts are ten in 1,533 or about one in 153, and so on. When all the probabilities are multiplied together, the odds that the Millisecond Pulsar would also be the one-radian pulsar are about *one in a billion.* "The odds are overwhelmingly against nature having arranged this placement. If we had to choose between coincidental placement near this key galactic location and purposeful placement by a galactic civilization, the odds seem to lean heavily in favor of the ETI alternative," wrote LaViolette.[60]

The case for Little Green Men is even stronger when considering the location of other unique pulsars in the context of the galactic superwave and its destructive power. Of the other four pulsars that emit visible flashes, two mark the closest and most recent supernovas to Earth, the Crab and Vela nebulas. "Is it just a coincidence that of all the supernova remnants in the galaxy, the two that happen to have unique placements relative to our solar system are among the few to be marked with pulsars,"[61] asked LaViolette rhetorically, comparing the Crab and Vela pulsars to flashing road hazard warning signs placed at freeway construction sites.[62]

It was these signs that led him to reconstruct the scene of the catastrophe much like an accident investigator. He found that the time between the Crab and Vela supernovas was approximately equal to the time it takes light to travel from the Vela site to the Crab Nebula. "It is, then, entirely reasonable that a superwave "event horizon," moving outward from the galactic center at the speed of light and reaching the Earth around 14,130 years ago, first passed the relatively nearby Vela site, causing its supernova to occur, and then, after traveling some 6,300 light-years farther on, passed the Crab Nebula site, causing its supernova also to occur," wrote LaViolette. It made sense, he argued, that if such a devastating astronomical phenomenon happened from time to time, advanced civilizations would surely attempt to communicate about it "since it is something that *all civilizations in the Milky Way have experienced in common.*" It would be the "talk of the Galaxy, hence the original title of his book."[63]

In summary, the odds that the pulsar cluster at the Galactic core's one-radian point is the result of coincidence are truly, as they say, astronomical. LaViolette put the odds at much less than one in 50 trillion or 10 to the 28th power to be exact.[64] Such numbers are simply unimaginable. As a result, LaViolette concluded the only alternative to Extraterrestrial Intelligence was that the universe itself had to be conscious and was trying to send us a message. In other words, the most likely explanation is that pulsars are evidence of post-Singularity, astroengineering of a magnitude our linear-thinking, pre-Singularity minds simply cannot imagine.

LGM – LITTLE GREEN MEN

In 2003, astronomers studying the Crab pulsar announced that certain giant pulses occurred in times as brief as two nanoseconds, thus essentially confirming LaViolette's theory that pulsar signals are artificial. "Such a short duration implies that they are necessarily being emitted from a region less than two feet in diameter. This has led this research team to assert that their findings invalidate most previously proposed pulsar radio emission models. On the other hand, these results confirm the suggestion proposed in 2000 that pulsar signals are of artificial origin and are generated by particle-decelerating fields projected close to the surface of a stellar ray source," wrote LaViolette.[65]

The ETI beacon pulsar model suggests any stellar source that emits cosmic rays, including neutron stars, white dwarfs and X-ray stars, could be used to generate pulsar signals by a civilization with the technology to beam and manipulate force fields near its surface. It may sound like far-out science fiction, but the U.S. military has already begun developing such technology.[66]

The implications are far-reaching. LaViolette thinks interstellar navigation is likely the primary function of the pulsar beacon network. For ETCs that have developed superluminal spaceflight pulsars could serve as an intergalactic GPS system. Spacecraft could use the unique properties of the signals to gage speed and location anywhere in the galaxy. In fact, NASA has used pulsar radio signals for just such purposes. A message on a plaque placed aboard the Pioneer 10 spacecraft, the first man-made object to leave the solar system, enabled any ETC that discovered it to find Earth by using a pulsar map to triangulate on our Sun's location. Ironically, the architects of that message were Carl Sagan and SETI founder Frank Drake.[67]

There may be even more to pulsars. LaViolette based his theory on the geometric symbolism of pulsar location in the context of the complexity of the signals, which defy natural explanation. The actual signals themselves have never been deciphered, at least in the public realm. Sagan thought pulsar signals might include ET communication, so it's possible there's been a top secret Majestic-12-like attempt to decipher them. Unfortunately, no one else seems interested. If SETI is any indication, LaViolette is about as popular in the astronomical community as Galileo was within the Catholic Church. Even though the neutron star lighthouse model has been shown to be as imaginary as Ptolemy's epicycles, there's no interest in resurrecting Little Green Men. LaViolette offered to submit his work to SETI Director Seth Shostak, but he wasn't interested.[68]

A simple check of its website shows the bean counting goes on as usual at SETI as far as pulsars are concerned.[69] Such lack of interest is completely at odds with SETI's mission and its history given its founding fathers' belief that pulsars might be evidence of Extraterrestrial Intelligence.

About a month before LaViolette called him out on *Coast to Coast AM* with George Noory, Shostak flaunted his bias against the very premise that pulsars could be ET signals in an editorial posted on space.com on December 1, 2005, in which he bloviated pulsar dogma. "Pulsars flash over the entire spectrum. No matter where you tune your radio telescope, the pulsar can be heard. That's bad design, because if the pulses were intended to convey some sort of message, it would be enormously more efficient (in terms of energy costs) to confine the signal to a very narrow band," wrote Shostak, who simply reiterated the outdated idea that broadband signals weren't doable.[70] In the 1970s, astronomers Robert Jastrow and Malcolm Thompson argued that the enormous power requirements of a broadband transmission meant that the only feasible way to send an interstellar signal would be to concentrate all power on just one frequency.[71] It was a textbook example of the limitations of linear thinking.

In fact, Broadband is the far superior choice for interstellar radio communication. As LaViolette shows, broadband is a feature not a bug.

Such signals are much easier to detect than a single frequency among billions, which is like "trying to find a needle in the cosmic haystack," according to LaViolette, who pointed to the development of particle-beam weapon technology that made interstellar broadband possible.[72] What's more, Disclosure Project witnesses emphatically refuted the assumption of a fundamental energy shortage. The truth is interstellar radio signals aren't just possible, they're ideal for a robust post-Singularity civilization capable of navigating the galaxy at superluminal speed, another concept that was inconceivable at the time- outside of highly classified channels.

In light of the SETI's strange lack of interest in its own Holy Grail, one can't help view the organization through the lens of the Majestic-12 operation. ET radio signals would've been a top priority of the intelligence gathering operation described by Corso. SETI could've been used much like Project Blue Book. The real investigation would take place in the classified world while the faux investigation/public relations program was fed to the public. It could be that behind the scenes there is, or has been, a top secret effort to decode the broadband signals of pulsars all-the-while international headlines trumpet the fruitless search for a single-frequency ET message.

SETI's Allen Telescope Array lists pulsar science among its capabilities.[73] Thus, SETI, like Blue Book, could funnel data on pulsars to classified projects. It could do this in secret while its failures to detect the lone alien channel carrying its version of *I Love Lucy* are widely publicized. Such publicity would create the illusion of negative evidence that would be of great benefit to a public relations campaign like the one recommended by Majestic-12 that was codified into policy by the CIA's Robertson Panel. It also fits the modus operandi of the UFO cover-up, which Corso described as a camouflage scheme. "In fact, we never hid the truth from anybody, we just camouflaged it," wrote Corso about the cover-up strategy.[74] If intelligence agencies taught classes, SETI's insistence on the doomed-to-fail search for the "cosmic needle in a haystack" along with its apathy towards the so-called "natural" broadband beacons called pulsars would serve as a prime example of Corso's camouflage scheme.

If SETI is a product of the government's secret UFO program it came into being after the original Majestic-12 operation had already spun out of control. Even so, SETI could still be operating as originally intended under the control of a faction of the splintered group. As Corso explained, Majestic-12 operations continued on long after the parent group went out of existence. And there is reason to believe this could indeed be the case. SETI has ties to Majestic-12.[75] Lloyd Berkner, who sat on the Robertson Panel, was Frank Drake's mentor. He encouraged Drake's Project Ozma, a precursor to SETI. What's more, Donald Menzel's protégé Carl Sagan was one of SETI's founding fathers and its most passionate advocate.[76] In fact, the cognitive dissonance between Sagan's passion for contact with other intelligent life in the universe and his bias against UFOs can best be explained by the Majestic-12 agenda. Sagan not only spearheaded the effort to get SETI up and running, he beat back critics lobbying congress to kill the program. When it became clear that public money would eventually dry up he arranged private funding. More so than anyone, Sagan was SETI's greatest patron saint, which made his reflexively dismissive attitude towards UFOs rather puzzling. Sagan estimated there were at least a million advanced ET civilizations in the Milky Way Galaxy that had to be capable of interstellar travel. He made the 'ancient aliens' argument that we may have been visited thousands of times in the past and that there might be artifacts of such ET visitation. He even claimed there could be an ET base on the backside of the Moon. Nevertheless, Sagan rubbished UFOs as nonsense and dismissed Ufology as pseudoscience. But it was Sagan who was guilty of pseudoscience. Stanton Friedman, coincidentally a college classmate, wrote an open letter to Sagan calling him out on his "false and misleading statements" about UFOs, reminding him that "every large scale study of flying saucers has produced a significant number of cases which not only cannot be identified, but which clearly indicate that some so called flying saucers are manufactured objects behaving in ways that we Earthlings cannot yet duplicate with our manufactured objects." What's more, he accused Sagan of following in Menzel's footsteps as a "UFO disinformation specialist."[77] Friedman's charge was confirmed by Disclosure Project witnesses, including Philip Corso Jr. "My dad said many times that Carl Sagan was CIA-sponsored and he had actually seen his payroll and credentials. He said he was a paid debunker."[78]

So perhaps SETI is a post-Majestic-12 program, possibly attached to the CIA, where Sagan took on a Hynek-like role. It's possible then that Sagan, who suggested pulsars might carry an ET signal, might've funneled pulsar data to a Majestic-12 program for decryption, all-the-while debunking UFOs in public. Perhaps Shostak plays a similar role today, reciting outdated pulsar dogma from over half a century ago while secretly passing on LaViolette's work to the classified portions of SETI just as Hynek was a go-between the public and classified portions of Blue Book.

Even if SETI didn't have a classified wing and wasn't an offshoot of Majestic-12, other forces could make it react to LaViolette's work as if it were Kryptonite. Shostak and SETI scientists face the proverbial rock and a hard place just like the priests in the Catholic Church when confronted with Copernicus and Galileo. Radio astronomers are people too. They may be no more capable of accepting a reality contrary to their personal interests than the priests were. When credibility is in question, reputations are at stake and careers are built upon a worldview increasingly contradicted by compelling evidence, utter denial is the last refuge.

Some will no doubt pooh-pooh the connection between the UFO cover-up and pulsars. Such self--styled skeptics will inevitably argue that pulsar science, right or wrong, has evolved naturally absent such conspiratorial shenanigans. And it is at least partially true. The limitations of our linear thought processes have contributed mightily to the evolution of a Ptolemaic-like neutron star lighthouse model. Here today at the dawn of the 21st century we still can't imagine that a vast interstellar civilization might occupy the galaxy. Unable to see too far into the future, scientists search for ETs just a little more advanced than we are. A civilization that is bound to its home world, burning fossil fuels, straining to blast single-channel signals off into the cosmic haystack. The inability to foresee exponential progress along with the "illusion of knowledge," as historian Daniel Boorstin put it, makes it easier to further obscure the Big Picture for those whose wealth and power depend upon perpetuating a crumbling paradigm. Last time around, Ptolemy's delusion of knowledge set the field of astronomy back for well more than a millennium. This time paradigm shift will be much more abrupt in the wake of the Singularity. In the not-too-distant future, AI will surely recognize pulsar signals as artificial.

Whether or not SETI is propaganda, the UFO cover-up has had a profound impact on the scientific community. If not for the atmosphere of hostility towards the idea of ET UFOs engineered by the Robertson Panel, pulsar's discoverers may not have been so reluctant to publish their original conclusions about Little Green Men.

PULSAR POLITICS

SETI's snub aside, LaViolette's other theories have gained traction in the astronomical community thanks to an abundance of successful a priori predictions. On his website, he documents no less than 12 confirmed predictions for subquantum kinetics theory and 15 for the galactic superwave theory.[79]

Despite such successes, the prospect of a pulsar beacon network built by superior extraterrestrials seems a bridge too far for the astronomical community. In 2000, at the 195th meeting of the American Astronomical Society in Atlanta, Georgia, LaViolette became the first scientist at a major scientific conference to present evidence of extraterrestrial communication. An abstract of the lecture entitled, *Evidence that Radio Pulsars may be Artificial Beacons of ETI origin*, is archived on the AAS website and the entire event is available on video.[80] Although the presentation was a success in that he received no criticism, he only got a handful of questions. It would seem that even though no one could argue with the theory, there was little interest. Since then, the march of science provided LaViolette with confirmation much like it has for his other theories. In 2003, the discovery that the crab pulsar emitted pulses in as little as two nanoseconds destroyed neutron star lighthouse radio pulsar emission models. In an update of his book, *Decoding the Message of the Pulsars*, published in 2006, LaViolette wrote that the discovery essentially proved pulsars emit artificial signals of ET origin just as he had proposed to the American Astronomical Society back in 2000.[81] Yet, as far as the establishment is concerned, it never happened. LaViolette has simply been ignored.

Curiously however, the idea of extraterrestrial beacons seems to have gathered steam, so to speak. In 2010, the ETI broadband beacon theory went mainstream- without LaViolette. In June 2010 *Astrobiology* published a theory by University of California Irvine professor and science fiction writer Gregory Benford, his twin brother James and nephew Dominic, who argued that ETs would indeed choose broadband radio broadcasts to get our attention. Yet, they weren't referring to pulsars.[82]

According to the Benfords, it would still be cost prohibitive to blast continuous broadband signals haphazardly in search of contact. But an advanced ET society with an economy on par with ours would be able to muster enough power for an occasional ten-minute broadcast at all viable points in the Milky Way in search of intelligent life. The signal would function somewhat like the hailing frequency from Star Trek, flashing periodically until noticed by an ETC savvy enough to be looking for such a sign. The broadband signal would serve as an alert to a much more subtle, cheaper-to-broadcast, message, much like the needle in the haystack that SETI has been seeking.

The Benford Bunch imagined a phased array of transmitters, either planet-bound or space-based, that would have a range dependent on how much energy an ETC could budget for the task.[83] The establishment press that had ignored LaViolette's work ate it up. From *Time magazine* to *Astronomy Now*, the press trumpeted the hypothetical broadband transmitters as "Benford Beacons." Even Seth Shostak, who had pooh-poohed the idea of broadband interstellar transmissions as 'bad design' in a snarky rebuttal to intelligent design proponents, was on-board with the concept of Benford Beacons.[84]

LaViolette called foul.[85] It's standard operating procedure in the scientific community to cite prior research in publishing new theories. The Benfords made no mention of his work on pulsed, broadband ETI beacons despite the fact that a simple Google search would have revealed a prior history established by LaViolette, who noted that his Starburst Foundation had issued press releases- that his book had been reviewed in numerous periodicals- that he had spoken about his work on pulsars on numerous radio shows including *Coast to Coast AM*- not to mention his presentation to the American Astronomical Society in 2000.

It sure looks like things aren't any different than they were a few hundred years ago when the Church did whatever it needed to do to fend off Copernicus and Galileo. The problem is the same as it's always been: politics and power. An ETI pulsar beacon network makes SETI look foolish and incompetent and perhaps even part of a much larger cover-up. On the other hand, the concept of Benford beacons is a lifeline for the flagging institution. The possibility of an intermittent broadband radio signal that would serve as a hailing frequency for the cosmic needle sought by SETI is certainly a preferable alternative to the career-ending hari-kari that would result upon acknowledgement of LaViolette's work. Thus, SETI's hostility towards the discovery of actual broadband ET beacons coupled with its enthusiasm for hypothetical broadband ET beacons can best be explained by what's in the best interests of the institution and the individual careers of those involved-just as it was with the Church last time around.

Unfortunately for SETI, the gambit came at a high price. In grabbing the lifeline offered by the Benfords SETI sacrificed one of its prime arguments against LaViolette's ETC pulsar beacon network. At its most fundamental level, the Benford ET beacon theory is based upon the flawed assumption that energy supply is a limiting factor for an advanced ETC. Again, linear thinking limits the ability to imagine ETCs much more advanced than we are, hence the concept of the Benford beacon. It's simply beyond our capacity to imagine a civilization that can move neutron stars around the galaxy and use them to broadcast radio signals. The main appeal of Benford beacons is that they're something we can conceive of and they don't violate belief systems or challenge any paradigms.

In contrast, LaViolette's theory has less than no appeal to an establishment threatened by the prospect of ETI, especially because he links the pulsar beacon network to the UFO phenomenon. In *Secrets of Antigravity Propulsion*, LaViolette wrote that secret efforts to develop field-propulsion technology were likely aided by the recovery of recovered UFO/ETVs, specifically citing the Roswell Incident.[86] He was even more explicit in *Decoding the Message of the Pulsars*. "The same force field projection technology that is used for UFO propulsion, and which also appears to be used in highly secret military weapons projects for producing aerial fireballs and possibly crop circles, may be the same technology that extraterrestrial civilizations are using to produce pulsar signals," wrote LaViolette, a Disclosure Project witness whose theories utterly invalidate the most sacred beliefs of the scientific establishment.[87]

It's obvious why Big Science, a wholly owned subsidiary of the military-industrial complex, shunned LaViolette in what may be a mistake of epic proportions. The implications of the pulsar network for planet Earth are profound.

THE MISSING LINK

Fermi wouldn't have been surprised by the discovery of the pulsar beacon network. He thought spacefaring ETs should exist so an intergalactic GPS would make perfect sense. But he likely would have been shocked to discover that the pulsar network broadcast included a message suggestive of a relationship between this Great Intergalactic Civilization and Earth.

LaViolette's research led him to conclude that pulsar signals were not only artificial, they were meant specifically for us. "From the vantage point of any other star system, parallax effects would cause these stars to have very different sky positions relative to one another and relative to the position of the galactic one-radian point seen from that location. Consequently, we are inevitably led to conclude that this message is meant for us, for residents of our solar system," wrote LaViolette, who noted that radio would be the "signal of choice" to communicate with a backward civilization such as ours.[88]

A post-Singularity ETC will surely have developed a much more efficient interstellar communications medium than radio waves, which are a poor means for calling home over vast interstellar distances. Recent experiments hint at such possibilities. Transmission of microwaves up to almost five times the speed of light has been demonstrated in the lab.[89] And that's just dial-up compared to the potential offered by quantum-entangled photon pairs, which have physicists exploring the possibility of instantaneous communication between any two points in space regardless of distance. Such developments strongly suggest the feasibility of a Galactic Internet for post-Singularity ETCs.[90]

Radio waves, it seems, are best suited for interstellar navigation and communication with emerging, pre-Singularity civilizations such as ours. The problem with the pulsar beacon network is that it's so far beyond us. Moving neutron stars around the galaxy is astroengineering on a scale only dreamt about by Carl Sagan.[91] It's difficult to imagine something we ourselves don't know how to do. Also, the message has been personalized in such a way that the mind balks. The pulsar beacon message is 'transitory' in that that it is not only targeted at a point in space – our solar system - but at a point in time – our recent past.

Nothing rests on a fixed point in space. The galaxies, including the stars, planets and everything else, are all in motion relative to each other. Thus, when pulsars marking key locations wander far enough, the message will be lost. Already, highly significant pulsars have drifted from sites critical to the message.

LaViolette's calculations show that the most accurate illustration of one-radian symbolism occurred between the years 1,750 and 1,800.[92] And, in another five thousand years the pulsars will have moved so much that the message will be gone.

The implications of such precise timing are truly mind-boggling. The Millisecond pulsar is almost 12,000 light years away, which means whoever placed the beacon sent the warning long before we had the capability to receive it or do anything about it. "Did the pulsar builders 12,000 years ago somehow foresee that earthlings would have developed radio telescope technology around the targeted time of the arrival of their message, plus or minus several hundred years? Or, could it be that human technological evolution is not just left to chance, that our development is externally influenced to follow some sort of prearranged timetable?" wrote LaViolette, who dismissed kneejerk skepticism about anything beyond our capabilities as "a small matter" in comparison to the incredibly, astronomically overwhelming odds against the natural occurrence of such exotic pulsars at such key locations. In fact, the only reasonable alternative to the ETI explanation was that the universe itself was conscious.[93]

Despite its intransigence, LaViolette called on the scientific community to conduct a thorough, objective study of pulsars. "Unlike a UFO encounter, which is transitory and leaves behind little evidence that could be used to convince skeptics, pulsars are continuously in the heavens sending their signals. Their data is well documented in scientific journals. But when properly and objectively studied, this data inevitably leads to the conclusion that a galactic civilization of unusually high advancement does exist and is attempting to communicate with us," wrote LaViolette, further citing the work of fellow Disclosure Project witness Alfred Webre, director of the ET communication study commissioned by the Carter White House, "In his book *Exopolitics*, Webre convincingly argues that a federation of galactic civilizations does exist, that they conduct themselves in accordance with a galactic code of law, and are led by a civilization or group of civilizations that are benevolent and very spiritually advanced. It stands to reason that the powers of good would ultimately dominate in the evolution of a galactic society, for technology always proceeds faster in societies that have made peace with their neighbors and whose populace regularly derives inspiration from the higher levels within."[94]

Ultimately, LaViolette thought the message sent by the builders of the pulsar beacon network was much more than a simple roadside danger sign. "I think this is the big test of a civilization. If you can make it through the superwave to defend your planet and not go into a dark ages afterwards then you have passed the test. You're able to advance and be part of the galactic club, so to speak," said LaViolette, likening the pulsar display to a stunt plane skywriting Einstein's most famous equation for the whole world to see.[95]

The pulsar beacon network is astroengineering on a level that Fermi paradox theorists expect in a Galaxy colonized long ago. The evidence that LaViolette presents is *Saganesque* in the sense that such extraordinary evidence obviously warrants extraordinary conclusions. Hence, the Galaxy has been colonized by a post-Singularity civilization and Earth is a part of this ongoing process. Our relationship to this civilization is the missing link that makes all the puzzle pieces fall into place.

The premise that Earth is part of an immense Galactic super-civilization resolves all UFO-related evidence, including ETVs, their human/humanoid occupants, the sheer volume of the sightings, alien abduction, the base discovered on the backside of the moon, etc. It explains why pulsars are targeted directly at Earth and why such a civilization would go to the trouble to move neutron stars around the Galaxy in an attempt to communicate with us. It explains the choice of radio signals, the precise locations in the sky and the time period for which the message was intended. Just as the Extraterrestrial hypothesis is the lone theory that resolves all of the UFO evidence, post-Singularity extraterrestrial transmigration hypothesis is the singular theory that reconciles all the various aspects of the extraterrestrial presence. What's more, the model for Galactic colonization developed by Fermi paradox theorists can be used to understand the UFO/ET phenomenon.

Fermi paradox theorists that assume the Galaxy is ours to colonize think we could do so by deploying self-replicating robots to other worlds. Mathematician John von Neumann called such a robot a 'universal constructor' capable of building copies of itself and any other machine. Once such a von Neumann probe reached a new star it would gather materials from the local environment and build copies of itself, which would be sent off towards other star systems to repeat the process. The original probe would then build a new colony and synthesize human colonists in a lab. Even if there were no habitable planets in the star system the von Neumann probe would be able to build a space station that could support a colony. It would be a mind-boggling project. Galactic colonization will be at least several degrees more complicated than crossing the Atlantic in the

Mayflower. Like the colonists of Terminus in the classic science fiction series *Foundation* by Isaac Asimov, such a colony might not understand its true origins or purpose until it reaches maturity. The Galactic migration process dreamt up by Fermi Paradox theorists is based on seeding life rather than the direct transplant of colonists. If this is indeed how it's done, we may not even know our status as a colony until we reach maturity, which if LaViolette is right won't be until after we demonstrate the ability to protect our civilization from the galactic superwave.

The Fermi paradox led us to devise ways we could expand out into the infinite heavens with self-replicating robots. And, although the visions of futurists have proved to be of limited value, the basic premise is valid. Nature abhors a vacuum. If extraterrestrial civilizations exist – and they do – and practical interstellar spaceflight is possible – and it appears to be – interstellar migration is inevitable. And, if there is an extraterrestrial version of the von Neumann probe, it might be found in the Moon.

CHAPTER 6

MOON

Physicist Paul Davies of the University of Adelaide has even raised the possibility of a Von Neumann probe resting on our own Moon.
— **Michio Kaku**

We walked over to one side of the lab and he said, by the way, we've discovered a base on the backside of the Moon.
— **Sergeant Karl Wolfe, 2000**

FIELD OF DREAMS

Pulsars are one example of extraterrestrial astroengineering on a grand scale. There may be others. LaViolette has identified a feature of the Crab nebula that also appears to be of artificial origin. Astronomers have long been puzzled by a tubular jet of ionized gas within the crab nebula that is strikingly inconsistent with the remnants of the supernova. The jet projects outward two and a half light years, its straight lines in sharp contrast to the natural turbulence of the stellar explosion. What's more, the jet projects its ionized gas against the direction of the blast thus eliminating the possibility that it was created by the supernova. Its origin remains a mystery. "Nevertheless, such off-center alignment is precisely the kind of thing an ETI civilization would do to ensure that the recipients of their message did not mistake it for a natural phenomenon, and, as we see, the Crab Nebula jet certainly did get the attention of our astronomers," wrote LaViolette.[1] Other peculiarities are suggestive as well. Its magnetic field traps cosmic rays causing it to emit synchrotron radiation, which led LaViolette to ask, "Could the jet be an example of a cylindrical force field shield deployed to intercept superwave cosmic rays?" In other words, the anomaly appears to be a demonstration of a galactic superwave shield. What's even more fantastic is that LaViolette found further symbolism characteristic of the pulsar beacon network that suggests this awesome cosmic display is meant as a hint to Earth that it should be prepared to build its own force field shield.[2]

If such a wondrous post-Singularity civilization were really colonizing the Galaxy one would expect to find other examples of astroengineering much closer to home. There should be, as Fermi paradox theorists expect, signs of higher extraterrestrial civilization - and there are - along with the telltale signs of life.

MARS MYSTERIES & PHOBOS PHOBIA

Speculation about extraterrestrial life on the red planet goes way back. In the late 1800s, astronomer Percival Lowell thought he saw canals that had been dug to transport water from the poles to cities around the barren and dying planet. Lowell's vision sparked the public's imagination, igniting a pop culture phenomenon. The plight of desperate Martians inspired H.G. Wells' science fiction classic *The War of the Worlds*, which of course was the basis for Orson Welles' infamous 1938 radio broadcast that became such a defining moment in UFO history.

A Martian invasion, however, was not in the cards. Lowell's vision faded in 1965 when the Mariner 4 space probe returned images of a Martian landscape that been battered much like the Moon. Subsequent missions confirmed what the pictures showed. Mars was inhospitable to life. With an atmosphere too thin to support liquid water on the surface, there wasn't much hope for anything more than bacteria.

Public interest cratered much like the surface of Mars in images published on the front pages of the *New York Times*. The pictures put an end to excitement about Lowell's Martians. The big let-down was the ultimate buzz-kill, triggering the decline of the American space program according to Richard C. Hoagland, former science advisor to Walter Cronkite and consultant to NASA.

Unfortunately, the first glimpses of Mars showed only one hemisphere. It wasn't until 1971 when Mariner 9 entered into Martian orbit that the entire planet came into focus. And when it did we learned that Mars had another side. One that was much more familiar. It wasn't alive like Earth, but it showed signs that it once might have been. There were volcanoes, including Olympus Mons, the biggest in the solar system at over 16 miles high and 300 miles across. There was evidence of a volatile climate that hinted at a time in the past when conditions may have been much more amenable to life as we know it. And there were canals. They were channels, actually, that appeared to have been dug into the rock, not by thirsty Martians, but by the geological processes of raging waters and father time, much like here on Earth. For all intents and purposes, it appeared as if Mars once had oceans and rivers and lakes.[3]

As Mars exploration progressed from the Mariner missions to the Viking missions to the Mars Global Surveyor and so forth, the picture coming back from Mars gradually undermined the belief that the red planet was hostile to life. Recent studies, including one by the University of Colorado that combined data from various NASA and European Space Agency Mars missions, show that Mars likely had an ocean of liquid water that covered more than a third of the planet over three billion years ago.[4] What's more, Mars once had a "global hydrological cycle" of precipitation, runoff, cloud formation and the accumulation of ice and groundwater very much similar to Earth's.[5]

The prospect of an ancient ocean on Mars raises many questions. It's a common belief that where there's water there's life. Naturally, it follows that if Mars had an ocean, it also had life. At a minimum, scientists believe it was likely hospitable to microbes. The big question is whether it could have evolved more complex life forms like Earth. And there is some rather striking evidence. In 2004 the Mars Opportunity Rover took a picture of what looked like a fossil on a rocky outcrop along the rim of a small crater.[6] The image looked so much like a common Sea Lilly found in the Earth's oceans 350,000 million years ago that it could've come from a paleontology textbook. Unfortunately, there is no way to confirm the discovery. The Opportunity Rover destroyed the find by grinding it up with its Rock Abrasion Tool.[7] "The raw "before" and "after" images can still be seen at the JPL Mars Exploration Rover Mission homepage," wrote Richard Hoagland about what amounted to a travesty of science.[8]

There are other glaring anomalies that have gone unexplained. Arthur C. Clarke called attention to striking images coming back from Mars in 2001, coincidentally the year that he and filmmaker Stanley Kubrick turned into a metaphor for the future. "There are some incredible photographs from [the Jet Propulsion Laboratory], which to me are pretty convincing proof of the existence of large forms of life on Mars! Have a look at them. I don't see any other interpretation," he said to Space.com.[9] "I'm now convinced that Mars is inhabited by a race of demented landscape gardeners," quipped the legendary scientist, who was quoted in the London Times about an image taken by the Mars Global Surveyor that appeared to show "bushes" that looked a lot like Banyan trees.[10] Indeed, the image could easily be mistaken for a satellite view of India or perhaps Sri Lanka, Clarke's adopted home, rather than Mars if not for the rest of the terrain. When asked about how confident he was about life on Mars, Clarke replied, "The image is so striking that there is no need to say anything about it -- it's obviously vegetation to any unbiased eye."[11] He went even further in an article written for *Aviation Week & Space Technology*. "And talking of stupidity, I feel that a current example is the refusal by everyone to recognize that we've already discovered life on Mars. How else can you explain the Mars Observer Camera's (MOC's) M0804688.jpg's striking resemblance to Banyan Trees? I'm beginning to wonder if there's intelligent life at NASA," thundered an exasperated Clarke.[12]

Finding trees on Mars is a bit like discovering a dinosaur on the Moon. But the more we learn about Mars, the less implausible the trees in the pictures appear to be. In 2008, NASA's Phoenix Mars Lander made an amazing discovery. "We basically have found what appears to be the requirements for nutrients to support life," said Phoenix Mars Lander chemist Sam Kounaves, who further explained, "This is the type of soil you'd probably have in your backyard. You might be able to grow asparagus pretty well, but probably not strawberries."[13]

Of course it would be difficult to grow Martian asparagus without water, a resource originally thought to be remarkably scarce on the frigid planet. Yet that assumption has also fallen by the wayside the wake of recent discoveries. In 2002, the Mars Odyssey spacecraft detected "enormous amounts" of subsurface water ice that caught scientists completely by surprise.[14] Ice on Mars is one thing, but plant life, as we know it, requires liquid water, something not thought to be possible until recently. In 2008 the

Mars Reconnaissance Orbiter found evidence of liquid water on the surface of Mars.[15] Scientists think dark streaks that appear on Martian slopes in the spring and fade in winter are caused by briny water flows, which would be prime spot to search for life.

According to astrobiologist Chandra Wickramasinghe, such a discovery was made long ago. In 1976, experiments performed by the Viking 1 and Viking 2 space probes on the surface of Mars found life, but the news was withheld from the public. Officially NASA claims these experiments were a failure, despite the opinion of the principal investigator of the project, Gil Levin, a friend and colleague of Wickramasinghe, who concluded otherwise.[16] A recent re-evaluation of the Viking data made in 2012 using what mathematicians call cluster analysis supported Levin's original conclusions that microbial life was indeed detected on Mars by the Viking probes. Remarkably, scientists even found evidence of a Martian "circadian rhythm," in the Viking data.[17] "I think there could be political and sociological considerations at work," said Wickramasinghe about NASA's reluctance to acknowledge the existence of extraterrestrial life on the red planet, which he said had "little to do with science."

Wickramasinghe, whom Clarke named a character after in *2010: Odyssey Two* said, "The discovery of liquid water on Mars combined with earlier discoveries of organic substances in a meteorite that came from Mars, and also of methane in the Martian atmosphere all point to the existence of life - contemporary life - on the red planet."[18]

Richard Hoagland recognized the policy recommendations of the Brookings Institute report warning against disclosures about the discovery of extraterrestrial life in Wickramasinghe's statement, thus confirming his long-held belief that NASA was depicting Mars as far more inhospitable than it was in reality.[19]

Hoagland, a former curator at the Hayden Planetarium and consultant to NASA who came into the national spotlight as science advisor to Walter Cronkite, is another revolutionary who has drawn the ire of the scientific community for his dissident views. Despite being dismissed as a pseudoscientist, his accomplishments have often overshadowed those of his critics. In 1980, in his paper entitled, *The Europa Enigma*, Hoagland predicted that a planet-wide liquid ocean hospitable to life existed beneath the frozen surface of the Jovian moon.[20] Seventeen years later, the Galileo spacecraft confirmed existence of the ocean and, like icing on the cake, detected organic compounds on Europa's icy shell of a surface. "I'm sure there's life there," said oceanographer and NASA consultant John Delaney who noted the discovery would "surpass anything that has ever taken place in human history."[21]

NASA, whose scientists ridiculed Hoagland's theory with few notable exceptions, hailed the discovery as its own without any acknowledgment of its former consultant. Fortunately, Ted Koppel of Nightline, and more importantly, Arthur C. Clarke, set the record straight.

Hoagland, like Wickramasinghe, was inspiration for Clarke's sequel to 2001. "I owe him a considerable debt of gratitude. He was the first to suggest that life might exist in the ice-covered oceans of Jupiter's satellite Europa," said Clarke of Hoagland's priority in the paradigm-challenging discovery.[22] It is, however, his other theories about extraterrestrial ruins in the solar system that have earned him harsh ridicule, and perhaps ironically, his greatest honor. The former Cronkite sidekick was awarded the International Angstrom Medal for Excellence in Science for his analysis of possible intelligently-designed artifacts in the Cydonia region of Mars.[23]

As the story goes, on the same mission in which evidence of microbial life on Mars was detected in 1976, the Viking Orbiter spacecraft took pictures that showed what looked like objects of artificial origin. The first object to draw such attention looked like a human face that had been sculpted Mount Rushmore-style onto a mile-long mesa, staring up into the heavens.[24] NASA dismissed the haunting image of a human face as a trick of light and it was all but forgotten until two digital imaging specialists, Vincent DiPietro and Gregory Molenaar, discovered another photo of the mesa taken from a different angle and time of day. If the face was an illusion, it shouldn't be there, yet the clear impression persisted thus throwing into doubt the trick-of-light explanation.

Intrigued by the possible discovery of extraterrestrial artifacts, Hoagland joined the investigation and discovered what he argues are the ruins of an ancient city, including several pyramids, in the Cydonia region of Mars. Mainstream scientists reacted much like they did when he first proposed the theory that Europa might have an ocean that harbored life. To them, the trick of light explanation held sway regardless of the second image, regardless of other anomalous objects like the pyramids, regardless of the mounting odds against such a natural occurrence, which should have been cause for further investigation, at the very least, it would seem, to the objective mind.

Despite being dismissed as an illusion, the face on Mars captured the public's imagination. Once again the prospect of Martians, albeit ancient, presumably dead ones, created great excitement. Hoagland's promotion of the unusual feature put the heat on NASA, which eventually bowed to public pressure. In 1998, the Mars Global Surveyor took high-resolution images of the so-called face and when the images were released to the public both the pro and con camps claimed victory. Hoagland and noted astronomer Tom Van Flandern both claimed the images confirmed a priori predictions made about the face.[25] "In my considered opinion, there is no longer room for reasonable doubt of the artificial origin of the face mesa, and I've never concluded "no room for reasonable doubt" about anything before in my 35-year scientific career," stated Van Flandern. [26] Unfortunately, the condition of the ruins, if they are indeed ruins, made it easier for the skeptics and debunkers to win the court of public opinion. To the casual observer it isn't immediately obvious that the mesa is artificial. The face, if it is one, is highly eroded, perhaps like Mount Rushmore would be long after the end of our civilization. Fortunately however, NASA has acquired many other astonishing images of Mars.

If the existence of Martian fossils, Banyan trees and artificial structures wasn't sufficiently incompatible with our "understanding" of our close neighbor, consider the enigma of the 'glass tunnels of Mars' discovered in other MGS photos.[27] The images, which simply cannot be explained by natural processes, show enormous translucent tube-like structures that appear in canyon crevices like the remains of a Martian subway system. The tunnels, which are distinct from the background terrain, are supported by arches spaced at regular intervals and are reflective like glass.[28] The best conventional explanation is that the tunnels are merely sand dunes. However, they appear nothing like other sand dunes seen on Mars. What's more, the sand explanation defies the geological processes consistent with the environment, both local and global, and fails to account for the distinct appearance of the tube structure. Ultimately, the suggestion that the tunnels are nothing more than an illusion caused by sand doesn't hold water.[29] "I'm still waiting for an explanation of that extraordinary glass worm. How big is it? It's one of the most incredible images that's ever come from space," said Arthur Clarke about the photos, which suggest a technological civilization once existed on the red planet.[30] But if such a civilization did exist, what happened to it?

The evidence amassed by NASA, beginning with the very first pictures of Mars' southern hemisphere, suggests that if there was a Martian civilization it was a casualty of planetary cataclysm. Astronomer Tom Van Flandern had a theory. According to Van Flandern, Mars was once the moon of a planet that exploded, its remnants forming the asteroid belt and perhaps changing the course of history on Earth.[31] The explosion that bombarded Mars' southern hemisphere also blasted the former moon into a new orbit around the Sun and sent asteroids raining down on Earth sixty-five million years ago, which ended the age of dinosaurs and set the stage for the evolution of mankind.

Despite the fact that the puzzle pieces fit, the scientific establishment wouldn't consider the exploded planet hypothesis absent a trigger mechanism that could cause a planet to explode. Van Flandern's alternative physics theory about gravitons just made things worse politically, violating yet another paradigm, further offending the orthodoxy. Politics and alternative physics aside, one can't help but wonder if the trigger mechanism might be LaViolette's galactic superwave? Gas giants like Jupiter are potential stars, a theme explored in *2010: Odyssey Two*. If this exploded planet was a gas giant, perhaps the galactic superwave caused it to explode just as it triggered the Crab and Vela supernovas? Whatever the case, such a violent episode, which blew away most of Mars' atmosphere, would certainly have doomed the Martians.

It's difficult to imagine how anything could survive the cataclysm that apparently befell Mars. But here on Earth the avian dinosaurs we call birds are still with us today. Could the Martians have survived in some form as well? The existence of a decimated civilization on Mars raises many questions. Might it have been an earlier attempt at seeding a colony in our solar system? Are the two civilizations related? If the Galaxy has indeed been colonized by a common ancestor - the first civilization to hit the technological Singularity - then the answer is yes.

Both Mars and Earth share a startling mystery in common. Both have unusual moons that appear to be hollow, a completely unexpected development that has paradigm-busting implications according to Russian astrophysicist Iosif Shklovsky, Carl Sagan's co-author on *Intelligent Life in the Universe*. "Well, can a natural celestial body be hollow? Never!"

thundered Shklovsky, who concluded way back in the late 1950s that the moons of Mars were artificial satellites.

Mars two small moons, Phobos and Deimos, were so tiny and so close to the red planet they caught Shklovsky's attention. He calculated Phobos' orbital motion and found it didn't support the assumption that the moon was a captured asteroid. Phobos' orbit was strange indeed. It was too close to Mars and it changed speeds from time to time. Shklovsky searched for natural forces that could account for Phobos' strange behavior but he came up empty. As observations accumulated, Phobos' predicted orbit didn't match its true position. The math showed the tiny moon had to be much less dense than an asteroid. In fact, it had to be hollow, like a tin can. Even the U. S. Naval Observatory agreed with Shklovsky's observations. "Phobos must have an artificial origin and be an artificial Martian satellite," he concluded, after exhausting all alternatives. What's more, he compared the football-shaped object to the Lunar Excursion Module. In other words, Phobos had to be a spacecraft.[32]

Unfortunately, Mariner 9's photos of Phobos caused a reprise of the Mariner 4 public relations debacle. Phobos didn't look like the international space station or the Millennium Falcon. It looked like a common asteroid, which kneecapped Shklovsky's theory much like photos of Mars' moon-cratered southern hemisphere killed off excitement about Lowell's Martians.

Shklovsky's theory was left for dead. Carl Sagan - whose early career was defined by his emphatic statements on the existence of extraterrestrial life - who had predicted that civilization might have evolved first on Mars hundreds of millions of years ago – who promoted Shklovsky's theory that Phobos was an artificial satellite – and who was dissuaded from taking the UFO phenomenon seriously by his superiors within the institution of astronomy - was the first human to lay eyes upon the surface of Phobos in a JPL laboratory.

One can only guess Sagan's reaction. According to biographer Keay Davidson, the iconic astronomer was sadly resigned to the fact that Phobos was nothing more than a space rock, but one can't help but suspect that the man who drove a red Porsche with the license plate PHOBOS might not have given up on Shklovsky's math so easily.[33] In the context of Sagan's body of work it seems likely he would've considered the possibility that Phobos was an asteroid that had been captured and hollowed out by a Martian civilization capable of astroengineering a space rock into spacecraft.

If Sagan didn't consider such a possibility, he should have. In 2010, the European Space Agency Mar Express mission confirmed Shklovsky's theory that Phobos was artificial. Unfortunately, neither Sagan nor Shklovsky lived to see the data gathered by the ESA Mar Express, which proved that Phobos was no ordinary space rock. Phobos is in fact hollow or "porous" as the ESA put it. "We conclude that the interior of Phobos likely contains large voids. When applied to various hypotheses bearing on the origin of Phobos, these results are inconsistent with the proposition that Phobos is a captured asteroid," read the European Space Agency report, thus confirming the findings of an earlier, ill-fated Soviet mission that Phobos was one-third hollow.[34]

In 1989, the Soviet probe Phobos 2 mysteriously failed amidst very unusual circumstances not long after establishing orbit around Mars in close proximity to Phobos. Just before its disappearance, the probe took a picture of a huge cylindrical object with rounded ends that appeared near Phobos.[35] It was the last image the space probe sent back to Earth. Phobos 2 was never heard from again.

The photo of the Phobos UFO, officially known as the Phobos Mystery Object or PMO, was made public by Russian cosmonaut Marina Popovich, who said the enormous fifteen mile-long object couldn't be explained. Speculation followed that the appearance of the PMO might have had something to do with the demise of the Phobos 2 probe.

Whatever the Soviet probe's fate, the Mars Express not only confirmed its observation that Phobos was one-third hollow, it was able to map its interior. Through the use of internal radar imaging and other techniques, Mars Express was able to determine that numerous "compartments" with right-angle walls, floors and other structures exist within Phobos and that these room-like areas have an atmosphere slowly leaking into space.[36]

The data coming back from Mars made Shklovsky's hypothesis that Phobos was an artificial satellite more and more plausible. In theory, a hollowed-out asteroid would make the perfect hull for a spaceship, providing protection from meteorites as well as cosmic rays. It would also be rich in materials, including water and oxygen. And, as we have seen, an asteroid would also provide effective camouflage against a more primitive and warlike species such as our own. Indeed, as the COMETA reported noted, our own scientists imagine that we could one day use such asteroids as "islands in space" to propel ourselves to other worlds. Unfortunately, scientific establishment groupthink doesn't allow anyone to propose a theory that some other civilization might have already done such a thing, much like it discourages consideration of the exploded planet hypothesis unless someone can explain in establishment-accepted physics how a planet can explode.

The same Brookings Institution "political and sociological considerations" that Wickramasinghe said prevented the announcement that life had been found on Mars back in the 1970s currently prevents the scientific establishment from acknowledging that the ESA data confirmed Shklovsky's theory that Phobos is an artificial satellite. Instead, Phobos is described as a pile of rocks smashed together by natural forces somewhat like the Great Garbage Patch in the Pacific Ocean. According to NASA, its cavernous, geometric rooms, floors, structures and atmosphere are nothing more than a "rubble pile" inside a thin regolith of a shell made from powdery dust.[37] What's more, Mars Express high-resolution photos that show Phobos is lined with mysterious grooves were originally explained away as fractures caused by a massive asteroid impact. When that explanation didn't fly the grooves were attributed to crater chains caused by meteor storms or "magically aligned impact crater strings," as Richard Hoagland called them, mocking NASA's unlikely explanation.[38]

According to Hoagland, the "shearing gravitational forces" of the tides of Mars are gradually tearing Phobos apart, exposing its artificial innards in a rectilinear surface pattern of crisscrossing grooves that can be seen in "descending fractal patterns."

NASA eventually came to agree with Hoagland about Mars' tidal forces fracturing Phobos. "The gravitational pull between Mars and Phobos produces these tidal forces. Earth and our moon pull on each other in the same way, producing tides in the oceans and making both planet and moon slightly egg-shaped rather than perfectly round," said a NASA press release that made no mention of the telltale rectilinear surface patterns raved about by Hoagland, who made the exotic suggestion that Phobos might be a "suspended animation ark," presumably built by the doomed Martian civilization.

Such speculation might sound far out, but Phobos is utterly fantastic. In fact, astronaut Buzz Aldrin called for a mission to Phobos to investigate a structure that's eerily reminiscent of the iconic extraterrestrial beacon in *2001: A Space Odyssey*. "There's a monolith there - a very unusual structure on this little potato shaped object that goes around Mars once every seven hours," said Aldrin, about the structure, which is as out of place as a five-story building in the middle of the Sahara desert. "When people find out about that they are going to say, Who [sic] put that there? Who put that there?"[39]

If Aldrin gets his wish and such a mission reaches Phobos, it will find a prime example of extraterrestrial astroengineering, albeit on a small scale relative to LaViolette's pulsars. Ironically, there's a much greater example much closer to home.

THE ROSETTA STONE OF THE SOLAR SYSTEM

The Moon is the straw that stirs the drink here on planet Earth, driving ocean tides as well as plate tectonics. Without the moon, complex life forms like us are much less likely and quite possibly impossible.[40]

For most our history, the Moon was beyond our reach, accessible only via the imagination. The onset of the space age changed everything, and our subsequent discoveries challenged popular scientific lunar mythology. In 1967, two years before the US put a man on the moon, noted astronomer Robert Jastrow predicted that moon rocks would be the clue that unlocked the mystery of our Moon's origin. There were competing theories. One school of thought was the Moon spun off the Earth as it formed. The other said the Moon was a rogue planet captured by Earth's gravity much like Phobos was thought to have been captured by Mars. One way or the other, Moon rocks were expected to resolve the issue. If they were much different from Earth rocks it would mean the Moon came from elsewhere. If they were just like Earth rocks then the Earth and Moon formed together in some manner. Whatever the case, Jastrow boldly declared, "The moon is a Rosetta Stone of the planets."[41]

It looks like Jastrow was right, but not in the way he imagined. Just like a high-quality UFO sighting that becomes less explainable because of the richness of the data – for example, the JAL Flight 1628 incident documented by former FAA administrator and Disclosure Project witness John Callahan – the more we learn about the Moon, the less explainable it becomes. NASA brought back 842 pounds of Moon rocks that not only didn't solve the Moon's mysteries, it deepened them. In 1972, science writer Earl Ubell wrote, "The lunar Rosetta stone remains a mystery. The moon is more complicated than anyone expected, it is not simply a billiard ball frozen in time and space, as many scientists had believed. Few of the fundamental questions have been answered, but the Apollo rocks and recordings have spawned a score of mysteries, a few fairly breath-stopping."[42]

None of the leading theories panned out. Darwin's fission theory and co-accretion theory had long been abandoned as untenable before we even got to the Moon, which surely didn't spin into existence because of the Earth's rapid rotation as Charles Darwin's son, astronomer George Darwin thought. Nor did it coalesce from a Saturn-like ring as others suggested. By the 1970s, the last of the leading theories, the intact capture theory, also fell by the wayside. The Moon wasn't a wayward asteroid captured by the Earth's gravity like Phobos was supposed to be. Physicists showed that such a large body would have smashed into the Earth or bounced off the atmosphere into deep space. What's more, Moon rocks proved conclusively that the Moon couldn't have formed elsewhere. In fact, it looked like the Moon was made from the Earth's mantle, but was completely lacking heavier elements. It should have large amounts of iron, but it didn't. And although our Moon is by far the largest in the solar system at about a quarter the size of our planet, it's over eighty times lighter than the Earth.[43]

Astronomers were stumped and facing embarrassment over not being able to explain the origins of our own Moon when the giant impact theory emerged to save the day. William K. Hartmann, senior scientist at the Planetary Science Institute in Tucson, Arizona and his colleague D. R. Davis suggested that the Moon was created when a Mars-sized planet collided with the Earth, blasting off a chunk of mantle that settled into orbit.[44] The theory violated long-standing taboos against catastrophic explanations for geological phenomena, but over time it gained general acceptance, in large part, because of the absence of any other explanation and because computer models showed the Earth could absorb the impact in such a way that the mantle from both bodies would form the Moon.

At first glance, the giant impact theory appears to resolve the mystery of the Moon's origin, but like the neutron star lighthouse pulsar model, it's fundamentally flawed. If a giant impact really occurred the Earth would be spinning much faster today than it is today. In order to cancel out the effects of the first collision, scientists proposed a second giant impact - perhaps thousands of years later – that came from the exact opposite direction, returning the Earth to its original rate of rotation. "This balanced double act sounds unlikely in the extreme. Two cosmic collisions that just happen to precisely return the planet to its natural rhythm? To us this explanation smacks of desperation!" wrote Christopher Knight and Alan Butler, authors of *Who Built the Moon?*[45]

The double giant impact is several orders of magnitude beyond unlikely all on its own, but there's more. The discovery of Earth-like oxygen isotopes in Moon rocks meant the Moon had to have originated at the same distance from the Sun as the Earth. This proved the Moon was not a captured asteroid and it meant that the hypothetical Mars-sized planet also had to have originated at the same distance, which is a big problem.[46] It's difficult to imagine how this planet could've occupied a similar orbit without incident for millions of years before smashing into Earth in such spectacular fashion. Also, because this planet didn't come from deep space it would have lacked the extreme speed and momentum necessary to knock the Earth so severely off its axis. A planet occupying a similar orbit to Earth would have had to have been three times bigger than Mars to leave Earth with a twenty-three degree tilt. But that doesn't compute either. Giant impact models break down in such a scenario.

Scientists are still tweaking the models, trying to make all the data fit.[47] But other evidence suggests their efforts will be in vain. A recent study made by a team of geologists found no geochemical evidence for the giant impact, leading them to conclude: "This [hypothesis] has arisen not so much because of the merits of [its] theory as because of the apparent dynamical or geochemical short-comings of other theories."[48]

Instead of resolving the mystery of the Moon in favor of one theory or the other, the evidence amplified it. Scientists simply latched onto the least impossible theory. "In fact, the more you look at either theory the more you realize that they're not at all plausible, the only reason they're used is because they're the only answers available... When you really look at it, it's so incredibly implausible, that to suggest that the Moon is artificial is less implausible," said Alan Butler.[49]

SPACE STATION

A myth spread by the anti-UFO establishment back in the day was that *astronomers don't see UFOs*. Debunkers claimed that if UFOs were real astronomers would see them arriving from space, but since there were no such reports there were no UFOs. Aside from the dubious assumption that astronomers would see such arrivals, it was an easily disprovable falsehood. Pluto's discoverer Clyde Tombaugh is one famous example, but there are many others. In fact, many astronomers have seen UFOs *on the Moon.*

For hundreds of years, astronomers have documented what they call Lunar Transient Phenomena, which include brilliantly blinking lights, moving shadows, objects as bright as stars seen within the body of the Moon, clouds, colored mists, shadows, moving objects and other weird, unexplainable sights. There've been thousands and thousands of these strange "happenings." In just one month in the year 1781, there were 1,600 documented sightings of unexplained lights in the crater Plato.

Intermittent lights were perhaps the most common, yet mysterious phenomenon, and there was no readily apparent explanation. The Moon has been volcanically dead for at least three billion years and some of these phenomena have been observed for more than two hours ruling out meteorite impact. Among the most puzzling incidents were multiple lights that appeared to be operating above the Moon reported by none other than the father of modern astronomy Sir William Herschel, who later saw up to 150 bright lights on the Moon during an eclipse. Other enigmatic incidents included an apparent electrical discharge that looked like "glitter" at the South Pole and a twelve-mile long bridge on the Mare Crisium crater that appeared seemingly overnight.[50]

Geologic features seemed to appear and disappear on the Moon. Rectilinear structures as well as strange, domelike structures were there and then they weren't. The bridge on the Mare Crisium crater was a dramatic example. The region had been thoroughly studied and was well known. Nothing like the bridge had ever been seen before and yet suddenly there it was. The discovery made in 1953 by science editor of the *New York Herald Tribune*, John J. O'Neill, was met with scorn by the astronomical community until it was confirmed a month later by prominent British astronomers Patrick Moore, a leading figure in the British Astronomical Association and H. P. Wilkins, director of the Lunar Section of the British Astronomical Association.

The bridge was extraordinary. Wilkins estimated it to be 20 miles long and a mile and a half wide, towering 5,000 feet above the lunar surface. When the Sun was low the bridge cast a shadow and sunlight could be seen streaming in underneath it. Once the bridge was no longer deniable it was branded a natural feature even though everyone knew this was wishful thinking. Wilkins let the cat out of the bag on a BBC radio broadcast. "It looks artificial," he said, "almost like an engineering job."[51]

Lunar transient phenomena was of such significance that NASA conducted a study called Project Moon Blink, which detected twenty-eight peculiar lunar incidents in short order. What's more, astronomer and astrophysicist Morris Jessup, who'd discovered numerous double stars, made an exhaustive study of LTP documented by a myriad of leading astronomers, which led him to conclude that lunar UFOs were alien spacecraft using the Moon as a base of operations.[52]

Rumors were that Apollo astronauts saw UFOs on the Moon. Publicly, they denied it, but official NASA transcripts taken from Mission Control-astronaut conversations and debriefing sessions showed otherwise. [53] Mercury, Gemini and Apollo astronauts all reported UFOs. The crew of Apollo 11 had a spectacular close encounter. During preparations for the historic Moon landing, Neil Armstrong, Edwin "Buzz" Aldrin and Michael Collins saw two "bogeys" performing dramatic maneuvers. At one point, they seemed to be joined together by a brilliant emission before splitting apart and departing at high speed. According to the astronauts, the spacecraft became brighter upon separation and seemed "to emit a force field taking the form of a blurry 'halo' around the entire craft."[54] The public never heard any of these UFO encounters. According to former NASA space program member Otto Binder, that's because NASA censored its broadcasts by switching to obscure channels during such events. What's more, Binder said he knew ham radio operators who had listened to the uncensored NASA broadcasts and had heard one of the astronauts blurt out, "These babies are huge, sir... enormous... Oh, God, you wouldn't believe it! I'm telling you there are other spacecraft out there... lined up on the far side of the crater edge... they're on the moon watching us..."

Close encounters on the Moon were just the tip of the iceberg. Both Soviet and US lunar probes took photos that upon close scrutiny appeared to show non-natural, artificial structures much like "the bridge" on Mare Crisium. The first sign something was seriously amiss on the Moon was a set of conspicuously statuesque shadows. Although NASA "feigned ignorance" about the shadows' origins, according to researcher Don Wilson, the long, telltale lines caught the eye of astute observers within the scientific community. The obelisk-like structures that cast the shadows earned the region in the Sea of Tranquility the nickname "Valley of the Monuments."

In 1990, old Apollo photos were an embarrassment of riches for researchers like Richard Hoagland, who began re-examining NASA's then twenty-five year old lunar photo library through the lens of the current computer technology and imaging software.[55] He quickly discovered structures he called "The Shard," and "The Tower" and other unnatural appearing objects, including evidence of what looks to be a vast domed structure in the Sinus Medii region.

The Shard looms a mile and a half above the lunar surface, making Earth architecture seem absolutely Lilliputian in comparison. The structure can't be explained by any known natural process. The Tower is even more incredible. "The Tower represents an enigma of the highest magnitude, because it rises more than five miles above the surface of the moon, and has been photographed from five different angles and two different altitudes. In all four photographs the same structure is visible and can be viewed from two different sides. The Tower exists in front of and to the left of the Shard in the Lunar Orbiter III-84M photograph. The top of the Tower has a very cubic geometry and appears to be composed of regular cubes joined together to form a very large cube with an estimated width of over one mile," said independent geologist Bruce Cornet, after making a thorough study of the photos.[56]

Hoagland and colleagues put two and two together and held a press conference in 1996 at the National Press Club to announce that the real reason President Kennedy was so desperate to land astronauts on the Moon and why NASA sent them to the Sea of Tranquility was to get an up-close and personal view of the monuments discovered on photos and in film taken during earlier lunar orbiter missions. NASA and its astronauts – nearly all military officers subject to secrecy orders - denied all of it.

It was high drama, especially for Hollywood. The Apollo Moon missions were a boon for tinsel town, which couldn't help but reflect in its own distorted way the schizophrenia of colliding paradigms. The quest for Big Box Office spawned movies like *Apollo 18,* a low-budget thriller about spidery aliens tormenting the astronauts, and academy award winner *Apollo 13,* a rousing story about the salvation of the doomed mission. Unfortunately, with the exception of Stanley Kubrick's masterpiece *2001: A Space Odyssey,* which was made before we landed on the Moon, Hollywood seems to have passed on the biggest story that came out of the Apollo program. Despite its Academy Award nomination for best screenplay adaption, *Apollo 13* missed an opportunity for an even more fantastic story. Lost in the human drama following the explosion of an oxygen tank and the imminent threat to the lives of astronauts Jim Lovell, Fred Haise and Jack Swigert, Apollo 13 managed to carry out an experiment that showed the Moon was hollow- an immensely more important fact than either lunar UFOs or alien artifacts on the Moon's surface.

The real lunar drama began on November 20, 1969, when Apollo 12 jettisoned its Lunar Model during preparations for return to Earth, sending it crashing into the Moon, which rang like a bell. Reverberations continued for more than an hour. Scientists were baffled. "None of us have seen anything like this on Earth. In all our experience, it is quite an extraordinary event... quite beyond our range of experience," said Frank Press of MIT.

On the following mission - *Apollo 13* - it happened again. During the struggle to make it back to Earth, the astronauts managed to carry out several experiments, one of which was to launch the spacecraft's third stage at the lunar surface in an attempt to measure the impact with seismic equipment put in place by Apollo 12.[57] Again the Moon rang like a gong. Reverberations continued for over three hours, penetrating to a depth of twenty-five miles. What's more, lunar scientists marveled over how it wobbled "almost as though it had gigantic hydraulic damper struts inside it," according to NASA contractor Ken Johnston.[58]

The moon rang every time the experiment was repeated. In the context of the Moon's low density, such ringing led some to conclude that the Moon had either an unusually light core or perhaps none at all. Scientists hoped a meteor impact large enough to bounce a shock wave off the core and back would reveal the answer. On May 13, 1972 they got their wish. Although the blast sent tremors deep enough into the Moon, none returned to the surface, providing further evidence that the Moon was hollow or "porous" like Phobos. Scientists were flummoxed, at least publicly. According to NASA scientist Farouk El Baz, secret experiments confirmed the existence of cavities within the Moon. "There are many undiscovered caverns suspected to exist beneath the surface of the moon. Several experiments have been flown to the moon to see if there actually were such caverns," said El Baz, who made the all too familiar claim consistent with the Brookings Institute recommendations that the results have been kept from the public.[59]

Other strange discoveries led investigative journalist and author Jim Marrs to question whether the Moon was the greatest UFO. Moon rock proved mysterious in various ways. The composition of the Moon is counter-intuitive. The heavier elements are not found deep in its interior, but on the surface, which is extremely hard like a shell. Astronauts attempting to penetrate the lunar surface with a custom-designed drill were barely able to make a dent. What's more, the Moon doesn't have a magnetic field, yet its rocks are magnetized and contain rustproof iron, which is unknown in nature. Rocks laced with what looked like processed metals including brass and mica as well as nearly pure titanium further puzzled scientists. "The abundance of refractory elements like titanium in the surface areas is so pronounced that several geochemists proposed that refractory compounds were brought to the moon's surface in great quantity in some unknown way. They don't know how, but that it was done cannot be questioned. These rich minerals that are usually concentrated in the interior of a world are now on the outside," wrote researcher Don Wilson, whose investigation into evidence gathered by both Soviet and U.S. Moon missions led him to endorse a Soviet theory that the Moon is a natural planetoid that has been hollowed out, converted into a spacecraft and steered into orbit around the Earth.[60]

In 1970 senior scientists at the Soviet Academy of the Sciences, Michael Vasin and Alexander Shcherbakov published their Spaceship Moon theory in *Sputnik*, an official Soviet government publication. "Abandoning the traditional paths of 'common sense,' we have plunged into what may at first seem to be unbridled and irresponsible fantasy. But the more minutely we go into all the information gathered by man about the moon, the more we are convinced that there is not a single fact to rule out our supposition. Not only that, but many things so far considered to be lunar enigmas are explainable in light of this new hypothesis," wrote Vasin and Shcherbakov who argued that the Spaceship Moon theory was the only theory that resolved the Moon's many mysteries, much like COMETA argued that the Extraterrestrial hypothesis was the only theory that resolved all the various aspects of the UFO phenomenon.[61]

The foundation for the theory was the Moon's low density, which led the Soviet astronomers to suspect it was hollow. Subsequent Apollo missions, including one that measured the Moon's motion, confirmed the findings. The reasoning went: If the Moon was hollow it had to be artificial.

If it was artificial it was likely a planetoid that had been hollowed out and made into a spacecraft by an extraterrestrial civilization, just as a small cadre of scientists and science fiction writers foresaw we ourselves would do one day. For the rest of us it was too far beyond the limits of linear thinking that spaceships must be metal behemoths and death stars are built one steel girder and rivet at a time. It was simply too far out, but not for Vasin and Shcherbakov, who imagined the Moon might be an ark of some sort, perhaps carrying the survivors of a planetary holocaust.

It should come as no surprise that the Spaceship Moon theory failed to make a dent in the scientific establishment. It was about as well received as the last Grand Paradigm Busting Theory. Fortunately, Vasin and Shcherbakov didn't have to wait until they were on their deathbed to publish like Copernicus and they weren't forced to recant or face the death penalty like Galileo. But they weren't taken seriously either. Researcher Don Wilson's initial reaction was typical. When Wilson, a teacher and amateur astronomer, was first introduced to the theory by a student he dismissed it out of hand as crazy. But he thought it would make a great premise for a science fiction novel, so he began to research the evidence gathered by the U.S. and Soviet Moon missions. "I soon was shocked to find out that *all the evidence from both the American and Soviet lunar programs and explorations supported the crazy spaceship theory*," wrote Wilson, who published his science fiction project, *Our Mysterious Spaceship Moon*, as a work of scientific fact.[62] And as Wilson noted, some would no doubt continue to call it science fiction. Nevertheless, the Spaceship Moon theory resolves the myriad of mysteries that is the so-called Rosetta stone of the solar system, including why the Moon's heavier elements are found on its surface, why it rings like it's hollow when struck and why moonquakes occur like clockwork in such precise, recurring patterns like the creaking and cracking of an old vessel at sea.[63]

The Spaceship Moon theory explains the highly unusual orbit of the Moon and how it came to be in place. "It is important to remember that something had to put the moon at or near its present circular pattern around the Earth. Just as an Apollo spacecraft circling the Earth every 90 minutes while 100 miles high has to have a velocity of roughly 18,000 miles per hour to stay in orbit, so something had give the moon the precisely required velocity for its weight and altitude.... The point – and it is one seldom noted in considering the origin of the moon – is that it is extremely unlikely that any object would just stumble into the right combination of factors required to stay in orbit. 'Something' had to put the moon at its altitude, on its course and at its speed," wrote science writer William Roy Shelton.[64]

Something also had to explain the 1,000 square kilometer cloud of water vapor detected on the Moon by Apollo 15. Moon rocks had shown its surface to be incredibly dry, as much as a million times as dry as the Gobi desert according to one estimate. NASA claimed the vapor cloud was caused by two tiny water tanks holding between 60-100 pounds of water Apollo 15 left behind, but the scientists who made the discovery rejected the explanation as impossible, concluding that the water had come from deep inside the Moon. The implications were profound. If the Moon were actually a spacecraft with an internal atmosphere the water vapor cloud might be easily understood as routine outgassing.[65] In fact, the Spaceship Moon theory explains why all natural explanations for the origin of the Moon have proven inadequate. It explains why the Moon is similar in composition to the Earth and yet much different and why no evidence of a giant impact or a rogue planet has been found. It explains why the Moon appears to have been both a hot world and a cold, dead world and why its crust is actually thicker than the Earth's.

The Moon has an outer shell of metallic rock and dirt that shows evidence of reinforcement, as well as an inner hull of metal 20 miles thick, enabling it to withstand the kind of asteroid strike that wiped out the dinosaurs. The dark patches on the Moon called maria, or seas as they were once thought to be, are one of the Moon's biggest enigmas. The maria are actually seas of lava rock that upon first glance appear to be evidence of volcanic activity. There's just one problem. The Moon is too small to generate enough internal heat to have produced the maria, which cover a third of its surface.[66] It was thought that perhaps the lava flows were caused by meteor impacts, but the evidence pointed to an internal source. Also, the maria are distributed non-randomly with four-fifths on the Moon's near side facing Earth, which made such a scenario further unlikely. Lunar expert astronomer Zdenak Kopal concluded the lava came from the Moon's interior, but was unable to explain how it got to the surface in the absence of volcanic eruptions. What's more, scientists found heavy metals including titanium, chromium, zirconium, yttrium and beryllium among others, amalgamated in the lava rock. These are super tough, heat resistant elements that only melt at 4,000 degrees. It didn't add up. There was no way to reconcile all the evidence.

The Moon is certainly a cold world now and it doesn't look like it could've ever been hot enough to produce the maria. This fundamental contradiction that has utterly stymied scientists is resolved if the Moon is a natural planetoid that has been hollowed out by an artificial volcanic process for use as a spacecraft or a space station, which explains why the evidence shows the Moon has both hot and cold origins and why lava from its interior laced with pure, processed heavy metals coats its surface. "This is the perfect material out of which to fashion and reinforce a spacecraft. Such metals were used not only in the Spacecraft Moon's inner hull but its outside exterior shell to withstand the rigors of their long space odyssey," wrote Vasin and Shcherbakov about the composition of the Moon's surface, which, despite the Moon's lack of a magnetic field, included magnetized rocks, as well as *rustproof* iron- something unknown in nature and beyond our technological capabilities to manufacture.

What's even more fantastic is that buried beneath each circular sea of metallic lava rock is another breathtaking Moon mystery foreseen by Vasin and Shcherbakov, who argued that if the maria were the result of artificially induced volcanism, the machinery necessary for such a large-scale operation might be detectable as a gravitational anomaly. Sure enough unmanned spacecraft orbiting the Moon experienced much stronger gravitational pull as they passed over the maria, causing the craft to both dip and accelerate. These regions of dense rock or mass concentrations called 'mascons' are buried twenty to forty miles below the lunar surface.[67]

Some lunar experts thought mascons might be the remnants of a gigantic meteor or asteroid, but physics dictated that these cosmic projectiles that travel at such tremendous velocity would vaporize upon impact. And again, the evidence didn't support the theory. Celestial bombardment was ruled out. Somehow, the maria came from within the Moon and suspicions were that the mascons had something to do with the process. There is no good natural explanation for these unlikely formations, especially in light of their unique relationship with the maria. "What they are is a major moon mystery. It now appears that the mascons are broad disk-shaped objects that could be possibly some kind of artificial construction. For huge circular disks are not likely to be beneath each huge maria, centered like bull's eyes in the middle of each, by coincidence or accident," wrote Wilson about the very real possibility of the discovery of extraterrestrial artifacts buried beneath the surface of the Moon, which sounds like the plot of a Hollywood blockbuster.[68] And in fact, it was.

Clarke and Kubrick's *2001: A Space Odyssey* was playing in theaters in 1968 as the real-life drama unfolded overhead. In rather striking fashion, the plot of the movie mirrors the discovery of the mascons, differing slightly in that it is a magnetic not gravitational anomaly that leads to the discovery of a manufactured extraterrestrial artifact buried beneath the surface of the moon. The plot was so similar that researchers Christopher Knight and Alan Butler mused about the possibility that Clarke, the great NASA-inspiring visionary, had some inside info.[69]

It's a good bet that not only was Clarke in the know about the mascons, but that he and Kubrick made the movie as an early attempt at Disclosure. In the film, the discovery of the extraterrestrial monolith is followed by a cover-up with dialogue drafted straight from the Brookings Institute report. In a scene at a lunar base located in the Clavius crater, Heywood Floyd, head of the film's fictional counterpart to NASA, briefs base personnel about the discovery of the alien monolith, requiring everyone to sign a secrecy agreement because of the potential for "cultural shock" and "social disorientation" if the public were to learn the truth without adequate preparation and conditioning.

There's little doubt that the Brookings report, unknown outside the higher echelons of NASA at the time, served as Kubrick's source material. In an interview with Playboy magazine shortly after the premier of *2001*, he quoted it verbatim. "In 1960… the Brookings Institution [sic] prepared a report for the National Aeronautics and Space Administration warning that even *indirect* contact – i. e. *alien artifacts* that might possibly be discovered through our space activities on the Moon, Mars or Venus or via radio contact with an interstellar civilization – could cause severe psychological dislocations. The study cautioned that 'Anthropological files contain many examples of societies, sure of their place in the Universe, which have disintegrated when they have had to associate with previously unfamiliar societies espousing different ideas and different life ways; others that survived such an experience usually did so by paying the price of changes in values and attitudes and behavior,'" said Kubrick, who took the opportunity to rail against the policy. "I would personally view such contact with a tremendous amount of excitement and enthusiasm. Rather than shattering our society, I think it could immeasurably enrich it," he said, just months before the crew of Apollo 8 embarked on the first real lunar expedition.

Richard Hoagland saw *2001* as an act of rebellion by Clarke and Kubrick against a cover-up they knew to be imminent. "It is now my firm belief – based on over thirty years of hindsight, coupled with the exhaustive research detailed in this book – that Arthur Clarke and Stanley Kubrick, at some point, decided to reveal the (to them) totally repugnant Brookings/NASA Study as part of their joint film: the imminent, *deliberate government censorship* of the greatest story ever told," wrote Hoagland in a 2001 update to *The Monuments of Mars* in concluding that the ultimate message of the film was "this is what will happen *if* they really find it." What's more, Clarke's own public comments suggest he knew what had been found on the Moon and what it meant. "I've said that one reason people disliked *2001* – mainly older people – is that they realize this film *is about reality* and it scares the hell out of them [emphasis added]...." said Clarke in an interview shortly after the premiere.[70]

One can't help but wonder if the prospect of an extraterrestrial artifact on the Moon scared the hell out of them, what kind of terror must the full implications of the lunar evidence evoke? Perhaps for the Brookings crowd the most terrifying scenes in *2001* are those in which the Earth, Moon, Sun and alien monolith all come into alignment culminating in a Total Solar Eclipse, a sign of a much more awesome, even larger reality. The total solar eclipse is a singular phenomenon in the solar system. "There is no astronomical reason why the moon and sun should fit so well. It is the sheerest of coincidences, and only the Earth among all the planets is blessed in this fashion," said the iconic science fiction author Isaac Asimov rather ironically.[71]

In fact, the evidence that suggests the Moon is artificial also implies the solar eclipse is not a coincidence at all. Total solar eclipses occur because the Moon is 1/400th the size of the Sun and it orbits the Earth at 1/400th of the distance between the Earth and the Sun.[72] "If you actually look at facts-we've had to come kicking and screaming to accept that the Moon cannot be natural. And that in fact whoever built it has deliberately left a message to say look what I've done. When you look at the evidence, and particularly all of the numbers involved, not just with its size, but with its movement, its spin, its orbit, its position is space, its relative mass and density, its size- all of it- its built like a Swiss watch," said Christopher Knight who flatly stated that the numbers are not up for debate and the implications are clear. According to Knight, the theory that the Moon is artificial is "waterproof."[73]

If the Moon is artificial and it's far beyond our present capabilities to build even as we are rapidly approaching our own technological Singularity then it seems a safe bet the Moon is the product of a post-Singularity civilization, which means it's not a cosmic ark carrying wayward ETs parked in Earth's orbit as originally proposed by Vasin and Shcherbakov. The Moon is more likely a manufacturing plant built for the development of advanced life on Earth in a project to colonize the Galaxy.

SERIAL LOTTERY WINNER THEORY VS. PARADIGM SHIFT

According to present day thinking, the most efficient way to explore a Galaxy filled with billions of stars and planets is to build and deploy a self-replicating robotic space probe. Such a probe, based on the concept of a universal constructor – a machine capable of fabricating any device given the raw materials and a construction program - would locate an asteroid or a moon near a habitable planet to begin assembly of a factory for the manufacture of more self-replicating probes, which would then be launched towards other star systems to repeat the process.

Our Moon is an ideal location for such a self-duplicating, star-hopping device called a Von Neumann probe for mathematician John von Neumann, who founded the mathematical laws of self-replicating systems. Although mainstream science regards the Spaceship Moon theory as science fiction, scientists still expect there may be an extraterrestrial Von Neumann probe waiting to be discovered on the Moon, perhaps buried beneath the surface just begging to be dug up like the notorious black monolith. In fact, the monolith is based on the concept of the Von Neumann probe according to Michio Kaku. Kubrick's original cut of *2001* included a ten-minute documentary-like prologue in which various scientists talked about how such probes would open up the galaxy to exploration.[74] But Kubrick cut the opening sequence just before the premier and the monoliths became "almost mystical entities" in the absence of the Von Neumann probe narrative.

By the mid 1980s, scientists could see far enough over the technological horizon to realize it would be possible for a Von Neumann probe to not only explore the Galaxy within a few million years, but to colonize it. In *The*

Anthropic Cosmological Principle, physicist Frank Tipler and astronomer John Barrow showed we could do so even with 1980s technology, although it would be ruinously expensive and take billions and billions of years, in Sagan parlance, just to explore the Galaxy. However, in the foreseeable future it would be technically feasible to build a von Neumann probe that could do the job in just a few million years for little more than the cost of a PC. "It would also be possible to use the von Neumann probe to colonize the stellar system. Even if there were no planets in the stellar system - the system could be a binary star with asteroid-like debris - the von Neumann probe could be programmed to turn some of the available material into an *O'Neill colony*, a self-sustaining human colony in space which is not located on a planet but is rather a space station. Inhabitants for the colony could be synthesized by the von Neumann probe. All the information needed to manufacture a human being is contained in the genes of a single human cell. Thus if an intelligent extraterrestrial species possessed the knowledge to synthesize a living cell - and some biologists claim the human race could develop such knowledge within 30 years - they could program a von Neumann probe to synthesize a fertilized egg-cell of their species. If they also possessed artificial womb technology - and such technology is in the beginning stages of being developed on Earth - then they could program the von Neumann probe to synthesize members of their own species in the other stellar system. As suggested by Eiseley, these beings could be raised to adulthood in the O'Neill colony by robots also manufactured by the von Neumann probe, after which these beings would be free to develop their own civilization in the other stellar system," wrote Tipler and Barrow in 1986.[75]

The implications were that the Von Neumann probe should be as ubiquitous as drones in the not-too-far-distant future, which means the Galaxy should be practically crawling with ET versions by now. In fact, the Moon itself is such evidence, but the policy put in place to preserve the current paradigm and prevent "cultural shock" and "social disorientation" has blinded scientists like Barrow and Tipler, who erroneously conclude that there's no evidence of such extraterrestrial colonists when what may be the ET equivalent of an O'Neill colony orbits the Earth once every month.[76]

The unfiltered evidence suggests that the Moon was created to facilitate the development of life on Earth, culminating in an advanced civilization capable of continuing the colonization process in another star system. As fantastic as that may sound the conventional explanation is far more unlikely. In the final analysis, the belief that we are the lone celestial lottery winners is the only alternative to the ultimate paradigm shift.

The Moon is the straw that stirs the drink of life here on planet Earth. Without it we wouldn't be here. The Moon stabilizes the Earth in its orbit around the Sun, helping maintain a 22.5-degree tilt on its axis, which gives us moderate weather. No other small rocky planet in the solar system has a moon as large as ours. Mercury and Venus have no moon at all.

Without a stabilizing force like our Moon, the weather on these planets is hostile to life, especially advanced life. Mercury is a good example. Life can't make it on Mercury not because it's too close to the Sun, but because of its tilt angle, which is almost non-existent. As a result, Mercury rotates on its axis facing the sun dead-on, dooming the planet to extremes. A tilted axis like ours distributes the Sun's energy across a planet more evenly. When there isn't any tilt sunlight blasts the equator like a laser beam. Mercury is hot enough to boil lead at the equator, yet the poles are frozen. Even if microbes somehow gained a foothold they would be driven into extinction long before evolving into more complex life forms. What's more, planets without a moon are highly unstable. Internal processes could cause a planet like Mercury to suddenly flip over, changing its tilt angle thus throwing its extreme climate into total chaos. A sea of bubbling lead at the equator could quickly turn into solid rock under a sheet of ice at one of the new poles. Any life form eking out a living on the fringes would be instantly wiped out. Such an event would reboot the system.

Our planet would be in the same boat without the Moon. Earth's tilt angle might vary by as much as 85 degrees, making the evolution of complex life impossible.[77] If Earth faced the Sun at the same angle as Mercury, some regions would experience unrelenting heat while others would be bathed in perpetual rain. Hurricanes and tornadoes would run amok, while others areas in permanent darkness would experience the deepest of deep freezes. Instead, the Earth has been blessed with a relatively moderate climate thanks to the Moon, which stabilized conditions within the narrow range of temperature in which water exists in a liquid state, thus making life possible and enabling the evolution of complex life forms.

If the Earth had a greater tilt angle the climate would be colder. Less would make it hotter. Too great a tilt could freeze the oceans and too little would polarize the climate in extremes. Unbearable heat at the equator and unfathomable cold at the poles would create an environment challenging for even simple life and hostile to biodiversity, another vital factor in our evolution. A moderate climate with an abundance of liquid water is the foundation for life on Earth.

The Moon not only regulates our climate, it also drives plate tectonics, another key element of evolution on Earth that isn't found anywhere else in the solar system. Evidence shows that the formation of the Moon is both the cause and the driving force behind continental drift.

At the dawn of life on Earth all the continents fit together like puzzle pieces forming one supercontinent called Pangaea, which broke apart drifting across the globe over the eons. The Moon appears to be the catalyst that set entire process in motion. Whatever force (technology) removed 70 percent of the Earth's crust used to form the Moon left a void that caused the remaining 30 percent to shift, thus initiating continental drift. What's more, the presence of the Moon in orbit continues to drive the continents across the globe an inch at a time every year, year after year. According to Geophysicist Nick Hoffman, without plate tectonics the Earth would be a water world where only the peaks of highest mountains rose above the surface of an endless ocean.[78] Such a world would be hospitable to life, but not intelligent life. Dry land is necessary in order to make use of fire and develop tools, both of which are considered essential to the development of intelligent life. Hence, the Moon is central to evolution of life on Earth. Without it we earthlings would be nothing more than microbes clinging to a tenuous existence. In fact, some think the Moon is evidence that intelligent life is rare and that we might be alone in the galaxy and perhaps even the universe.

In *Rare Earth: Why Complex Life is Uncommon in the Universe*, astrobiologists Peter Ward and Donald Brownlee find seemingly endless reasons why a civilization like ours shouldn't exist. Rare Earth theory says that a planet must occupy a position in the galaxy not too close to the center, edge or halo, have the right planetary mass, orbit a sun of the right size and at the right distance within the habitable zone, have a neighbor like Jupiter among other highly unlikely conditions, which include a large moon.

Rare Earth turns the Drake Equation on its head in proposing that the odds of finding another planet like Earth capable of evolving higher life forms are like the odds of winning the lottery - not just once – but again and again. "While primitive organisms such as microbes are very likely abundant across the galaxies, advanced life, depending as it does on a myriad of special circumstances, is altogether another story," wrote Ward and Brownlee, whose theory violates the Copernican Principle and makes Sagan's estimate that the galaxy likely had a million technological civilizations seem wildly optimistic.[79]

The commonly accepted theory that the Moon is the result of a freak cosmic accident is the centerpiece of the Rare Earth concept. "Although there are dozens of moons in the solar system, the familiar ghostly white moon that illuminates our night sky is highly unusual, and its presence appears to have played a surprisingly important role in the evolution of life. The Moon is just a spherical rock 2000 miles in diameter and 250,000 miles away, but its presence has enabled Earth to become a long-term habitat for life. The Moon is a fascinating factor in the Rare Earth concept because the likelihood that an Earth-like planet should have such a large moon is small," wrote Ward and Brownlee, arguing that the Earth may be the lone garden spot in the universe.[80]

If the Moon is in fact not the result of a far-fetched cosmic collision, then Rare Earth theory falls apart. If the Moon is actually an artificial body then all the so-called chance circumstances that led to complex life on Earth were not by chance at all, but by design. Mainstream science doesn't account for the Moon's anomalies or acknowledge the political and sociological considerations referenced by Wickramasinghe that make such paradigm-threatening discoveries forbidden knowledge. As a result, Ward and Brownlee are apparently unaware of evidence that the Moon is artificial. They're unaware that microbial life was discovered on Mars back in 1976 and they don't know about the red planet's Banyan trees or that its tiny moons might also be artificial.

As far as mainstream science is concerned NASA failed to detect life on Mars even though this is only political, not scientific fact. As a result, Ward and Brownlee theorize on the premise that the Moon is the result of a freak accident akin to a cosmic roulette wheel hitting the same number on consecutive spins.[81] And so in true garbage-in-garbage-out fashion they erroneously conclude that we may be alone in the galaxy. If mainstream science recognized paradigm-busting discoveries about the Moon one could not escape the exact opposite conclusion. Instead of Rare Earth what we have is Routine Expansion of a Galactic civilization.

A space station was just the type of evidence that scientists like Fermi, Teller, Sagan, Barrow, Tipler, etc., would expect to see if the Galaxy had been colonized. What they didn't imagine was that such a structure would be made from what looks like a natural, celestial object. If the Moon looked like a *Star Wars Death Star* there would have been no Fermi paradox. But it doesn't. The Moon is a much more subtle example of extraterrestrial engineering. Researchers Knight and Butler found that the Total Solar Eclipse couldn't possibly be a coincidence. It had to be a sign purposely engineered to draw our attention to the Moon and its role in the development of complex life on Earth.

There's much more to the eerily precise relationship between the Earth, Moon and Sun that gives us the TSE. The system is further encoded by a "planetary identification number," which Knight and Butler liken to a Personal Identification Number or PIN code that we've all become so familiar with in the digital age. The most fundamental and unique ID for any planet would be the number of days it takes to orbit its sun. On Earth, a year is 365.25 days. Rounding up, our PIN would be 366, the number of days in a leap year, used to compensate for the extra quarter day per orbit. In fact, this number is encoded in the Earth's size relative to the Moon. The Earth is 366 percent larger than the Moon, which the authors call a "regulator" for its roll in stabilizing Earth's environment for the development of advanced life. What's more, the Moon's size relative to the Earth is also its PIN. Although a month is about 30 days because of the aggregate motion of the Earth-Moon-Sun system, the Moon actually completes one orbit around the Earth in 27.322 days. "The regulator was also engineered with a PIN number that was meaningful to the intended intelligent creatures. That number would be the reciprocal of the planet's PIN number – the mirror image of 366," wrote Knight and Butler, who were astounded to find that the Moon was 27.322 percent the size of the Earth.[82]

Any variation of the Giant Impact theory is unlikely in the extreme to produce such meaningful, non-random numbers, especially in the context of the TSE. And the numbers just kept coming up, adding layer upon layer of improbability. Knight and Butler thought the encoding might be some sort of litmus test for the complex life (us) the Moon was built to bring about. "The consequence of these arrangements would not be lost on the new life forms because they would easily realize that for every 10,000 of their planetary days, the regulator would complete exactly 366 orbits of the planet.

Surely they would spot the use of round base-ten numbers and the PIN number 366 being echoed by the regulator? But then, if they did not recognize these message patterns it would mean that they still lacked the intelligence or the imagination to be considered mature," wrote the researchers, who were awed by the odds against such random occurrences, much like LaViolette was with the pulsar beacon network. They concluded in very similar fashion that, "we are confronting a whole list of non random-looking values that add up to create what would otherwise be the most unlikely series of chance events in the history of the cosmos." What's even more remarkable, the Earth-Moon-Sun clockwork that gives us the Total Solar Eclipse is a time-sensitive message just like LaViolette's pulsar beacon network.[83]

When the Earth was young the Moon was much closer, possibly as much as ten times closer than it is today.[84] The proximity of the Moon drove enormous tsunami-sized tides, greatly accelerating the process of erosion, thus seeding the oceans with the minerals necessary for the evolution of life. With each orbit, the Moon stirred the primordial soup, drifting further away at a rate of 3.8 centimeters per year. There was no such thing as a Total Solar Eclipse in the past and there won't be one in the future. In 15 billion years the Moon will be 1.6 times farther away from the Earth than it is now.[85]

Much like LaViolette with the pulsar beacon network, Knight and Butler concluded the "Unknown Creative Agency" that built the Moon had to be God, ETs, or time-traveling humans from an alternate future Earth. But the totality of the evidence suggests that a post-Singularity civilization built and placed the Moon in orbit to seed advanced life on Earth in the process of colonizing the Galaxy. The Moon is the extraterrestrial equivalent of an O'Neill colony/von Neumann probe and we are part of a much larger civilization spread throughout the cosmos. The mathematical symbolism and time-sensitive messages encoded in both the Earth-Moon-Sun system and the pulsar beacon network are evidence of this great cosmic civilization and its relationship to Earth. Both have been timed to appear in the sky in this window of Earth history, although the eclipse is going to be with us a lot longer than the pulsar warning signals.

There are sure to be many surprises within the basic framework of post-Singularity extraterrestrial transmigration. Methods for colonization will surely be far in advance of the von Neumann probe concept. The most obvious difference will be the amount of time it takes to saturate the Galaxy.

Singularitarian Ray Kurzweil has said that a post-Singularity civilization will "expand outward at at least the speed of light (with some suggestions of circumventing this limit)."[86] The collective testimony of witnesses like the Disclosure Project's Mark McCandlish, Aerospace legend Ben Rich, Paul LaViolette and others indicates that this post-Singularity ET civilization operates at superluminal speed. LaViolette has even speculated that pulsars are part of an intergalactic infrastructure, acting as a GPS system for intergalactic travel.

Faster-than-light transport opens up all kinds of possibilities including direct transplant of a population. And there are simply more possibilities than our pre-Singularity minds can imagine. There may be more than one type of colony as well as multiple attempts to seed a single solar system, themes explored in Arthur C. Clarke's, *2010: Odyssey Two*. Perhaps civilization has arisen before only to crash short of interstellar status? Maybe we're the subjects of some sort of grand experiment? Is there an intergalactic hierarchy? Is there a governing body?

It's very likely that the story of interstellar migration will have many, many subplots. There will be no doubt countless questions regarding the super-civilization and its relationship to its colonies. There is no bigger question than our relationship – or apparent lack thereof – with this parent civilization. LaViolette thought we might have to demonstrate our maturity by building a shield against the galactic superwave. Knight and Butler wrote that our failure to recognize the true nature of the Moon might lead its creators to conclude that we "lacked the intelligence or imagination to be considered mature."[87] Our lack of development might actually run quite a bit deeper. If there is a primary reason why they don't land on the White House lawn, metaphorically speaking, this might be it. Whatever the case, it seems that interface between the super-civilization and Earth represents a significant challenge.

CHAPTER 7

INTERFACE

In virtually every case there are one or more concrete physical findings that accompany or follow the abduction experience, such as UFO sightings in the community, burned Earth where UFOs are said to have landed, and independent corroboration that the abductee's whereabouts are unknown at the time of the reported abduction event. Seemingly unexplained or missing pregnancies, a variety of minor physical lesions, odd nosebleeds, and the recovery of tiny objects from the bodies of experiencers are also widely seen.
— Psychologist John Mack, 1994

Some people have experiences that are so strange, they attribute them to alien intervention of some kind… I had one of those experiences myself. To say it was aliens is to assume a lot. But to say it was weird is to understate it. It was extraordinarily weird… I wouldn't try to publish a paper about these things, because I can't do any experiments… I can't cause myself to be lost again for several hours. But I don't deny what happened. It's what science calls anecdotal, because it only happened in a way that you can't reproduce. But it happened.
— Nobel prize–winning chemist Kary Mullis, 1998

BACK TO THE WHITE HOUSE LAWN

The idea that visiting extraterrestrials would introduce themselves by actually landing on the White House lawn is silly in the extreme. The whole premise rests on the assumption of parity between civilizations as if alien visitors from another planet would be just like dignitaries of a foreign country. Just a few hundred years of progress in our own world shows how communication would be difficult at best. Aside from the language and cultural barriers, which would be considerable all by themselves, imagine the challenges we would face if we had to travel back in time just a few generations to discuss climate change or the Internet with our own recent ancestors. As this mental exercise shows, communication between disparate civilizations is problematic at best. That's why scientists expect ETs trying to communicate with us will use math. It's a universal language. Carl Sagan gave us a classic example in his novel turned Hollywood blockbuster, *Contact*, about the discovery of an ET radio signal using prime numbers as a hailing frequency. The underlying assumption in such contact scenarios is that ETs attempting to communicate with us will be completely alien, having evolved independently on a planet in a distant star system. But if the Galaxy, including Earth, has been colonized by a post-Singularity civilization this assumption is false. We're all related. They may be extraterrestrial, but they're not completely alien. In this scenario, the beginner's math is a poor choice for a cosmic hailing frequency. As LaViolette, Knight and Butler argue, it's likely that the greater cosmic civilization will expect an emerging colony to reach a minimal level of development before meaningful communication can take place. It seems reasonable that a civilization like ours would be required to demonstrate a basic understanding of its place in the Galactic hierarchy, which explains the enigmatic mathematics encoded in both the Earth-Moon-Sun system and the pulsar beacon network. Our failure to recognize this signal is a sign we haven't reached a level of development that warrant's direct communication. Such contact may be undesirable or even impossible as long as we persist in reinforcing our flawed worldview with Serial Lottery Winner theories rather than face a world-altering paradigm shift.

Absent such a quantum leap in development, communication with our parent civilization will likely remain limited to the symbolism exemplified by the TSE, the pulsar beacon network *and unambiguous UFO incidents*. In his book, *Exopolitics*, researcher Alfred Webre showed how the appearance of a real UFO was in itself a symbolic message. The idea dates back to psychologist Carl Jung, who not only concluded that some UFOs were real objects under the control of "quasi-human" pilots, but that these higher intelligences made such appearances as psychological conditioning tools meant to guide humanity towards spiritual evolution.[1] "The content of these extraterrestrial communications can be interpreted contextually, through a process analogous to the principles that psychologists use to interpret dreams. According to the context communication theory, verified flights by UFOs over intercontinental ballistic missile bases and nuclear power facilities are warnings to humanity about the dangers of nuclear war," wrote Webre.[2]

Some recent examples include dramatic close encounters in the heavily restricted airspace over Washington D.C. and the Dome of the Rock in Jerusalem. On July 26, 2002, fighter jets scrambled to intercept a UFO in the nation's capitol exactly fifty years after the 1952 Washington National sightings. Two F-16's rattled D.C. neighborhoods at low altitude in the middle of the night chasing a bright blue object in vain.[3] The incident marked a key event in UFO history, perhaps reminding the Powers That Be of the true Powers That Be.

In 20011, a UFO appeared in Jerusalem over the Dome of the Rock shrine, a site that holds special religious significance for 3.3 billion Christians, Muslims and Jews. Such a high-profile venue guaranteed witnesses to the event. In short order, videos of the Dome UFO began appearing on YouTube. Skeptics and debunkers reflexively cried hoax, but there were four videos, each taken from different angles. Although photographic evidence is problematic, there was no evidence of a hoax. "The ET intelligence behind the UFO orb phenomenon at the Dome of the Rock may be signaling the importance to the leaders of these three religions of being alert to using peaceful non-violent conflict resolution over disputes that may arise at this site and elsewhere in the Middle East over religious issues," wrote Webre, who concluded that the Dome UFO was "more probably than not" a real extraterrestrial incident.[4]

The most spectacular example of context communication that ties the entire post-Singularity, Earth-Moon-Sun, UFO phenomenon together occurred in Mexico City during a TSE on July 11, 1991. "This was no ordinary eclipse. Before it occurred, some Mexicans were talking about an ancient Mayan prophecy known as the 'Dresden Codex.' Despite a gulf of 1,200 years, the prophecy was believed to have predicted that the 1991 eclipse would usher in major Earth changes and greater cosmic awareness, specifically from encounters with the 'Masters of the Stars.' With such a cultural buildup, thousands of Mexicans were ready for the event and watching the skies. Many of them had camcorders," wrote historian Richard Dolan.[5] UFOs were seen for over thirty minutes before, during, and after the Total Solar Eclipse. Video evidence flooded the studios of Mexico's TV news magazine *60 Minutos*. Television journalist Jaime Mausson conducted a thorough investigation of fifteen videotapes sent by witnesses from a wide area that stretched over two hundred miles. The videos were of such good quality that the appearance of classic metallic discoid craft, hovering, maneuvering and passing in front of clouds, was clear and unambiguous. According to Dolan, the event marked the beginning of a UFO wave that ran throughout the '90s in Mexico.[6]

The symbolism was breathtaking - especially in the context of the Dresden Codex – and the message was clear: *We are the Masters of the Stars. We built the Moon. We seeded life on Earth.*

The Total Solar Eclipse not only draws attention to the engineering of the Earth-Moon-Sun system, it also reveals the Sun's corona, acting as a natural coronagraph like the SOHO space telescope astronomers use to block the Sun's glare in order to study its atmosphere. According to LaViolette, understanding solar weather is critical for an emerging technological civilization. Cosmic dust and radiation that arrives with a galactic superwave is a potentially lethal threat that can ignite the Sun, causing solar flares that could destroy life on Earth. The Sun could even go supernova. By periodically flashing the Sun's corona at us, the TSE reinforces the warning encoded in the pulsar beacon network. What's more, the appearance of UFOs further links the TSE to the pulsars. ETs appear to use the same force field projection technology for both UFO propulsion and the production of pulsar signals.

Failure to recognize and respond appropriately to these symbolic messages from what is, for all intents and purposes, our parent civilization, is surely received as a sign that the colony seeded on Earth has not fully matured, which makes a reception on the White House lawn unwarranted. Despite our perceptive deficiencies, it appears such attempts at symbolic communication are not entirely in vain. Just months after the close encounter eclipse, the world saw the Soviet Union dissolve, the cold war officially come to an end, and the rise of the Disclosure movement. Witnesses to subsequent close encounter events in Mexico testified for the Disclosure Project at the National Press Club in Washington D.C. on May 9, 2001, which would seem to fulfill, to some degree, the Dresden Codex prophecy of major Earth changes and greater cosmic awareness. Perhaps Jung was right that these symbolic UFO events have an impact on the collective subconscious much like dreams.

Unfortunately, such contextual communication doesn't appear to have been enough to shake us from our nightmares. Despite clear warnings that nuclear warfare is unacceptable to the Great Galactic civilization from which we spring, we still live in Dr. Strangelove's world, one hair-brained miscalculation from an unimaginable catastrophe. Such warnings imply that our lack of development runs much deeper than mere failure to recognize communication from our more advanced parent civilization. We're not simply under-developed or behind schedule. Something has gone terribly wrong here with the project to develop a new Galactic outpost. Like the hypothetical self-reproducing carbon nanobots that escape the lab prematurely, we appear a threat to turn the biosphere into grey goo. In fact, according to Alfred Webre, we've experienced an "evolutionary disaster" here on Earth that has landed us in a planetary quarantine. [7]

CLOSE ENCOUNTERS OF THE ABSURD KIND

At the 2001 Disclosure Project press conference, one of the major themes was extraterrestrial opposition to the weaponization of space. The implications were that ETs might prevent primitive, warlike species like us from venturing out to wreak havoc. In 2005, scientists within the Disclosure movement, including Hal Puthoff and Bruce Maccabee, published an article in the *Journal of the British Interplanetary Society* advocating the quarantine solution to Fermi's paradox. They argued that recent developments in science, including Inflation theory and M-theory made Fermi's paradox so much stronger that it was more probable we were in some sort of planetary quarantine than we were alone in the universe. Puthoff and company suggested that ETs might adopt such a strategy for our own protection and because they might value the intellectual innovations of an uncontaminated species over direct contact.

In the quarantine scenario, high quality UFO sightings were part of what these scientists called a 'leaky embargo' meant to condition us to the existence of Galactic civilization. ETs apparently in tune with the Brookings Institute report would surely be aware of the overwhelming threat open contact posed to an emerging civilization such as ours. Hence, these incidents were designed to hint at the truth without providing enough evidence to cause a sudden catastrophic shock to Earth societies. Puthoff and colleagues suggested that such careful tactics might be a sign of extraterrestrial ethics, which appeared to be at least neutrally benevolent, meaning they haven't invaded or wiped us out, but they also haven't helped us prevent war, famine, etc.

The publication of such a paper in a mainstream journal was a coup for the Disclosure movement, but it's ultimately of limited value as far as the true agendas and ethics of extraterrestrial civilization is concerned because it failed to factor in the so-called alien abduction/contact experience phenomenon. Reports of such close encounters are by far the most difficult aspect of the UFO phenomenon to come to grips with for a Disclosure movement that is based on the premise that the extraterrestrial presence is benign. The possibility that ETs regard us as a lower life form to study, tag and track as we do animals in the wild threatens that narrative, engendering something akin to climate change denial among ufologists. The good news is that the message embedded in the abduction phenomenon reveals not the cold indifference of a superior power, but the corrective actions of Galactic civilization.

In the early years, most UFO researchers scoffed at reports of face-to-face encounters with UFO occupants as simply too far out. Alien abduction became the taboo within the taboo. Complicating matters, self-proclaimed "contactees" tied red ribbons around all the leprechaun's trees with sensational stories about contact with flying saucer occupants.[8] Much like misidentifications, mistakes and hoaxes hid the signal of real UFO/ETV sightings, the absurd stories of George Adamski, Howard Menger and others who claimed that "space brothers" took them joyriding around the solar system helped to obscure real close encounters.[9]

Adamski was the most notorious of the bunch. He claimed to be in regular contact with golden-haired, Zeus-like Venusians with whom he occasionally dined on hamburgers and apple pie at a favorite restaurant.[10] Of course, his claims evaporated upon investigation. What's more, evidence suggested he was part of an intelligence operation likely related to the Robertson panel policy to debunk UFOs. It was surely no coincidence that Edward Condon, whose rigged study was used to deep six the UFO phenomenon once and for all, chose to focus on the contactees rather than the actual UFOs. Putting the spotlight on their absurd stories helped to kill serious scientific interest in the phenomenon.

If Adamski was the most notorious of the contactees, Billy Meier was the most enigmatic. A one-armed, Swiss-born, grade school drop-out somehow able to describe in plausible terms the advanced physics of ET propulsion systems, Meier claimed to have been given messages meant for all mankind by a beautiful blue-eyed, strawberry-blond woman from the Pleiades star system in the Taurus constellation named Semjase.[11] Meier's wild tales came with a plethora of photos. Most were obviously made with miniature models, but a few were of such quality as to be endorsed by no less a figure than Michael Malin, the NASA contractor who ran the Mars Observer Camera on the Mars Global Surveyor spacecraft. "It took us two years to figure out you're never going to prove [Meier's story] and you're never going to disprove it. It's just there," concluded UFO investigator Britt Elders. Whatever the ultimate reality of the Meier episode, it was quite literally not believable, whether true or not.

Flying saucer reports became synonymous with contactee stories, thus relegating the UFO subject to the realm of fantasy, which was the goal of the disinformation campaign set in motion by the Robertson panel. Wild stories camouflaged the truth like red ties around every tree in the old Irish folk tale helped the Leprechaun hide his stash of gold. APRO investigator Dr. Olavo Fontes discovered such a pot of gold in Brazilian farmer Antonio Villas-Boas, whose report was obscured by the forest of contactee fairy tales. At first blush, Villas-Boas' story seemed even more absurd than the new age, space brothers-have-come-to-save-the-Earth yarns spun by those in the contactee camp. While working at night in his fields near San Paolo in 1957, he claimed to have encountered a landed UFO/ETV and alien beings that forcibly took him aboard as he tried to run. They subjected him to some sort of medical procedure, which eventually led to a sexual encounter with a beautiful female humanoid alien.

At face value, such a claim appears totally absurd. Science assures us that extraterrestrials would be completely alien to Earth. "There may be some convergent evolution because there may be only one best solution to an environmental problem- something like two eyes, for example, for binocular vision at optical frequencies. But in general the random character of the evolutionary process should create extraterrestrial creatures very different from any that we know," wrote Carl Sagan, who said sex between extraterrestrials and humans was preposterous, like trying to cross a human being with a petunia.[12] According to 20th century science, truly alien extraterrestrials shouldn't be able to breathe our air or move about freely in our gravity field, much less have sex with a Brazilian farmer. Villas-Boas story simply couldn't be true, but he was no ordinary contactee. In fact, he was the antithesis to the flying saucer celebrities of the 1950s. Villas-Boas was initially reluctant to report the incident. He wrote to a magazine that published articles about flying saucers and eventually the report found its way to APRO (Aerial Phenomena Research Organization) headed by Jim and Coral Lorenzen, civilian UFO researchers and counterpart to Keyhoe and NICAP.

APRO's Fontes expected to unmask a hoaxer upon interviewing Villas-Boas, but instead found him credible. Unlike contactees who glorified their so-called space brothers with new age mystical jargon, Villas-Boas described his abductors in down-to-earth terms. "[He] did not think the crew were angels, supermen or demons. He believed them to be human beings as we are, only coming from other countries on some other planet. He declared that because one of the crew… pointed to himself, then to the earth, then to some place in the heavens," wrote Fontes in his report for APRO. What's more, Villas-Boas was embarrassed about the sexual interlude, a detail he had initially withheld, but felt compelled to try to explain. After being forced aboard the spherical craft by smallish humanoid beings in white uniforms who spoke to each other with "guttural" sounds, he was stripped naked and subjected to a medical examination in which blood was drawn and a liquid substance was applied to the skin all over his body. Next, he was placed in a small room with a bed and left to wait until a naked female appeared. The woman looked human from the neck down and had a body that Villas-Boas described as "much more beautiful than any I have ever seen." Her face was also humanoid, but large blue, catlike eyes and angular features made her look distinctly alien, as did other aspects of her appearance. Her long blond, almost white hair, and dark red arm and pubic hair were exotic to say the least. To his surprise Villas-Boas became "uncontrollably" excited, which led him to suspect that the liquid coating he received was some sort of aphrodisiac. With the purpose of the encounter self-evident, he and the alien woman proceeded to have sex. According to Villas-Boas, the experience was mostly typical with the disturbing exception that "some of the growls that came from her at certain times nearly spoiled everything, as they gave the disagreeable impression of lying with an animal."[13] Afterwards, the woman quickly lost interest and dismissed herself. Before leaving, she signaled him, pointing to her stomach and then to the heavens. Villas-Boas felt used. He likened himself to a Triple Crown racehorse put out to stud. "All they wanted [was] a good stallion to improve their stock," he said.[14] In short order, he was given his clothes, a cursory tour of the ship and returned to the fields where he watched the craft depart at unearthly speed.

Villas-Boas never promoted his story nor profited from it like the space brother celebrities. He didn't have ties to intelligence agencies like Adamski or stacks of photos like Billy Meier. He didn't have any evidence to corroborate his story at all, although Fontes noted that a medical examination showed the young farmer suffered from weakness and nausea, along with small bloody lesions, all symptoms consistent with radiation poisoning. In the final analysis, Villas-Boas's account only sounds absurd if one assumes extraterrestrials must be completely alien. In other words, there was no good reason to write-off the Brazilian famer's experience other than sheer disbelief. In fact, according to historian Richard Dolan, the incident stood out as the first clear-cut case of alien abduction.[15]

Through the lens of Webre's context communication theory, the message of this uncomfortably intimate close encounter appears to be about the nature of the extraterrestrial presence and its relationship to humanity on Earth. The goal may not have been to actually conceive a child, but to show us that they're not completely alien. What better way to demonstrate that they're not as incompatible with us as a petunia? What's more, the message foreshadowed the reproductive component of the alien abduction phenomenon, which appears to be part of an operation to correct the defect suffered by humanity in its evolution here on Earth.

Because Villas-Boas did not promote his story it was unknown until MUFON first reported it in 1962. If not for a lack of publicity, it would rightfully be known as the beginning of the modern close encounter/alien abduction age. Instead, that distinction went to the second known case.

The contactee fad of the fifties faded in the sixties, but encounters of the up close and personal kind did not. In 1961, before the Villas-Boas case had come to light, a similar incident occurred near Portsmouth, New Hampshire.[16] Betty and Barney Hill, a middle-aged interracial couple returning from vacation in Canada in the middle of the night, were intercepted along a lonely road in the countryside by a highly advanced craft that seemed to be tracking them. At first, the Hills tried to convince themselves that they were seeing some sort of conventional phenomenon, a falling star or a military craft of some sort. But the manner in which the object danced about the sky, hovering and then darting about, frightened them, especially when it came within a few hundred feet of their car. As it hovered just above the treetops, Barney parked and got out for a closer look. He saw a disk-shaped object with a double row of windows and a crew of strange humanoid beings staring back at him. Certain they were about to be captured, he ran screaming hysterically, jumped in the car and took off down the highway. In short order, the craft appeared directly overhead and the couple fell into a trance upon hearing a series of electronic beeping sounds. A short while later, the sounds repeated and both Betty and Barney returned to full consciousness- 35 miles south of the original close encounter.

The Hills didn't plan to tell anyone about the incident, but the couple suffered from post-traumatic stress that was simply impossible to suppress. What's more, Betty discovered a dozen perfectly circular shiny spots the size of a silver dollar along the trunk of their car that made a compass spin wildly. Afraid of having been exposed to radiation, Betty made a report to nearby Pease Air Force Base. Unfortunately, by the time of the Hill incident, Project Blue Book was little more than a public relations UFO debunking operation. After a cursory investigation, Blue Book cited "insufficient evidence" in its conclusion that the object was "in all probability Jupiter."[17] As a result, the Hill's turned to Keyhoe and NICAP for an actual investigation. Betty had been experiencing recurring nightmares commonly suffered by trauma victims.[18] In these terrifying dreams she and Barney ran into a roadblock on a lonely country road set up by a group of "intelligent humanoid beings," who took them aboard a strange craft for physical exams of some sort.

NICAP science advisor Walter Webb investigated the Hill case. Like Fontes with the Villas-Boas investigation, Webb expected to catch the Hills in a hoax, but was instead convinced otherwise. "I cross examined them together, separately, together, requestioned them again and again. I tried to make them slip up somewhere, and I couldn't. Theirs was an ironclad story. They seemed to me to be a sincere, honest couple driving home from vacation, late at night on a lonely road, when suddenly something completely unknown and undefinable descended upon them. Something entirely foreign and alien to their existence," said Webb about the Hills, who discovered under questioning they couldn't account for two hours during the trip home. A period of amnesia known as 'missing time' would turn out to be a common feature of the contact experience.[19] It was these missing memories that drove Betty's obsessive desire to understand what had happened to them that night. In fact, the attempt to lift the Hill's memory blackout opened up a new frontier in UFO research and unlocked further communication from Galactic civilization.

The Hill's were referred to distinguished psychiatrist and neurologist Benjamin Simon, a Lt. Colonel in the Army known for having great success in treating post-traumatic stress disorder. Simon used hypnosis to help soldiers recall repressed memories of traumatic events in order to reverse serious psychosomatic symptoms such as blindness and amnesia. His unique abilities seemed a perfect fit for Hill's, who had clearly suffered some sort of trauma. Betty had recurring nightmares and Barney developed a variety of maladies including exhaustion, insomnia, high blood pressure, ulcers and facial ticks.[20]. Simon treated the Hills for a six-month period in 1964. He warned them upfront that he didn't believe their story, but he agreed to treat them because of Barney's symptoms, which resisted conventional medical treatment, and to resolve the source of Betty's nightmares. Simon used separate sessions and post-hypnotic suggestions to prevent cross-contamination of the Hills' memories and to shield them from the emotional trauma. Consequently, the Hills were unable to quiz each other about the sessions, which were very intense and emotional, especially for Barney who became almost hysterical at times.

Under hypnosis, both Hills described the scene in Betty's nightmares. After the beeping sounds that immediately preceded the couple's memory blackout, Barney was directed by a 'mind voice' to drive into the woods where the car stalled as they encountered a roadblock and a group of small, non-human beings. The Hills found themselves under some sort of mind control. Although terrified, they were powerless to resist. "I felt like the eyes had pushed into my eyes," said Barney about his experience with the strange humanoids that whisked them aboard their craft.[21]

The beings communicated amongst themselves with humming sounds but they spoke to Betty and Barney in English, which Betty thought they heard telepathically. The couple was placed in separate examination rooms that resembled a surgical theater. Barney was given an eye, ear and throat exam and an anal probe. They took skin samples from his arm and placed a cup on his groin that he thought was used to extract a semen sample. Betty received similar treatment, including hair and nail clippings, as well as what she understood to be a pregnancy test in which a long needle was inserted into her naval, an unfamiliar procedure at the time that would later become a common practice in medicine.

Betty did her best not to look at her captors, which she described as grotesque.[22] They were grey-skinned, hairless, diminutive, yet barrel-chested creatures with oversized heads and large wrap-around eyes like a cat.[23] After the exam was over, Betty asked the leader of the alien crew where they were from. In response, he made a star map appear on the wall like a window.[24] The image was in 3D like a hologram. Betty saw stars of various sizes, some of which were connected by solid and dotted lines indicating established routes and expeditions. Soon after, the Hills were returned to their car. Simon didn't believe in UFOs and he didn't think the Hills' story was literally true. He did his best to convince Barney that he had been influenced by Betty's nightmares – that he had somehow absorbed them – and, as a result, the abduction was merely a dream.

Simon was in a difficult spot according to researchers Stanton Friedman and trustee to Betty's estate, her niece Kathleen Marden, who teamed up for a comprehensive review of the Hill case.[25] If Simon validated the Hill's abduction experience his professional reputation would be at stake. He had to accept the Hill's initial sighting of a 'flying vehicle' of some sort, thanks to Pease AFB radar, however, he wouldn't accept the abduction scenario that followed the electronic beeps.[26]

Simon's professional bias caused him to misinterpret Betty's nightmares as the source of her trauma rather than a symptom. Instead of treating her like one of his soldiers suffering from amnesia after witnessing a buddy's grisly combat-related death, Simon tried to blame the victim. But the dream theory was just as inadequate as the weather balloon cover story and the Venus explanation were for other UFO incidents. It didn't account for the corroborating evidence discovered as a result of the hypnosis sessions. It didn't explain the scuffmarks on Barney's shoes, the tear in Betty's dress, the shiny, magnetic spots on the trunk of their car, etc.

Barney thought the dream explanation was absurd. He rejected it outright, noting ironically how he wished it were true. Because he worked nights and slept during the day, the couple never actually slept together. He couldn't have heard her talking in her sleep, making it impossible to have "absorbed" her dream. Even if he had, he didn't see how it was possible for her dream to become his reality. Simply put, he found the dream theory laughable.[27]

The Hills demanded confidentiality all throughout the investigation. They didn't want to become part of the lunatic fringe. By the time of their abduction experience the contactee movement had gone a long way toward helping the Robertson panel achieve its goal of stripping UFOs of their special status. The Hills were afraid of ridicule. They were socially active members of the local community. Betty thought she might lose her job as a child welfare worker for the State of New Hampshire. Barney had been appointed to the U.S. Civil Rights Commission and was being considered for the state's Human Rights Commission. They were the polar opposite of fame-seeking contactees. They were afraid if their story got out it might destroy their lives and everything they'd fought so hard to build. Unfortunately for them, word did get out and the press caught wind of it. What's more, some NICAP members and some of their friends violated confidentiality agreements and spoke to a reporter about the investigation, including the hypnosis sessions.[28]

Against their wishes, the Hill's story went public in 1965 on the front-page of the *Boston Traveller*. Instantly their lives turned upside down and they became reluctant participants in a public dialogue about their ordeal. In 1966, the story of the Hills' UFO abduction became a national sensation with the publication of journalist John Fuller's best-selling book *The Interrupted Journey*, and ultimately, the Hill experience became part of our cultural mythos in 1975 with the broadcast of NBC's television movie, *The UFO Incident*, starring James Earl Jones and Estelle Parsons.

Debunkers like Phillip Klass and Robert Sheaffer were empowered by Simon's dream theory, while UFO researchers stood down having themselves had trouble accepting the alien abduction scenario. But those intimately familiar with the investigation like Rev. John D. Swanson of Christ Church in Portsmouth had no doubt about the sincerity of the Hills. "First let it be said that I do not and cannot doubt the veracity of the Hill's account and I believe in the factual reality of their experience. Anyone who has spoken with them, has heard the recordings made when they were under hypnotic recall, and has examined all the evidence, cannot doubt that what they describe did in actuality happen," said Swanson.[29]

Others were equally impressed by the Hills. Others like Mensa member Marjorie Fish, who became a major contributor to the substantiation of the Hill's experience. After reading Vallee's *Anatomy of a phenomenon*, Fish developed a burning interest in UFOs, especially the Hill case. She was fascinated by the star map Betty had seen aboard the craft.[30] So much so, that she attempted to build a 3-D model using astronomical data on stars in the local neighborhood to see if she could identify the star cluster Betty drew during a hypnosis session. She used nylon fishing line and color-coded beads to represent different types of stars. Unfortunately, the data available at the time was limited. Her initial efforts were unsuccessful. She had expected to find many patterns that might match Betty's map, but instead found none. Fortunately, Fish was persistent. "It was only after she had data from the newly published 1972 *Catalogue of Nearby Stars* by Wilhelm Gliese, and built yet another model using this new data, that she found one – and only one – three-dimensional pattern that fit, angle for angle, line length for line length, what Betty had drawn… a real eureka moment," wrote Stanton Friedman about Fish's breakthrough, which caught the attention of J. Allen Hynek. In his new incarnation as UFO proponent, Hynek arranged for Fish to present her model at the Adler Planetarium at Northwestern University. Friedman and Condon staff scientist David Saunders, author of *UFOs? Yes! Where the Condon Committee Went Wrong*, attended the presentation.

The map Betty Hill had been shown featured sixteen stars connected by solid and dotted lines representing travel routes. Fish limited her search to the local cosmic neighborhood, which consisted of about 1,000 stars that fell within 55 light years of the Sun. Using Fermi-like reasoning and the latest research, she filtered out stars unlikely to have planets or support life, including stars that were too dim or too unstable, double stars, etc. Saunders and astronomer George Mitchell of Ohio State University gave Fish's model the thumbs up. In fact, it was so accurate that Mitchell used it as a teaching aid. It was an amazing achievement. All the stars in the model are Sun-like stars where life might be found, despite the fact that only five percent of the stars in the local neighborhood were thought capable of supporting life. What's more, all the suns in the pattern are aligned in a plane, something unknown before Fish's work that made interstellar travel much more efficient. Friedman marveled that the match with Betty's drawing would utterly vanish if there were even slight variations in the size of the suns in the pattern, noting that the odds were upwards of a million-to-one against such a coincidence.[31]

Fish's model not only provided compelling evidence of the accuracy of Betty's memory under the direction of Simon's hypnosis, it also proved that the Hills couldn't possibly have perpetrated a hoax. Fish showed that the data necessary to create the map was unavailable until years after the incident, putting any such doubt to rest. In December 1974, *Astronomy magazine* published an article about the discovery called *The Zeta Reticuli Incident*. Fish had concluded that Zeta 1 and Zeta 2 Reticuli in the reticulum constellation were the home stars of Betty and Barney's captors. The article got a bigger reaction than anything *Astronomy magazine* had ever published. Fish's theory gave the Hills' extraterrestrial interventionists a plausible backstory. Zeta 1 and Zeta 2 are a billion years older than the Sun and are close enough to each other to encourage intelligent life to develop space travel. Either star would be twenty times brighter than Venus in the sky to inhabitants of their neighbor's solar system. If intelligent life developed on Zeta 1 it would've been able to see planets in orbit around Zeta 2 and vice versa. They're much closer neighbors than we are to our nearest cosmic companion, Alpha Centauri, which is 39.4 light years away. In fact, a trip from Zeta 1 to Zeta 2 would only be a matter of "light-weeks." There's no doubt that if a Zeta 1 planet had a civilization like Earth there would've been a Kennedy-like plan to land a little gray man on a Zeta 2 planet. With a billion year head start, such a civilization would've passed through the technological Singularity long ago.

Not everyone was impressed. Predictably, Carl Sagan pooh-poohed the significance of Fish's map, giving the establishment the voice of authority it needed to safely ignore such extraordinary evidence. He accused Fish of choosing stars just because they matched Betty's map, somehow failing to recognize the use of Fermi's logic in star selection for the model. If anyone should have recognized such reasoning it would be Sagan. It was he who introduced the world to Fermi's famous question in his book *Intelligent Life in the Universe*. It seems more likely that Sagan's response to *The Zeta Reticuli Incident* had more to do with "political and sociological considerations" than the significance of Fish's model. Also, it seems the value of a computer model is somewhat dependent on whether it challenges establishment views like Fish's model or supports them like the Giant Impact theory, which is wholly dependent upon computer modeling.

In retrospect, the contactee movement helped camouflage real close encounter experiences like the Villas-Boas and Hill incidents, which signaled the beginning of the modern contact/abduction era. In terms of context communication theory the Villas-Boas encounter showed that our assumption about how truly alien extraterrestrials would be is dead wrong. If the Hill case has such a symbolic message it would seem to be that consciousness is the key component in the interface between pre-Singularity humans and the post-Singularity civilization that engineered life on Earth.

A BRIEF HISTORY OF (MISSING) TIME

By the 1980s, it was clear the Villas Boas and Hill cases weren't just one-off incidents. Much like UFO sightings, alien abduction reports became an embarrassment of riches. These reports usually featured reluctant witnesses who'd had a dramatic, close-range, UFO sighting that coincided with a block of missing time, which served to mask traumatic encounters with humanoid beings that were distinctly nonhuman. Although many different types have been reported, those most commonly associated with alien abduction are small, gray-skinned humanoids with oversized heads and large, wraparound eyes who communicate by telepathy and perform physical examinations with an emphasis on reproduction.

Contrary to popular misconception, alien abductees did their best to ignore the troubling events and go about their lives, but were unable. They often suffered from traumatic, recurring nightmares and nagging questions about what had happened to them. Although the reports shared a common narrative, not all such close encounters fit neatly within the box. The Travis Walton incident is a case in point.

In 1975, a seven man logging crew on their way back to town after a long day's work in the Sitgreaves National Forest in eastern Arizona came upon a bright disk-shaped UFO hovering at treetop level.[32] Twenty-two year old Travis Walton got out of the truck to look at the craft. As he approached, he was hit with a beam of light that lifted him up and knocked him off his feet. The rest of the crew fled in terror thinking he'd been killed. After the initial panic subsided, the loggers returned to the scene but found no trace of their coworker. In a state of near hysteria, they drove into town and reported the incident to police, who organized a search party in spite of extreme skepticism about the story they'd been told. When repeated searches found no physical evidence, the police began to suspect murder. Suspicions remained even after every one of the loggers passed a lie detector test, an outcome that would happen by chance only one time in a million.[33]

Five days later, Walton called home from a local phone booth, exhausted and eleven pounds lighter. He remembered awakening in what he thought was a hospital room until he realized he was surrounded by hairless, nonhuman creatures with oversized heads and big eyes. In sheer terror, he reacted like a cornered animal, scattering the alien humanoids. Bewildered, he wandered the ship alone until a well-built, perfectly human-looking man over six feet tall with long blond hair wearing a one-piece blue suit and transparent helmet appeared, motioning for him to follow. He was led to a hangar containing several disk-shaped craft and three more humans, two men and a woman. All looked similar, but not identical, like they were family. The woman placed what appeared to be an oxygen mask over Walton's face and his next memory was of awakening on the pavement in Heber, Arizona watching the UFO/ETV shoot off into space.

Walton thought his ordeal had only been a matter of hours, but he'd been missing for five days. Like his coworkers, he passed a lie detector test. Nevertheless, skeptics and debunkers dismissed the case as a hoax despite the fact that there was no evidence of a hoax and despite the fact that every member of the logging crew rejected significant offers to confess to the media. Walton's desire to tell his story led to the publication of *The Walton Experience* in 1978, which eventually became the 1993 film *Fire in the Sky*. Unfortunately, the film was anything but a documentary. The scenes on board the alien craft were pure b-movie horror flick fiction. What's more, Walton's Hollywood experience gave his critics the ammunition they needed to perpetuate the hoax for wealth and fame claim. Walton fired back in 1996. Turning the tables on his critics, Walton said his experience taught him a great deal about humanity. "It's given me some real insight into people and the kind of contortions that their reasoning goes through when confronted with something they cannot accept."

One such skeptical contortion was the argument that all abduction accounts were similar because the story had become widespread in popular culture, TV and movies in particular. In reality, the reverse was true. The movies didn't introduce the greys to the abductees. It was the abductees that introduced the greys to the movies. Reports of the little humanoids with oversized heads long predated *The UFO Incident, Fire in the Sky, Close Encounters of the Third Kind*, etc.[34] In fact, J. Allen Hynek was *the* direct link between such reports and pop culture. Spielberg used his Close Encounters classification system for the title, made him a consultant on the film and, as if to underscore his importance to the story, gave him a cameo appearance in the climactic contact scene with the little, big-headed grey humanoids. Although the plot was fiction, the scenes were essentially an amalgamation of the Air Force's Project Blue Book files.

Like weather balloons, crash test dummies and the Venus explanation, the so-called skeptical theory about alien abduction simply didn't hold water. What's more, *Alien Agenda* author Jim Marrs noted that it didn't account for the reproduction angle in abduction reports, which was also well established long before pop culture and its Hollywood hacks got ahold of the story. While the Hill and Walton cases grabbed all the headlines, abduction accounts quietly began to accumulate. In 1967, a police officer had a close encounter and twenty minutes of missing time while on duty. Hypnosis sessions conducted by Dr. Leo Sprinkle revealed a brief encounter with beings that said they were trying to prevent humans from destroying the Earth. In October 1973, two men on a fishing trip in Pascagoula, Mississippi reported being taken aboard a hovering UFO by strange robot-like entities.[35] In August 1975, just three months prior to the Walton abduction, Sergeant Chuck Moody, a Vietnam veteran with fourteen years in the Air Force, had an alien abduction experience with eighty-five minutes of missing time while observing the Perseid meteor shower not far from Holloman Air Force base. Subsequent physical problems, not unlike those experienced by Barney Hill, led him to seek answers. With the assistance of the civilian UFO organization APRO led by Jim and Coral Lorenzen, Moody recalled an encounter with beings that told him he had been taken aboard a ship used for "observing" and that they were among a number a different races that worked together. According to these beings, it was up to them to accept us.[36] By 1977, the Lorenzens had compiled enough material - two decades worth of abduction reports – to write a book.

Sometimes a single case was of such significance that it resulted in a series of books. In 1979, veteran UFO researcher Raymond E. Fowler published *The Andreasson Affair*, the first in a series about the mind-boggling alien abduction experiences of Betty Andreasson, a devout Christian and "simple, unsophisticated country girl," who turned to ex-Blue Book astronomer J. Allen Hynek and his new UFO research organization, the Center for UFO Studies (CUFOS) for help. Hynek had run a nationwide advertising campaign asking the public for UFO sighting information. At the urging of her family, Betty responded to an ad in a local newspaper, setting in motion an investigation led by Fowler, a highly-regarded Hynek associate and former member of NICAP.[37]

The incident that caused Betty to write to Hynek happened in 1967 on a night when she was at home with her seven children and her parents. It began with a power outage accompanied by a bright reddish light streaming in through the windows. Betty's father went to investigate and was shocked to see four small, gray-skinned humanoids with oversized heads and large wraparound, catlike eyes coming from the light source near a small hill towards the back of the house. Dressed in form-fitting dark blue uniforms with boots, the "Halloween freaks" as Betty's father Waino Aho called them, entered the house by passing directly through a closed door. From that point on conscious memory faded leaving Betty and her family with a telltale block of missing time.

By the time Hynek founded CUFOs and was able to act on Betty's letter those memories had been lost for a decade. It was 12 years after the incident when *The Andreasson Affair* was finally published, which as Marrs observed, made it difficult for debunkers to argue that it was a hoax for money scheme, especially in the wake of the year-long investigation run by Fowler and his team. Dr. Harold J. Edelstein, director of the New England Institute of Hypnosis, led the effort to recover the missing time memories for Betty and her eleven year old daughter Becky, who also had conscious recall of the event.[38]

The story that unfolded under hypnosis was beyond anyone's ability to fabricate. The gray humanoid intruders placed Betty's family in a state of suspended animation and took her aboard their craft. They communicated telepathically and were able to take control over Betty, who was unable to resist their commands. She was subjected to the familiar medical exam, including the insertion of a long needle into her navel. Unlike Betty Hill she felt no pain. A long needle was also inserted into her head via her nose to remove a tiny artifact. It was the first report of what appeared to be some sort of implanted device.[39] Reports of "alien implants" would become more common among abductees over time.

The removal of the implant hinted at an earlier abduction experience. Sure enough, further probing showed that she had endured such experiences periodically throughout her life, beginning when she was seven years old. The events that Betty Andreasson described were breathtaking, both in their detail and their scope. The implant was originally placed when she was thirteen during an alien intervention that included other procedures suggestive of the removal of reproductive material.[40] The tiny device was retrieved when Betty was thirty during the incident that prompted her to answer Hynek's ad. After the implant removal procedure and physical examinations, she was taken to another planet and exposed to scenes and events that were difficult to understand or describe. What's more, she was told that she had been chosen to show the world something of great significance that would affect all mankind.[41] The message was implanted in Betty's subconscious like a time-release pill. The Grays told her she wouldn't be able to remember portions of the message that were revealed in subsequent abductions until the time was right. Researchers attempts to recover these memories were unsuccessful. Betty experienced great debilitating pain whenever they tried to probe these experiences under hypnosis. In 1987, the investigation resumed when Betty's painful memory block suddenly vanished and she was able to recall further experiences.

At age thirty-six, she was taken and made to witness the extraterrestrial genetics program in action. She saw the removal of a fetus from a fellow abductee and its subsequent placement into a liquid-filled device. It was explained to her that environmental pollution would eventually render human beings on Earth unable to reproduce, making such actions necessary to perpetuate the species.[42] And finally, in her forties, her abduction experiences culminated with lessons about "spiritual" technology in which alien devices produced out of body experiences meant to demonstrate that human beings were much more than flesh and blood.[43]

The Andreasson affair was so utterly fantastic that it would've been easy to dismiss it as just another contactee story if not for the investigation conducted by Ray Fowler and CUFOs. Betty was subjected to intensive scrutiny, which included extensive background checks, character references, lie detector tests and psychological evaluations. "They were telling the truth with regards to the 1967 incident… In the opinion of this analyst, the results are conclusive," said a report issued by the Psychological Stress Evaluator about Betty and her daughter.[44] At the conclusion of his investigation, Ray Fowler had no doubts about the reality of the Andreasson affair. "Never before have I or investigators scrutinized the overall background of a witness so thoroughly… Under hypnosis, Betty not only recounts but *relives* her UFO encounters. She does this in intricate detail with corresponding emotion, trauma, and body movements. She is able to provide detailed drawings that tally exactly with her verbal testimony. Weeks, months and even years later she is able to relive selected segments of her experience upon demand by a hypnotist," wrote Fowler.[45]

J. Allen Hynek endorsed Fowler's investigation, challenging debunkers like Philip Klass and Curtis Peebles, who ignored the Andreasson case in their books. "Those who still hold that the entire subject of UFOs is nonsense will be sorely challenged if they have the courage to take an honest look at the [Andreasson] book. For whatever the UFO phenomenon is – or are – it is not nonsense. It would take an imagination of the highest order to explain the reported happenings described herein as mere misidentifications of balloons, aircraft, meteors, or planets! Neither is there the slightest evidence of hoax or contrivance," wrote Hynek.[46]

Extraterrestrials made Betty Andreasson a witness to their human genetics program and implanted a message for humankind about the operation in her subconscious. The message showed we weren't facing an alien invasion, but an extraterrestrial intervention meant to save the human race from the lethal toxicity of its industrial civilization, which is a symptom of the catastrophic error in our evolution written about by Alfred Webre. Our situation might be somewhat analogous to Barrow and Tipler's hypothetical von Neumann probes that need to be reprogrammed or repaired after deployment. It appears the real alien agenda is to correct the error in our evolution, put project Earth back on track, and to prevent the human race from turning the surface of the Earth into gray goo like renegade self-reproducing carbon nanobots.

In terms of context communication theory, the symbolism of the Andreasson message is just as mind-blowing as the content. The fact that this message was received by an organization founded by Hynek, the face of the government's official UFO investigation/public relations program, is of tremendous significance as is the use of the subconscious mind as a medium of communication. It may be a clue that consciousness itself is a key component of the interface between Earth humans and our post-Singularity parent civilization.

The mental roadblock of missing time led UFO abduction researchers like Budd Hopkins into the subconscious minds of the abductees that came to him for help. Hopkins, a successful New York artist who developed an interest in UFOs and abductions during 1975, the year of the Travis Walton incident, decided to conduct his own investigation.[47] He teamed with licensed psychologist Aphrodite Clamar, Ph.D. who evaluated potential abductees and conducted hypnosis when it became necessary. Hopkins was the first to argue that missing time was a typical feature of the alien abduction experience, which he said was far more common and widespread than previously thought.

In 1981, Hopkins published the results of his study in *Missing Time,* a groundbreaking work on the proliferation of the UFO abduction phenomenon and its implications. Like other witnesses, the folks Hopkins studied were not publicity seekers. They were ordinary people who were confused and anxious about their experiences. They had scars and "scoop marks" that corresponded to the medical procedures they said had been performed on them by non-human beings and they described their experiences in great detail with remarkable consistency.

The publication of *Missing Time* brought forward other key witnesses. After reading the book, Indianapolis housewife Debbie Tomey contacted Hopkins about a similar series of strange events. The investigation that followed shed new light on the purpose of the extraterrestrial research program. Like Betty Andreasson, Tomey experienced a lifetime of contact that began when she was a child. Upon sexual maturity, gynecological exams became part of her ET abduction experience and after a UFO sighting in 1977 she became pregnant. Much to her doctor's surprise, the fetus disappeared. During the investigation, she told Hopkins that, "someone took my baby."[48] During an abduction incident in 1983, Tomey was reunited with the child she thought she'd lost, but the pretty little girl didn't look completely human like us or alien like them. Her pale skin, oversized head, large blue eyes, tiny nose, pink lips and white wispy hair made her look like an alien-human hybrid child. What's more, the child apparently had plenty of siblings. On a subsequent abduction incident, Tomey was told that nine other children had been created from tissue taken from her body.

Tomey's natural family, including her mother and two children, were involved as well. Tomey and her mother both had identical scars on their lower legs that coincided with abduction incidents that occurred when they were children. Such scars and scoop marks appeared again and again among abductees. According to Hopkins, physicians who had been shown the marks thought they were suggestive of surgery. Nevertheless, the naysayers dismissed such evidence out of hand and accused Hopkins of creating hypnotically induced fantasies. According to Richard Dolan, such criticism was unfair at best. Licensed psychologists performed hypnotic regressions in many of the cases Hopkins investigated. Also, when Hopkins himself performed hypnosis, he used protocols specifically designed to lead witnesses away from the alien abduction scenario. In fact, 25 potential abductees had been weeded out after hypnosis failed to uncover such memories. No psychologist who had ever observed him work had any worries about his competence and some actually came to him for help. What's more, hypnosis wasn't always necessary to remember alien contact. "In roughly one-fourth of the abduction cases I've investigated, the subject has recalled virtually all of his or her basic abduction scenario prior to hypnosis," said Hopkins.[49]

Despite the Hill's *Interrupted Journey*, Walton's *Fire in the Sky* and Hopkins' *Missing Time*, the general public was largely unaware of the UFO abduction phenomenon. That all changed in 1987 when horror novelist Whitley Strieber wrote about his own alien abduction experience in *Communion: A True Story*, which sold millions of copies and became the number one best-selling paperback during its first three months on the *New York Times* best seller's list. Strieber was the highest profile witness to come forward. His early works *The Wolfen* and *The Hunger* were adapted for the Big Screen, making him a hot commodity in Hollywood. Recent blockbusters *The Day After Tomorrow* and *2012* were based on Strieber novels. *Communion* also found its way onto the silver screen with Christopher Walken in the lead role, but it was more B-movie than blockbuster. The film failed the book and flopped badly at the box office.

According to Strieber, his odyssey began in 1985 when he awakened one morning with the disturbing memory of a barn owl staring at him through his bedroom window. Anxiety and other unusual physical ailments triggered memories of what was apparently an alien abduction experience, which led him to contact Bud Hopkins, setting in motion an investigation. Sessions began in March 1986. Dr. Donald Klein of the New York State Psychiatric Institute performed Strieber's hypnotic regression in Hopkins presence. Under hypnosis, the memories came flooding back. His barn owl turned out to be another commonly reported feature that Hopkins called a "screen memory," which served to mask the more frightening underlying experience. "The function of a cover story is to soften a disturbing memory and render it more benign and acceptable," explained Hopkins. In Strieber's case, the underlying traumatic incident was a home invasion by non-human intruders. The alien crew included the familiar short gray beings with oversize pear-shaped heads and big black slanted eyes, smaller gray beings with rounded eyes, short, stocky blue-gray beings with broad human-looking features and a robot-like entity. They took Strieber aboard their craft for medical procedures, including an implant. Strieber resisted his captors, whom he referred to as visitors, warning them that they had no right. The "visitors" disagreed. "We do have a right," they insisted.[50] It was a claim Hopkins had heard many times before.[51]

As the investigation unfolded, Strieber discovered he had endured a lifetime of such abductions that began when he was a child, much like Betty Andreasson, Debbie Tomey and others. He went on to write three more books about his contact experiences and founded the website Unknowncountry.com.

Skeptics didn't take him seriously. Some believed his first person account of alien abduction was simply a literary device. That he'd made himself a character in one his fantastic horror stories, similar to what best-selling author Richard Bach had done in 1977, with a first person account of his friendship with a modern day Jesus figure in *Illusions: The Adventures of a Reluctant Messiah*. The assumption that Strieber was a hoaxer was perpetuated in popular culture by the TV show, *The X-Files*, which featured what looked like an obvious spoof, portraying him as a money-grubber looking to cash in by creating a new "non-fiction science fiction" literary genre in an episode called *Jose Chung's From Outer Space*. Others believed it was either an outright hoax or the delusion of a fantasy-prone personality. It had to have been a frustrating situation for an author. What's a writer of tall tales to do when he claims that his tallest tale of all is actually a true story? Strieber subjected himself to both medical and psychological exams and passed a lie detector test administered by the managing director of Polygraph Security Services of London, who found him to be truthful about everything, including the question about the physical reality of his alien abductors.[52] He also found indirect support from the academic community in Kenneth Ring, a psychologist at the University of Connecticut who conducted a study of the fantasy prone personality thesis. He found no difference between UFO witnesses and alien abductees and a control group of non-UFO witnesses. The study poured cold water on the skeptical theory that UFO abduction experiences were the product of chronic daydreamers and Dungeons and Dragons aficionados. They were not. In fact, all such efforts to characterize abductees as a group have failed. They seem to come from all parts of society at random.[53] Such a result should've been taken as a sign that the UFO/alien abduction phenomenon deserved further study. Instead the academic establishment continued to ignore the subject on the weak assumption that it was nothing of significance. There were few notable exceptions.

EARTH HOMO SAPIENS VERSION 2.0

Temple University historian David Jacobs, whose doctoral dissertation *The UFO Controversy in America* was published by Signet in 1976, was initially skeptical about alien abduction, but was inspired by Budd Hopkins' work to begin his own investigation. "I had begun to understand that if abductions were really happening, they could be the key to the UFO mystery because they allowed us to enter inside the UFOs," wrote Jacobs, whose study helped confirm Hopkins' work and furthered developed the alien abductee narrative. In 1992, Jacobs published *Secret Life: Firsthand Accounts of UFO Abductions*. Both Hopkins and Jacobs found that abductees were made to interact with what appeared to be their alien-human hybrid offspring and that they weren't merely a source of genetic material; they were also an essential social component in the development of an alien-human hybrid race.[54] What's more, abductees not only experienced abductions throughout their lives, they were often paired with other abductees in childhood. These "abductee couples" developed intimate relationships completely unknown in their everyday lives until discovery in adulthood. Once uncovered, such relationships were often so powerful that they took precedence over all others. Jacobs' study included a couple, "Dena and Ray," who experienced such an overwhelming feeling of belonging together that they divorced their spouses in order to marry. Hypnosis revealed they'd had an intimate relationship as adolescents that took place exclusively during abductions. Perhaps the most significant abduction witness, Betty Andreasson divorced her first husband with whom she had seven children and married fellow abductee Bob Luca, who had contact experiences in both 1944 and 1967 just like Betty. Although they had no memory of meeting during these events, it was their abduction experiences that eventually brought them together.[55]

Jacobs found the alien-human hybrid program to be extensive, widespread and troubling. In 1998, he published *The Threat*, a grim assessment warning of alien infiltration. According to Jacobs, successive generations of alien-human hybrids were becoming more and more human in appearance, while retaining ET mental capabilities such as telepathy and what he called mindscan, the ability to access and control the human mind as if it were a computer. These were hybrids that could easily pass for human, but weren't. Jacobs worried that the end result would be something akin to a biological coup d'état. Human-looking aliens would assume control of Earth.[56]

Historian Jacobs' work was of great value in helping substantiate the alien abduction/contact experience, but his Cold War era take on the alien agenda was more appropriate for the Hollywood slush pile than an intelligence assessment about the motives of a post-Singularity civilization. Harvard Psychologist John Mack, the highest profile academic to buck the establishment with an investigation of the taboo within the taboo, came to completely different conclusions.

Mack, who wrote a Pulitzer Prize-winning biography of T.E. Lawrence, was "an intense skeptic" when he first met Budd Hopkins in 1990. But it didn't take long for him to see the folly of his assumptions. He quickly realized the abduction phenomenon *was* a threat. Not in the way Jacobs imagined, but in the sense that it challenged the entire Newtonian-Cartesian Western worldview. Like other researchers, including Hopkins, Jacobs, Sprinkle and John Carpenter, Mack found that people weren't imagining alien abductions because they were crazy, sexually abused, fantasy prone or delusional, but the alien abduction experience could drive them crazy.

"These individuals reported being taken against their wills by alien beings, sometimes through the walls of their houses, and subjected to elaborate intrusive procedures which appeared to have a reproductive purpose. In a few cases they were actually observed by independent witnesses to be physically absent during the time of abduction. These people suffered from no obvious psychiatric disorder, except the effects of the traumatic experience, and were reporting with powerful emotion what to them were utterly real experiences. Furthermore, these experiences were sometimes associated with UFO sightings by friends, family members, or others in the community, including media reporters and journalists, and frequently left physical traces in the individuals' bodies... In short, I was dealing with a phenomenon that I felt could not be explained psychiatrically, yet was simply *not possible* within the framework of the Western scientific worldview," wrote Mack, who was a childhood friend of Thomas Kuhn, author of *The Structure of Scientific Revolutions* and originator of the concept of paradigms and paradigm shift.[57]

There was no one better suited to consult with than Kuhn, who thought that Western science had become as dogmatic as religion. He advised Mack to think outside its structures, forms and conventions, collect raw data and look for a pattern to emerge. Mack heeded Kuhn's advice, opting for a more Heisenbergian approach rather than a strictly empirical investigation, which he thought was doomed to fail. Abductions followed a trend in UFO sightings that led scientists to conclude ETs may be using a "leaky embargo" strategy to gradually condition Earth civilization to their presence.[58] Never in hundreds of thousands of UFO sightings has an incident lasted long enough for the major news media to gather at the scene. Such reports raised speculation about ETs but weren't enough to prove their existence. It was the same with abductions. "It is as if the agent or intelligence at work here were parodying, mocking, tricking and deceiving the investigators, providing just enough physical evidence to win over those who are prepared to believe in the phenomenon but not enough to convince the skeptic. In this apparently frustrating situation, there may lie a deeper truth and possibility. It is as if the phenomenon were inviting us to change our ways, to expand our consciousness and ways of learning, to use, in addition to our conventional ways of knowing and observing, methodologies more appropriate to its own complex, subtle, and perhaps ultimately unknowable nature," wrote Mack about the challenges of investigating the alien abduction phenomenon. Instead of attempting in vain to keep separate observer and observed, subject and object, Mack considered he and his alien abductee subjects to be co-investigators.[59]

In 1994, after an initial three and a half year study of 76 alien abductees out of over a hundred potential cases, Mack ignited a firestorm of controversy with the publication of his book *Abduction: Human Encounters with Aliens*. Mack found the agenda behind the abductions appeared to have two primary objectives: to raise human consciousness and to create a new life form by fusing two species together. What's more, information gathered from abductees suggested that Earth was part of a much larger interconnected cosmic system, which led him to conclude that alien intervention may be "some sort of corrective initiative."[60]

As one familiar with the subject would expect, the establishment reacted hysterically. Harvard rebuked Mack with an unprecedented investigation aimed at revoking his tenure. A special committee found Mack irresponsible for considering the possibility that alien abductees were actually describing real events. Mack's attorneys, including Daniel Sheehan, who would later represent the Disclosure Project, along with the support of other researchers, forced Harvard to back down and reaffirm Mack's academic freedom.[61] "Harvard University isn't going to take action against someone who takes unorthodox views, and with whom it may disagree. John Mack may win the Nobel prize and go down in history as the modern Galileo," said committee chairman Arnold Relman, tongue firmly planted in cheek.

Despite such official capitulation, Mack's colleagues made it clear that Harvard didn't endorse his work. The knives were out. The scientific community at large accused Mack of pseudoscience and continued to insist that alien abductions must be the result of delusions. One reviewer in a psychoanalytic journal called Mack's book a "subversive assault on psychoanalysis as a science." Mack fired back at such critiques, which he said, "reflect a misunderstanding of the nature of rationality and reason, and even of science itself." What's more, he accused his dissenters of essentially arguing that any information that didn't fit their beliefs was invalid. *It can't be; therefore it isn't.* The same old logical fallacy that has embarrassed many a prominent scientist was the heart of the argument. "To exclude data because it does not fit a particular view of reality can only, in the end, arrest the progress of science and keep us ignorant," wrote Mack, refuting the debunkers, which included Carl Sagan, who claimed that alien abduction was nothing more than hallucinations caused by sexual abuse, sleep paralysis, temporal lobe epilepsy and other such trauma. [62] In the documentary *Touched,* Mack called him out. "Carl Sagan says gratuitously on the basis of nothing this is hallucinations and he wrote an article on that. He didn't do any work," Mack whinged, "I mean, what does he know about hallucinations anyway, you know."[63]

Sagan was out of his field just like his mentor Donald Menzel was when he debunked James McDonald, an atmospheric physicist best suited to analyze reports of UFOs operating in the Earth's atmosphere. Likewise, Mack, a psychologist, was far and away more qualified to assess matters of the mind and to receive a message embedded in the subconscious of a population of abductees. Hence, Mack was undeterred by Harvard, Sagan and an establishment desperate to defend a crumbling paradigm just like it had a few hundred years ago.

In 1999, after working with over a hundred additional abductees from the U.S. and around the world, Mack published *Passport to the Cosmos: Human Transformation and Alien Encounters*. Nearly ten years of research had a transformational effect on Mack and his subjects, who found their alien contact experiences were about much more than a program to breed alien/human hybrid babies. Together they found that the "terror of confronting a more powerful biological entity from another world," as General Twining allegedly put it, had utterly shattered their view of reality, as it was designed to do. Once past the initial trauma they discovered the alien contact experience had caused a profound shift in consciousness, an "awakening" or awareness of a higher reality. As a result of their experiences, abductees developed "an intense concern for the planet's survival and a powerful ecological consciousness."[64] Ultimately, alien contact experiencers developed an "authentic identification with the purpose of the whole phenomenon," which was to raise human consciousness so that we would stop destroying our environment and dooming ourselves to extinction.[65] If the project to transform consciousness failed and human beings succeeded in committing ecological suicide, alien-human hybrids were Plan B.[66]

Such a scenario is consistent with the hypothesis that the Earth is the product of a post-Singularity civilization that has, or is in the process of, colonizing the Galaxy. If the project here on Earth has truly become FUBAR, as it appears, an intervention, or "some sort of corrective initiative," as Mack put it, would seem the natural response of such a parent civilization.

CHAPTER 8

SYNTHESIS

Not only will men of science have to grapple with the sciences that deal with man, but — and this is a far more difficult matter — they will have to persuade the world to listen to what they have discovered. If they cannot succeed in this difficult enterprise, man will destroy himself by his half-way cleverness.
— Bertrand Russell

No problem can be solved from the same level of consciousness that created it.
— Albert Einstein

The end cannot justify the means, for the simple and obvious reason that the means employed determine the nature of the ends produced.
— Aldous Huxley

STARWORKS

Driven by technology, the exponential rate of scientific progress has left our linear thinking minds racing to catch up. In the blink of an eye on a cosmic timescale, we've made a difficult transition from the belief that we were the crowning achievement at the center of all creation to understanding that we're just a tiny grain of sand adrift on an unimaginably immense cosmic ocean. There are so many stars and the Universe is so vast that Carl Sagan's catch phrase 'billions and billions' couldn't possibly do it justice. It's obvious we can't be the only island of life in the Universe or the first technological civilization to have come this far. Even Kurzweil admits his belief that we're in the lead is extremely unlikely. Fermi quickly realized we should've been visited by advanced ETs many times by now, but by the 1970s the high volume of authentic UFO sightings made the ETH seem inadequate to many ufologists. Extraterrestrial visitation seemed too simplistic an explanation for the phenomenon and all its associated manifestations. Yet the reports, especially the abduction accounts, indicated an alien presence. Clearly, the Extraterrestrial hypothesis was in need of an update and a couple extra terms, especially in light of our own impending Singularity. What I call post-Singularity Extraterrestrial Transmigration hypothesis (PSETH) explains the totality of the UFO evidence, as well as its association with anomalous data gathered by our space programs.

The puzzle pieces fall into place when we insert our civilization into an ongoing project to colonize the galaxy. PSETH explains why the Moon appears to be a space station placed in a precise orbit designed to bring about advanced life on Earth and the time-sensitive symbol of the Total Solar Eclipse. It explains why extraterrestrials are humanoid, why some of them appear to be humans just like us, and why sexual relations between interstellar species are possible. It explains why ETs would stage an intervention to fix the error in our evolution and engage in an alien/human hybrid genetics program to preserve the species. It explains why an advanced ET civilization would move neutron stars around the galaxy to warn us about the lethal threat of the galactic superwave.

The model for interstellar colonization proposed by John Barrow and Frank Tipler is useful as a guide for understanding how intelligent life might spread throughout the Galaxy, but there will be many surprises because it's impossible, to imagine the technological innovations of a post-Singularity civilization or the situations it will face and the problems it will have to solve. For example, Barrow and Tipler argue that because machines will be able to synthesize DNA, humans can be manufactured and grown by robots in an industrial fashion at remote interstellar colonies.[1] It's technically plausible, but in the real world, rolling off of an assembly line might not work for living beings. Abductees, who are a natural resource for information about this unimaginable stellar civilization, report having been made to interact with hybrid babies in order to facilitate their development.[2]

The size and scope of ET operations here on Earth is difficult, if not impossible, for our pre-Singularity minds to grasp. In 1991, aerospace industry mogul Robert Bigelow commissioned a study from Budd Hopkins and David Jacobs to estimate the total number of alien abductees in America. In turn, the research team hired Roper to conduct a carefully crafted survey of almost 6,000 randomly selected people across the United

States to determine whether they had experienced the telltale signs of alien abduction, including missing time, unusual lights, puzzling scars, terrifying figures, etc. The Roper poll was the largest and most statistically accurate poll of its kind and it showed that there were likely millions of alien abductees in America alone.[3] Carl Sagan seized upon what Jacobs called an "embarrassingly high number" to ridicule abduction research. "If we believed the conclusion drawn by those who bankrolled and interpreted the results of this poll, and if aliens are not partial to Americans, then the number for the whole planet would be more than a hundred million people. This means an abduction every few seconds over the past few decades. It's surprising more of the neighbors haven't noticed," quipped Sagan, making the familiar argument that *it can't be; therefore it isn't.*

It was convincing rhetoric, especially back in the day, but as Mack noted, it wasn't science. A species-wide, consciousness-altering, alien-human hybrid operation requiring over a hundred million unwitting participants was, and probably still is, simply inconceivable at our current level of development. But as we approach our own technological Singularity, futurists like Ray Kurzweil envision a human-machine civilization of nearly infinite capability, able to produce at will any thing, situation or environment imaginable, engineering reality to its liking. For a civilization of this magnitude such an operation may be the equivalent of a high school science project. What's more, according to Kurzweil, if such a civilization exists it would have the ability to prevent us from detecting it. Like LaViolette, Knight and Butler, Kurzweil expects an advanced civilization will have a minimum standard for contact. "Perhaps it will reveal itself to us when we achieve the next level of our evolution, specifically merging our biological brains with our technology, which is to say, after the Singularity," wrote Kurzweil, who nevertheless proclaimed his belief that we are alone in the universe, the first to approach the ultimate technological summit.[4]

In reaching such a conclusion, Kurzweil had to confront Fermi's paradox, which he did without ever once discussing flying saucers or UFOs. In *The Singularity is Near,* published in 2005, four years *after* the Disclosure Project press conference at the National Press Club in Washington D.C., there is no lunchtime discussion between Kurzweil and colleagues about the evidence for UFOs, alien abduction or anything of the sort. It was just five years since the publication of historian Richard Dolan's first volume of *UFOs and the National Security State,* but Kurzweil made no references to the work that Edgar Mitchell called "thorough and Monumental." It was a mere eight years since Corso's *The Day After Roswell*, 11 years since Mack published his first book about alien abduction and 24 years after Bud Hopkins put his finger on the phenomenon of missing time. It was also 53 years after the CIA's Robertson panel recommended UFO sightings be debunked. In fact, most of Hynek's so-called "embarrassment of riches" of UFO evidence accumulated after 1950, when Fermi and his colleagues famously chewed on flying saucers over lunch. Nevertheless, Kurzweil omits the entire subject. He bases his conclusion on the apparent *absence of evidence* that our solar system has been transformed into a cosmic computer and the assumption that the activities of at least one among billions of hypothetical, post-Singularity technological civilizations should've gotten our attention by now.

Like other Fermi paradox theorists, Kurzweil's conclusion is built on the assumption that all extraterrestrial civilizations will have evolved independently - like so many tiny isolated islands in the Cosmos - as we assume we have. This basic assumption is at the core of Fermi paradox arguments that not all advanced civilizations would choose to ignore us or study us or quarantine us or leave this universe for a new one of their own making. Such thinking is a foundational pillar of the current Western Scientific paradigm, much like Ptolemy's assumption about the geocentric universe was the load-bearing wall of its day. This elemental error prevents Fermi paradox theorists from considering that life on Earth, and perhaps all life in the universe, and perhaps even the universe itself, is the product of a previous technological Singularity.

It's ironic that the politics of paradigm shift discourages establishment scientists like Kurzweil from considering the work done by Fowler, Hopkins, Mack and others because the world described by alien abductees is the world of Kurzweil's singular technological utopia.

THE DAY AFTER THE GREAT TECHNOLOGICAL QUANTUM LEAP

From the beginning of the space age, engineers have tried to build completely remote controlled spacecraft, but astronauts, who were the face of the space program, rebelled. "No bucks, no Buck Rogers," as the old space industry adage goes. The astronauts won the day, but Kurzweil believes the engineers will eventually prevail. "I have always considered the science fiction notion of large spaceships piloted by huge, squishy creatures similar to us to be very unlikely," wrote Kurzweil, who assumes a post-Singularity civilization will achieve space exploration exclusively through the use of nanotechnology, which means there's no need to consider UFO reports, the Disclosure movement or the eyewitness accounts of alien abductees. *It can't be therefore it isn't.* Of course, Kurzweil can't imagine what actual nanotechnology of a post-Singularity civilization will be like. No one can. Except quite possibly Betty Andreasson, who learned that alien craft were scalable. At one point during her contact experiences, Betty witnessed a large spacecraft reduce to the size of a car. The ETs explained to her that they could make their craft, *including its crew,* larger or smaller at will, suggesting the possibility that a nano space probe could also function as a macro space probe. This might explain why some ET craft appear to shrink to a point in an instant and wink-out rather than zip-off in a flash.

Scalable nanotechnology is just the type of unforeseeable technological development one would expect from a post-Singularity civilization. Such possibilities are why it's downright silly for Kurzweil to assume that all advanced spacecraft will be limited to nanosize. Ironically, it's a great example of the limitations of linear thinking, much like Benford beacons in comparison to the pulsar beacon network. Such a proclamation is reminiscent of others from the past like *heavier-than-air flight is impossible* and *spaceflight is utter bilge,* etc. It's not scientific fact. Far from it. But it plays one on TV. It's also a meme that acts like a vaccine for the mind, immunizing the scientific community against UFOs. It's nothing more than a pretext to reject the Disclosure movement, which is symptomatic of a crumbling paradigm.

Futurists like Kurzweil ignore the extraterrestrial presence and there are many things they can't possibly anticipate, but their predictions about the technological Singularity make a good a beginner's guide to the world where real UFOs come from.

The merging of biology and technology on Earth is already underway as we rapidly approach our own local Singularity. Cochlear and retinal implants that restore the ability to hear and see, along with increasingly lifelike Luke Skywalker-type prosthetic limbs are just the beginning. Soon every body part will not only be replaceable, but upgradeable, including the brain, the very epicenter of perception. Nothing will impact us more than brain augmentation through nanotechnology. Nanobots the size of brain cells will be like a computer upgrade from the room-sized ENIAC to a quantum computer for our frontal lobes. It boggles the mind to imagine what the world will be like when everyone is as smart as Einstein and has telepathic connectivity to the Internet and everyone else. "The most important application of circa-2030 nanobots will be literally to expand our minds through the merger of biological and nonbiological intelligence. The first stage will be to augment our hundred trillion very slow interneuronal connections with high-speed virtual connections via nanorobot communication. This will provide us with the opportunity to greatly boost our pattern-recognition abilities, memories, and overall thinking capacity, as well as to directly interface with powerful forms of nonbiological intelligence. The technology will also provide wireless communication from one brain to another," wrote Kurzweil, unwittingly providing an excellent explanation for the telepathic communication reported by extraterrestrial contact/abduction experiencers.[5]

Andreasson abduction researcher Ray Fowler speculated about such technology back in 1990 when the Singularity was just an obscure, far-out, science fiction fantasy, if-ever-comes-true-at-all concept. "Parapsychology and the New Physics are both relatively new branches of human science. Significantly, both seem to be revealing the bare rudiments of the super technology demonstrated by the aliens. For example, parapsycholgical experiments indicate that the powers of telepathy, levitation and telekinesis may be inherent but usually latent in the human mind. One cannot help but wonder how much more such powers would be manifested in a super-mind millions or billions of years in advance of the human mind. Most likely, super rich minds would display exactly what Betty and other witnesses have described- telepathy, levitation and telekinesis," wrote Fowler.[6]

Ironically, instead of citing real world examples of the Singularity found in alien abduction literature, Kurzweil turned to the realm of make believe to illustrate Arthur C. Clarke's third rule that "any sufficiently advanced technology is indistinguishable from magic" in the introduction to *The Singularity is Near.* "Consider J.K. Rowling's Harry Potter stories from this perspective. These tales may be imaginary, but they are not unreasonable visions of our world as it will exist only a few decades from now. Essentially all of the Potter 'magic' will be realized through the technologies I explore in this book. Playing quid-ditch and transforming people and objects into other forms will be feasible in full-immersion virtual-reality environments, as well as in real reality, using nanoscale devices," declared Kurzweil[7]

Adding further irony, corroboration for Kurzweil's predictions can be found in the experiences of abductee Jim Sparks, who had contact with beings able to manipulate their appearance at will through what he called a seamless form of *virtual reality*.[8] Harvard psychologist John Mack, who first interviewed Sparks in 1996, called his case "one of our richest and most detailed documentations of an abduction history," noting that Sparks had total conscious recall of his experiences without the aid of hypnosis. According to Sparks, ET's walk through walls and float in thin air. Their ships appear and disappear. "It's not magic, demons or angels. It's just advanced technology," wrote Sparks, whose description of extraterrestrial machinery dovetails with the Singularity foreseen by Kurzweil[9] "The aliens use thought-activated technology, and their machines are at least partially biological and can interact with us as if they were alive. Their ability to take in, process and project information is so vast that they can see the future coming," wrote Sparks, who should've written the forward to *The Singularity Is Near*, but because of paradigm dynamics he and fellow ET contact experiencers remain invisible to Kurzweil and his colleagues who mistakenly believe we are the Top Dog in the universe.[10] The day after the Singularity they expect it is we who will first spread among the stars, making the Galaxy our oyster. But it's not going to happen that way. It's possible to ignore the Disclosure movement, but not the civilization that inspired it. When we hit our Singularity – if we make it that far – we will be in their world.

Much of this grand civilization is beyond our ability to imagine. But over the last seventy years or so, we've managed to learn some of the basics. The first thing to know about who *They* are and what they're like is they're much like us. Intergalactic civilization is primarily humanoid in form. When we emerge into the post-Singularity world and come face to face it will be somewhat like Villas Boas described. Like meeting someone from another country, but instead they're from another planet or maybe even another dimension outside of spacetime. It seems the tentacle-wielding, antenna-laden space alien of sci-fi lore is indeed a myth. ETs appear to be variations on a theme, perhaps engineered to best fit the local environment of different star systems. Real-life patrons of a Star Wars bar would appear to be much more humanoid than George Lucas ever imagined. One might suspect convergent evolutionary forces at work. It could be that a humanoid form is the best vehicle for the evolution of intelligence. But if life in the Galaxy was seeded by a post-Singularity civilization that was human or humanoid then the spread of the human form is likely by design.

The most common types of ETs include the Grays, the Reptilians and the Nordics. The Grays have been so widely reported that they've become part of pop culture. Even people who know nothing about UFOs or alien abduction are familiar with the child-sized ET and its big head and almond-shaped eyes. The Reptilians are insect-like with a reptilian face. They have eyes with elliptical pupils like a cat. The blue-eyed-blond Nordics also have catlike eyes. They look human like us, but they seem "beyond-human."[11] Witnesses also report truly non-human looking beings, including tall, bug-eyed entities that look like a praying mantis. Just how many different extraterrestrial races exist is unknown. At the Disclosure Project press conference, Sgt. Clifford Stone, a member of a disaster recovery unit that brought him into direct contact with both living and dead ETs, said the U.S. government had catalogued 57 different types. Betty Andreasson's Grays told her that there were seventy different ET races involved with Earth.[12]

The situation could be incredibly complex. According to a recent NASA study on data gathered by the Kepler spacecraft, there are over 17 billion planets in the Milky Way galaxy similar in size to the Earth.[13] If even a small fraction of them have been seeded in the project to colonize the galaxy there will be millions upon millions of extraterrestrial races.

It may seem daunting to sort out, but Galactic civilization appears to be a humanoid civilization and it may very well be a human-centered civilization. Human beings much like us may have been the first to hit the Singularity somewhere else, long ago. The Grays may be the key to the mystery. There are different types. Many witnesses have reported Grays that exhibit automated behavior as if they were a form of biological robot.[14] Corso described the beings recovered at Roswell in much the same fashion. "Perhaps we should consider the EBEs as described in the medical autopsy reports humanoid robots rather than life forms, specifically engineered for long-distance travel through space or time," wrote Corso in a report for General Arthur Trudeau.[15]

Corso wasn't too far off the mark. According to Betty Andreasson Luca, the gold standard among ET contact witnesses, the Grays were a type of device remotely controlled by tall, Nordic-like beings called "Elders." During an abduction in 1967, Betty witnessed an operation the ETs called biobics. She was told the Grays famously big black eyes degraded over time with exposure to natural light and needed to be replaced with lab grown eyes.[16] After the installation, the elder performed a task that seemed somewhat analogous to synching a digital camera with a Mac or a PC. In fact, Andreasson said the Grays were a "living camera" only far more sophisticated. They did the bidding of the elders, who could see through their eyes and guide their actions much like the marines guided genetically engineered alien bodies in the 2009 James Cameron blockbuster *Avatar*.[17]

But not all Grays are robotic drones. Witnesses also report another class, slightly taller, which they describe as doctors, nurses and leaders. And then there's the Betty and Barney Hill Grays, whose origins trace back to the Zeta Reticuli star system thanks to a star map seen aboard their craft.

The post-Singularity world that ETs inhabit must be incredibly complex. In a galaxy with 17 billion Earth-sized planets, one can imagine there might thousands, maybe even millions, of different types of grays just as there are different types of human beings here on Earth. According to Alfred Webre, Earth is a microcosm of the cosmos. "As above, so below." We are but one small fractal in much larger pattern. It appears that pattern may be largely human and it may be that extraterrestrial humans were the first to hit the Singularity. In fact, Andreasson told investigators that the elders were at the top of the chain of command among ETs. Ultimately, no matter who was first, biological robots are the signature of the Singularity, which appears to be a rabbit hole that winds its way right out of space/time.

Some Fermi's paradox theorists think a post-Singularity civilization will create a new universe and disappear into it never to be seen or heard from again. They may be at least partially right. Alien abductees/contact experiencers appear to provide some measure of confirmation that post-Singularity ETs are indeed able to leave this universe *and* re-enter at will. What's more, they're able to bring us back and forth with them.

Abductees studied by John Mack told him that not only had they been spirited away from their daily lives, they'd been taken to a world outside of time. Mack's subjects had the impression that some of their abduction experiences were "not occurring in our space/time universe," but in some other "dimension" of reality in which there was no such thing as time.[18] The ETs validated such impressions through Betty Andreasson. "The future and the past are the same as today to them- Time to them is not like our time, but they know about our time," said Andreasson who was told by the beings, "The place with you is localized. It is not with us."[19]

In this timeless dimension, abduction experiencers report encountering translucent entities and beings of light in addition to the Grays, Nordics, Reptilians and other extraterrestrials.[20] They also report experiencing transformative energetic and vibrational effects. "For abductees a strong physical vibration that seems to affect and even change the cells and molecules of their bodies is a central aspect of the encounters," wrote Mack about technology used to transport abductees from their homes into alien spacecraft, other planets, and ultimately into other dimensions.[21] "It's racking just to go through the window because they have to alter your vibration in order to get a solid object to pass through another solid object, literally," explained Mack abductee Karin, whose description matched other abductees including Betty Andreasson.[22] When Andreasson asked how she was made to pass through a solid wooden door she was told, "By controlled vibrational levels. It is very simple, those structures are very loose."[23]

Such advanced technology fits Arthur C. Clarke's definition as indistinguishable from magic. Yet there's more. Mack reported that contact/abduction experiences sometimes occurred in a non-physical state.[24] Like an out-of-body-experience or a near-death experience, the abductee's astral body can be detached from his or her physical body, which is left behind for the duration of the encounter. Betty Andreasson experienced several astral abductions at the hands of ETs who told her this method was used when physical contact was too risky on account of potential witnesses.

According to Andreasson, the Grays use technology to free the astral body. During one such abduction episode, she saw a gray being initiate the process by manipulating a small device attached to a belt it was wearing.[25] What's more, the ETs told her they had what could best be described as *spiritual technology*. "They have technology that Man could use… It is through the spirit… If Man will just study nature itself, he will find many of the answers… Man will find them through the spirit. Man is not made of just flesh and blood."[26]

Perhaps the most surprising revelation about the alien abduction experience is that such contact results in spiritual epiphany. Mack noted that the vibrational energies used to transport abductees through solid objects also "appear to be associated with some sort of shift of consciousness, spiritual awakening, and the sense of connecting with other dimensions of reality."[27] Although these encounters are initially traumatic, Mack found that their cumulative effects were ultimately transformative. The utter obliteration of one's personal worldview resulted in an "ontological shock" that triggered profound personal transformation and spiritual growth.

It might seem counterintuitive that ET contact would be a spiritual experience given fears about alien invasion, but the capacity for spirituality appears to be yet another facet of brain function that will be greatly enhanced by the Singularity. Neuroscientists have found an area of the frontal lobes that they call the "God module" because of its activity during intense mystical experiences. According to Kurzweil, the Singularity will enhance this capacity just as it will amplify our other cognitive functions, including intelligence, memories, etc.

"When we can determine the neurological correlates of the variety of spiritual experiences that our species is capable of, we are likely to be able to enhance these experiences in the same way that we will enhance other human experiences. With the next stage of evolution creating a new generation of humans that will be trillions of times more capable and complex than humans today, our ability for spiritual experience and insight is also likely to gain in power and depth," wrote Kurzweil in his book, *The Age of Spiritual Machines*.[28]

The possibility that artificially intelligent robots will one day unlock the doors to heaven seems like the utterly fantastic plot of a Philip K. Dick novel. Whether they are called replicants, androids, cyborgs, transhumans or something else entirely, scientists of the post-Singularity will not only be many orders of magnitude smarter than they are now, they will also have an acute sense of the spiritual.

One can imagine that transhuman scientists of the future will master the quantum field, where consciousness and physical reality become entangled, so to speak. It was this nexus of science and spirituality that drew John Mack's attention in the course of his investigation. "Efforts to understand the light, energy, and vibratory phenomena that abductees confront take us far beyond this subject and into theoretical questions about the underlying nature of the universe. This is territory where theoretical physics and spirituality touch each other, if they do not completely converge," he wrote in comparing abductee's experiences with those of mystics who practice eastern spirituality and the possible relationship of such experiences to the latest discoveries in modern physics.

In the 1970s, writer Gary Zukav (*The Dancing Wu Li Masters*) and physicist Fritjof Capra (*The Tao of Physics*) popularized the link between consciousness and physical reality with bestsellers about the similarities between quantum physics and Eastern mysticism. The idea that consciousness and reality are interconnected again captured the Zeitgeist in 2004 with the surprise hit documentary film, *What The Bleep Do We Know!?* Although the movie was well-received by the general public, the same could not be said of the scientific community which panned it as new age "quantum mysticism." But if consciousness does have an effect on the physical world, as quantum physics shows, it would seem the ultimate cognitive function enhanced by a technological Singularity.

It's no accident that consciousness itself is central to the alien abduction experience. It's both the medium and the message. John Mack was uniquely qualified to receive that message. He is among the most important researchers in UFO history and he may indeed go down as a modern Galileo. Unfortunately, he was struck and killed by a drunk driver while in London in 2004.

Although Mack never made the connection between the alien abduction phenomenon and the great technological quantum leap, which was little more than far-out science fiction at the time of his death, he recognized the significance of the latest discoveries in physics. New subatomic particles that implied the existence of other dimensions and the *zero-point energy field* made abductee's experiences credible. Mack cited astrophysicist Rudolph Schild, who wondered if UFOs and aliens had found a way to master the quantum energy field. Schild's hunch gave Mack the genesis of an explanation for aspects of alien abductee's experiences. "Some experiencers have the impression that the changes in their vibratory frequency or 'energy fields' are an accommodation or attuning to the higher frequency of the beings themselves, the energies that surround them, and 'universal energy fields.' This change is also felt in some way related to the capacity of the beings to bring the human body through a solid object, an ability that many experiencers have been told we all potentially possess… It would not be surprising, he suggests, that abductees would feel such intense vibrations as they encounter these unusual energies."[29]

Disclosure Project witness Mark McCandlish got a glimpse of the ETs quantum field mastery that Schild could only dream about when he stumbled upon the ARV and its zero-point energy propulsion system. According to McCandlish, tapping the zero-point slows electrons in their orbit, which has a mass-canceling effect on matter. It could be this mass-altering process that enables ETs to move through solid objects. What's more, it might also explain close encounters with luminous entities and "translucent" beings that do not appear to be completely solid. It may even be the doorway to another dimension.[30]

The zero-point energy system described by McCandlish fulfills Kurzweil's prediction that the Singularity will result in new and exotic technology that makes it possible to engineer reality itself, which is likely the reason Hercules Aerospace referred to zero-point energy science as the "fundamental enabling technology." This is the world we will emerge into the day after the Singularity.

CLOSE ENCOUNTERS OF THE REMOTE MIND

Alien abductee/contact experiencers are our primary source of information about the post-Singularity world inhabited by extraterrestrials. They provide a snapshot of what that world actually looks like, but not much about how it works, its governance, etc. Fortunately, there is another way to glean information about this civilization, and again, consciousness is the key. An intelligence-gathering technique developed by the military during the Cold War known as Remote Viewing can open up another window into the world where real UFOs come from.

It seems when it comes to warfare, paranoia trumps worldview. Despite deeply rooted institutional bias against psychic phenomena, Strangelovian fear of an intelligence gap led both the U.S. and Soviet Union to develop psychic spy units.[31] In the U.S., research for the project ultimately code-named Star Gate was done at Stanford Research International (SRI) by engineer Hal Puthoff, who would later become a Disclosure Project witness, physicist Russell Targ, and well-known psychic Ingo Swann, who helped develop a set of protocols for accessing information about a remote target through psychic means. Swann demonstrated the effectiveness of the technique by targeting Jupiter in advance of NASA's Pioneer 10 mission. He made 12 unanticipated observations later confirmed by Pioneer 10, including the existence of Saturn-like planetary rings.[32]

As a result, the CIA and the military began training units of remote viewers. The program had its limitations and its share of failures, but in general, it was an invaluable intelligence asset for over twenty years before U.S. taxpayers knew anything about it. In 1995, it was officially shut down amidst controversy after it was made public on *Nightline* with Ted Koppel, *Larry King Live* and other mainstream media outlets. But according to former Army Captain David Morehouse, one of the first remote viewers to write about his experiences as a psychic spy, RV units likely still exist in secret because the technology is simply too valuable to abandon.[33]

Whatever the present status of the government's remote viewing program, its past successes give strong support to Morehouse's argument. In one striking example, the program drew praise from President Jimmy Carter. In 1978, America's psychic spies were the difference in a race to recover a Soviet spy plane that disappeared into the African jungle. Spy satellites failed to spot the crash site and CIA teams sent to recover the craft also had no luck *until they were given remote viewing data*. "She went into a trance. And while she was in a trance, she gave some latitude and longitude figures. We focused our satellite cameras on that point and the plane was there," said the former President in amazement.[34]

Remote viewers weren't just spies the enemy couldn't hide from, they were advanced scouts in the post-Singularity world. They often saw UFOs. Even when they weren't looking for them. While remote viewing a Soviet submarine, Ingo Swann discovered a disk-shaped craft tracking along with it high above in the atmosphere. Joe McMoneagle, one of the most prolific remote viewers, had a similar experience. At a target site he found his mind drawn to an object overhead. It was a classic metallic disc with rotating outer edges that he estimated to be traveling at 4,500 miles per hour. Such coincidental sightings led Puthoff and company to include UFO incidents in the target pool. "McMoneagle, going down to his zone to find what he believed would be some operational target, was often surprised to find himself looking around the cramped, curved interior of an unearthly ship, filled with skinny, large-eyed humanoids- who often stared back at him, wondering what the hell he was doing there," wrote science writer Jim Schnabel about the deeply strange circumstance of remote viewing close encounters.[35]

Such intelligence would be of great interest to whatever Majestic-12 projects might still be in operation. Whoever is in charge of making policy about the extraterrestrial presence surely knows that remote viewers have seen alien bases on both the Moon and Mars. This agency must also be aware that these bases have been seen on Earth. Remote viewer Pat Price discovered alien bases embedded inside various mountain ranges and under the Earth's oceans. There were four primary bases, each one heavily shielded against discovery. According to Price, they were located in the Pyrenees Mountains bordering Spain and France, Mount Inyangani in Zimbabwe, Mount Ziel in Australia and Mount Hayes, northeast of Anchorage, Alaska. What's more, they were "manned" by personnel that appeared completely human, but had significant differences in internal physiology. Joe McMoneagle also remote viewed Mount Hayes in Alaska. He saw underground infrastructure unlike anything he had ever seen. "It's like walking into a place I have no familiarity with at all," he said.[36]

Remote viewing data on the Great Galactic post-Singularity Civilization is simply fantastic, but it can't be taken at face value. With the help of Puthoff and Targ, Ingo Swann meticulously developed a method for separating the target signal from the noise, which was considerable.[37] As it happens, there are many obstacles to correctly perceiving psychic data, including one's own imagination and the thoughts of another remote viewer who had previously viewed the target. Therefore, Swann insisted that remote viewing data required real-world corroboration. The Pioneer 10 Jupiter mission and the Soviet spy plane episode are prime examples. Without such validation, Swann said remote viewing intelligence might turn out to be worthless. That was especially true when it came to extraterrestrial targets. Corroboration for RV data on the great Galactic civilization is a little harder to come by, but it has happened.

In 1991, as the Soviet Union was crumbling, its Phobos II space probe was lost on approach to Mars. Ironically, the Soviets turned to American remote viewers to solve the mystery. Perhaps President Reagan was right. In a speech before the United Nations just four years earlier he said the nations of the Earth would forget their differences if confronted by an extraterrestrial threat. Or maybe the Russian space agency no longer had access to the Soviet psychic spy program? Whatever the case, the remote viewing report on the fate of the Phobos II read like a scene from a James Cameron screenplay:

A disc-shaped object, Object 1, arose from the planet's surface to meet the probe, briefly perused it, then returned to the surface. Another object, already in space, was also attracted. Object 2 moved into close proximity and, in an act having some similarity to an "IFF" [Interrogation, Friend or Foe aircraft transponder] query, directed a very powerful, wide, penetrating particle beam into the interior of the space craft. Shortly afterward, Object 2 departed. The directed energy was neither reflected nor absorbed by the probe's skin. However, the beam inflicted serious damage upon the space craft's electronic components, altering or rearranging their material structure at the molecular level to such a degree that circuits became paralyzed in turn rendering many systems dysfunctional.

By Swann's standards, such a report might've indeed been dismissed as science fiction if not for real-world feedback provided by the Soviets. Not long after the American remote viewing team delivered its report, Cosmonaut Marina Popovich made public a photo taken by the Phobos II spacecraft just before it lost communication. The photo showed an unidentified object in close proximity to the probe as it approached Phobos. Popovich, a legend worldwide, raised the possibility that the object was an alien spacecraft. Remote viewers welcomed the photo as feedback that they'd been on target. The oddly shaped object in the photo closely resembled drawings they had made of the craft that took out the Soviet space probe.[38]

Kurzweil argued that a civilization that had passed through the Singularity would be able to hide itself from us. That indeed seems to be the case. "It appears that whoever is up there does not want us to know about them," said David Morehouse. Technology that we attempt to deploy is closely scrutinized by ETs. Anything that would reveal their activities is decommissioned, according to remote viewers, who've discovered what looks like an ET antimissile defense system. Scores of small, grenade-like devices orbit the Earth that intercept and destroy manmade craft, including satellites. Real-world feedback also exists in this instance. In 1993, a Titan 4 rocket carrying Top Secret military hardware exploded shortly after takeoff. Officially the cause was attributed to mechanical failure, but according to Titan 4 project manager, Col. Frank Stirling, Air Force video showed an object hitting the missile just before it exploded. Disclosure Project witness Robert Jacobs told of a similar incident caught on film when a UFO intercepted an ICBM launched from Vandenberg Air Force Base.[39]

Remote viewers can go where our satellites and missiles apparently aren't allowed, but without real-world feedback it's uncertain whether they've hit their target or gone off into the wild blue yonder like former Army Major Ed Dames and his private team of RVers did in 1993 when Dames announced that a group of Martians living in an underground base in New Mexico would soon reveal themselves to the world. This was the flipside of the Carter anecdote. A spectacular failure. When remote viewing doesn't work it's difficult to know what went wrong. Its developers have only demonstrated that it works, not how. The underlying mechanisms that deliver the data are unknown.[40] The protocols are designed to filter out imagination and prevent leading, but such contamination is always a threat. And then there are the known unknowns and the unknown unknowns. Some say ETs can block remote viewers, even editing their perceptions like a Hollywood movie, which seems entirely plausible given first-hand witness testimony about their abilities to manipulate consciousness and create screen memories. On the human side of affairs there's always the possibility of counterintelligence operations and sabotage.

RV intelligence failures like the Martian New Mexico episode highlight the importance of feedback, especially with extraterrestrial targets that include bases on the Moon, the remnants of a Martian civilization beneath the surface of Mars, the Gray's home planet and the Galactic Federation. There is no direct feedback on any of these targets. There are no photos of the Gray's planet for a famous Cosmonaut to reveal to the world, but there is indirect feedback in the form of alien abductee/contact experience eyewitness testimony given to researchers like Hopkins, Mack, etc.[41]

Remote viewers seeking answers about the Grays found they'd lost their home planet to an ecological catastrophe similar to what is unfolding here on Earth today. In a desperate attempt to adapt, the Grays altered their genetic code and became unable to reproduce. With their civilization at a crossroads, they turned to the Galactic Federation for help.[42] It appears the advanced Grays are members of a vast, interstellar quasi-governmental body that operates as a collaborative, non-authoritarian council somewhat like the United Nations. In a plot worthy of *Star Trek*, the advanced Grays obtained permission to use Earth as a gene pool, both to rejuvenate their own stock and to help humanity, it would seem, in our similarly failing endeavor to sustain a viable civilization. Unfortunately, according to Carter White House futurist Alfred Webre, our current state of arrested development has left us without a say in the matter. Based on an alternative RV method called Scientific Remote Viewing, Webre concluded that Earth has no representative advocating for our exopolitical or genetic interests in the universal project to hybridize Grays with humans. "Earth is now in political isolation, and does not participate directly in Universe government. In effect, we have defaulted on our Universe privileges, including that of self-government. The more advanced and evolved civilizations tend to be more involved in Universe governance," wrote Webre who concluded that it was in our best interests to follow the example of the Grays and solicit the help of the Galactic Federation, which presides over the ever-expanding post-Singularity cosmic civilization.

The narrative developed by remote viewers tells us we haven't yet achieved advanced civilization here on Earth. What's more, we're behaving more like renegade self-reproducing carbon nanobots escaped from the lab, turning the Earth's biosphere into gray goo, much like the Grays did to their home planet. As a result, we're stuck in an evolutionary dead end. "An advanced civilization possesses a sense of cosmic responsibility, and can oversee the creation and development of new intelligent planetary life," wrote Webre, who further explained that such a civilization must be spiritually advanced before it is granted license to develop new worlds and to participate in Universe governance, which is a familiar process because Earth's governmental and political systems are "holographic fragments of larger forms in Universe society."[43]

According to Webre, Earth is a soul-bearing, "life-experiment" planet, a "universal commons" ripened for development. Such planets are grown like gardens. Advanced civilizations cultivate a new intelligent civilization over periods measured in billions of years.[44] On such timescales, the strife and dysfunction here on Earth may be no more than a blip in post-Singularity planet development. A small glitch that corrective measures like the Gray alien-human hybrid program and possibly our own local Singularity can fix. To this point in history real civilization has not yet taken hold on Earth. Civil war is an oxymoron. War, as Webre points out, is nothing more than "legally sanctioned murder." Real civilization is unachievable amidst warfare. If Cosmic intervention succeeds and an advanced intelligent civilization can be established on Earth, humanity will have the opportunity to spread throughout the cosmos somewhat like its rudimentary von Neumann probe model, which is like a holographic figment of artificially intelligent imagineering in the post-Singularity universe.

The case for remote viewing intelligence about the Grays, their home planet, the alien-human hybrid program and the Galactic Federation is compelling. Alien abductee experiences and futurist's predictions about the Singularity are consistent with the RV narrative, but RV intelligence must be validated by feedback, especially with such exotic targets. Fortunately, the ultimate, real-world feedback exists for the Great Cosmic post-Singularity Civilization.

THE SINGULARITY IS HERE

Where are they?!! Stanton Friedman doesn't think Fermi posed his famous question as a paradox. "He was known to be an outstanding teacher. One of his techniques was to ask questions that forced students to think," wrote Friedman about Fermi, who died in 1954.[45]

Whatever Fermi's true intent, the scientific community has gone to great lengths to build upon his premise in an attempt to find out *where they are*. Astronomer Frank Drake formalized Fermi's off-the-top-of-the-head calculations about the likelihood of extraterrestrial intelligence as the Drake Equation, which is the basis for SETI. By the time Stanley Kubrick went looking to make an epic science fiction film in the 1960s, scientists following in Fermi's footsteps thought an extraterrestrial von Neumann probe might be found on the Moon. At the time, the possibility that the Moon itself was the equivalent of a von Neumann probe/O'Neill colony was simply a bit too far over the horizon to see with linear vision. If the Moon looked like an artificial construction instead of a natural planetoid it would meet our cultural expectations. The debate would be over. We could point to it as definitive evidence of advanced ET civilization. But it doesn't, so we call the Total Solar Eclipse the "greatest coincidence" and explain it away with Serial Lottery Winner theories.

Meanwhile, the scientific establishment goes on looking for signs of ETI that meet our expectations about what it should look like. The search for the heat signature of a Dyson Sphere is a prime example. An enormous artificial construction encapsulating an entire star to collect all its energy is just the kind of technology an emerging civilization might imagine, but would be long obsolete to a post-Singularity civilization that can harness the zero-point field. It should come as no surprise that efforts to scan the skies in the infrared spectrum haven't produced any evidence of a Dyson sphere.

While the evidence of extraterrestrial intelligence we expect to find remains elusive, the definitive evidence that the Singularity happened elsewhere long ago stares us in the face. The proof is in the stars. "Kurzweil once told me that when he gazes at the distant stars at night, perhaps one should be able to see some cosmic evidence of the singularity happening in some distant galaxy. With the ability to devour or rearrange whole star systems, there should be some footprint left behind by this rapidly expanding singularity," wrote physicist Michio Kaku in his book *Physics of the Future*.[46]

Paradoxically, such 'Saganesque' evidence exists in our own Galaxy, but Kaku, Kurzweil and their colleagues in the scientific community are oblivious to it because modern astronomers cling to the natural model for pulsars - much like their predecessors in the Church did with the geocentric model - even though it's as broken as Ptolemy's epicycles. Once again, the politics of paradigm shift have prevented futurists like Ray Kurzweil from understanding that we're not the first to come this far.

At the January 2000 meeting of the American Astronomical Society, physicist Paul LaViolette presented extraordinary evidence that pulsar radio signals are the product of extraterrestrial intelligence, inadvertently proving that the "footprint" that Kurzweil expects should exist if the Singularity had already happened elsewhere, does, in fact, exist. If science, like the universe according to abductees, is truly self-correcting, perhaps one day in the near future Kurzweil will circle the chart showing the non-random distribution of pulsars on page 23 in LaViolette's *Decoding the Message of the Pulsars* and write *The Singularity is Here!*

"What beings could have performed such an immense engineering feat as this? The powers required to accomplish this go beyond anything we can conceive," wrote LaViolette, who concluded, "Unlike a UFO encounter, which is transitory and leaves behind little evidence that could be used later to convince skeptics, pulsars are continuously in the heavens sending their signals. Their data is well documented in scientific journals. But when properly and objectively studied, this data inevitably leads to the conclusion that a galactic civilization of unusually high advancement does exist and is attempting to communicate with us."[47]

In attempting to decode the message of the pulsars LaViolette stumbled upon Kurzweil's proof that the Singularity has already happened. The implications are staggering. The Galaxy, and maybe the entire Universe, is occupied by a post-Singularity civilization that has engineered the Earth-Moon-Sun system as it spread throughout the heavens. If we manage to achieve our own Singularity we will join the Great Galactic Club and have the opportunity to seed life on a new world like the mythical von Neumann probe.

There's no guarantee we'll make it. The evolutionary defect that has stunted human consciousness threatens to turn our local Singularity into a Terminator apocalypse. The military is by far the largest developer of artificial intelligence. Although the Pentagon claims it won't take humans out of the loop, robots that kill can be made as autonomous as a driverless car.[48] We've had the ability to destroy ourselves since the middle of the last century, but soon the decision may be out of our hands. It could be that warfare inevitably leads to extinction for technological species approaching the Singularity. Again, there's nothing civil about war. Cultures that rely upon warfare for conflict resolution haven't yet achieved true civilization. What's worse, a culture that builds its economy around warfare may not be able to turn off the war machine.

Long before Eisenhower warned about the "unwarranted influence" of the military-industrial complex, the country's most decorated soldier blew the whistle on militarism in *War is a Racket*. According to Major General Smedley Darlington Butler, who was awarded 16 medals, including the Congressional Medal of Honor twice, war is the darkest scam of them all. "War is a racket. It is possibly the oldest, easily the most profitable, surely the most vicious. It is the only one international in scope. It is the only one in which the profits are reckoned in dollars and the losses in lives. A racket is best described, I believe, as something that is not what it seems to the majority of the people. Only a small 'inside' group knows what it is about. It is conducted for the benefit of the very few, at the expense of the very many. Out of war a few people make huge fortunes," said Butler, who quit the military and went on a nationwide speaking tour in the 1930s.[49] Butler gave twelve hundred speeches in seven hundred towns and cities, explaining to swelling crowds what war profiteering really meant.[50] Average corporate profits of six-to-twelve percent skyrocketed to three, four, five hundred percent - even as high as eighteen hundred percent - in times of war.

Unused and unnecessary goods paid for with tax dollars gathered dust in warehouses. In the context of World War I, this meant mosquito netting for soldiers deployed in locations devoid of mosquitoes and horseback saddles for an overseas cavalry that didn't exist.[51]

For Big Business, war wasn't just an excuse to gouge taxpayers. It was also a great opportunity to expand into new markets. "I spent 33 years and four months in active military service and during that period I spent most of my time as a high-class muscle man for Big Business, for Wall Street and the bankers. In short, I was a racketeer, a gangster for capitalism. I helped make Mexico and especially Tampico safe for American oil interests in 1914. I helped make Haiti and Cuba a decent place for the National City Bank boys to collect revenues in. I helped in the raping of half a dozen Central American republics for the benefit of Wall Street. I helped purify Nicaragua for the International Banking House of Brown Brothers in 1902-1912. I brought light to the Dominican Republic for the American sugar interests in 1916. I helped make Honduras right for the American fruit companies in 1903," said Butler.[52]

Despite Butler's speeches and Eisenhower's warning, war is more profitable than ever for insiders who know what it's really all about. There is no greater example of war racketeering than the Iraq war, which is widely known to have been fought on behalf of American oil interests. There is no greater example of someone who knows what it's all about than Dick Cheney and Halliburton, the company he set up to profit from warfare. Through the military-industrial complex revolving door, Cheney made Halliburton the top corporate war profiteer, scoring $39.5 billion in government contracts.[53]

The Iraq war ignited an orgy of war profiteering. The bipartisan Commission of Wartime Contracting estimated as much as $60 billion in graft overall. Bribes, kickbacks and other schemes were rampant.[54] In one glaring example, $9 billion dollars in cash shipped to Iraq on giant brick-like pallets just flat-out disappeared.[55]

Warfare has become so ingrained in our culture that one might assume it's a natural state of human affairs, that it's an innate part of human nature hardwired in our genes. But that doesn't appear to be true. Award-winning science journalist John Horgan found that evidence supporting a biological basis for warfare was flimsy at best. What's more, the archaeological evidence for warfare only dates back about ten thousand years. In fact, war appears to be a recent cultural innovation. In his book, *The End of War*, Horgan argued that warfare was more like a contagious disease than a biological imperative. What's more, the disease of war could flare up for an infinite variety of reasons, or as Butler might've said, an infinite variety of *pretenses*.[56]

The archeological record for warfare may reflect the error that occurred in the course of our evolution. "We humans are the children of a universal cataclysmic event suffered in the course of our planetary evolution. Our subsequent planetary isolation accounts for the severely conflicted, violent, ignorant, and confused state of our history and our society. It is no accident that humans are cursed with war, violence, poverty, ignorance, and death. The violence of the 20th century would not have occurred on a normal life-bearing planet that had not experienced such an evolutionary disaster," wrote Alfred Webre.[57]

This evolutionary error somehow affected the development of our consciousness, which is reflected in our greed. ETs told Betty Andreasson point-blank that greed was the root of all our problems. "Man seeks to destroy himself [through] greed.... He could be advanced so far, but greed gets in the way... Man is very arrogant and greedy and he thinks that all worlds revolve around him."[58] John Mack received the same message from the population of alien abductees he studied. "Growth without restraint has become an end in itself, as the reports of economic "indicators" endlessly intone, ignoring the inevitable collapse that cannot be far off if the multiplication of the human population continues unchecked and the pillaging of the earth does not stop," wrote Mack, who concluded, that the UFO abduction phenomenon "seems to be intricately connected with the nature of human greed, the roots of our destructiveness, and the future consequences of our collective behavior."[59]

Evidence of our destructive behavior is becoming impossible to ignore. According to environmental researchers, the oceans have become "plasticized."[60] Plastic waste is everywhere, but it is especially concentrated in state-sized patches. The Great Garbage Patch of the Pacific Ocean is the largest of five such garbage patches found around the world. Located between the U.S. West Coast and the Hawaiian Islands, the Great Garbage Patch is twice the size of Rhode Island. Dead albatross filled with plastic litter the area.[61] Sadly, death and destruction caused by toxic pollution dumped into the ocean is just part of the story. There are enormous dead zones devoid of life caused by overfishing, which afflicts 90 percent of the world's fisheries.[62]

The skies are also showing the effects of having been used as an open sewer. Recently, China began experiencing toxic weather events dubbed 'airpocalypse' and 'airmegeddon.' Industrial smog so thick that visibility is reduced to mere yards has brought cities like Beijing to a standstill. Schools and airports have been forced to close amidst traffic halted by invisible streetlights. The population forced to wear surgical masks and sometimes gas masks with filters just to breath. Researchers have described Beijing's atmosphere as nearly "uninhabitable for human beings." Such incidences only figure to increase as industrial civilization continues to burn fossil fuel in ever increasing quantities."[63] The toxic pollution that we pump into the atmosphere drives climate change, increasing the frequency and intensity of so-called hundred-year storms like Superstorms Katrina, Sandy and Haiyan and the more recent Maria, which decimated the Florida Keys and destroyed Puerto Rico and several other islands in the Atlantic Ocean.

In a global economy based on ever increasing consumption, it's clear the party won't last. According to the *Living Planet Report,* published every two years by the World Wildlife Fund, the Zoological Society of London and the Global Footprint Network, we have exceeded the biocapacity of the Earth, living so far beyond our means that by 2030 we'll need the resources of two Earths to support our lifestyle. "We are acting ecologically in the same way as financial institutions have been behaving economically - seeking immediate gratification without due regard for the consequences," said ZSL co-editor Jonathan Loh in 2008, referring to the great financial crisis that brought the global economy to its knees. Wall Street banks that caused the crash with assorted frauds and scams, peddling toxic sub-prime, mortgage-backed securities that they themselves bet against in the midst of a housing bubble, were bailed-out at taxpayer's expense.[64] "The consequences of a global ecological crisis are even graver than the current economic meltdown," Loh warned[65]

Our ET benefactors have been even more explicit. "YOU ARE KILLING YOUR PLANET. YOUR PLANET IS DYING," they told Jim Sparks and a group of abductees during a PowerPoint-like presentation showing Earth's environmental degradation, which led him to become an environmental and political activist. Sparks told John Mack, "I learned if we can't take care of ourselves and our planet, how can we ever expect to join the galactic neighborhood?"[66]

During an encounter with a group of reptilian humanoids, Sparks received an even more troubling message. "Your air, your water is contaminated. Your forests, jungles, trees, and plant life are dying. There are several breaks in your food chain. You have an overwhelming amount of nuclear and biological weapons that have brought about nuclear and biological contamination. Your planet is overpopulated. Warning: It is almost too late, unless your people act. There are better ways of deriving your energy and food needs without causing your planet any damage. Those in power are aware of this and have the capability of putting these methods into worldwide use," said ETs to Sparks. Unfortunately, instead of using ET technology to usher in a new world, we've used it to make weapons and money, furthering the racket that is the military-industrial complex.[67]

The cultural quandary in which we find ourselves is a reflection of the limitations of our collective consciousness, which is a product of the error in our evolution. "A powerful barrier keeping us locked within a terrestrial isolation is our Earth-bound culture. Our imprisoned culture repeats its patterns of waging wars, building military establishments, supporting tyrannies, weaponizing outer space, oppressing populations, committing genocide, and engaging in mass mind control of humanity. Our culture is now hijacked by elites, that maintain this destructive agenda and deny Earth its Universe citizenship.

"From the perspective of those who monitor Earth on behalf of Universe society, there is a moral bottom line to our collective behavior on Earth. What keep us imprisoned in quarantine are the violent, regressive patterns of our war-like society. In the eyes of Universe society, war and ecocide have negative consequences for human civilization. Perpetual warfare and ecological degradation of the planet mark us as a backward civilization incapable of participating in the advanced Universe scheme of things," concluded Alfred Webre.[68`]

Fortunately, ETs aren't the aliens we assume them to be. The Moon and the pulsar beacon network show that extraterrestrials come from an advanced, post-Singularity civilization that has spread throughout the Cosmos. Earth is one developmental project among countless others in an ever expanding Universe Society. True aliens might see our behavior and simply decide to drop an asteroid on us like one might pour a pot of boiling water on an out-of-control anthill, but real ETs see a defective Universe project that needs fixed. The ETs themselves told hand picked spokesperson Betty Andreasson this was what was happening. "Betty's mentors have told us that they have always coexisted with Man and are genetically related. They have identified themselves as caretakers of the forms of life that have developed on earth. Over their existence, they have conducted a long-term genetics program to prolong and improve life on this planet," wrote Raymond Fowler in the conclusion to his decade long investigation of the Andreasson affair.[69]

Betty also received a stark warning about the damage we are doing to the environment, including its relationship to the hybrid program. "The reason given for the sudden acceleration of their genetics program was that Man was going to become sterile. His many-faceted pollution of the environment was out of control. It would lead to the death of life on this planet," wrote Fowler who cited a litany of environmental threats including drugs, acid rain, pesticides, pollution, animal and plant extinction, global warming, AIDS and radiation leaks from atomic plants.[70] Since Fowler published *The Watchers* in 1990, industrial assault on the environment has been unrelenting, ever increasing in scope. Recent examples include the 2010 British Petroleum Deepwater Horizon oil spill that fouled the Gulf of Mexico and the ongoing 2011 Fukushima nuclear meltdown that is leaking 400 tons of radioactive groundwater into the Pacific Ocean every day.[71]

In the course of their experiences with the Extraterrestrial intervention, Alien Abductee/Contact Experiencers have been made to feel the impact that environmental devastation is having on the Earth. They've also come to understand that they're not victims. In fact, it appears that these individuals volunteered to assist in the re-engineering of human civilization on a soul level before being born on Earth. "Both men and women come to feel despite their anger that they are taking part – even that they have chosen to participate – in a process that is life creating and life-giving. Furthermore, for most abductees the hybridization has occurred simultaneously with an enlightenment imparted by the alien beings that has brought home forcibly to them the failure of the human experiment in its present form," wrote Mack, whose abductees made the painful discovery that they had a dual alien-human identity. "I'm a gray in my soul," Mack abductee Karin told him.[72]

The idea that abductees themselves may be ETs who have come into this world through the birth process as part of a planet-saving mission may sound like new age, space-brother mysticism, but as abductee Jim Sparks said, it's simply a matter of advanced technology. In the post-Singularity world consciousness is uploadable. It's transferable between devices just like a computer file. The body itself is the ultimate device. Imagine an iBody. These are the terms that abductees use when describing what it's like to take a human body on Earth, which entails a much more "dense embodiment." One abductee described it as somewhat like putting on a wet suit and scuba gear.[73]

How it all works is impossible to foresee for futurists like Kurzweil. Consciousness is a thorny subject that science can't fully explain. In the Western Scientific paradigm, there is no soul. Consciousness is a product of the brain. It doesn't exist apart from the body. After the Singularity, it will become apparent that the soul is a discrete entity that inhabits the body, which is a vessel, a piece of equipment. This relationship between the body and soul can be managed with technology. ETs told Betty Andreasson-Luca they had "spiritual technology." Her out of body abduction incident is a prime example. Betty saw a gray ET use a small device to detach her soul from her body during an abduction event.

The possibilities of such technology are surely limitless. As Kurzweil correctly surmised, it's possible to have a dual identity. Musing about the post-Singularity future, he wrote, "I'm able to change who I am quite readily... I can combine my thought patterns with someone else's and create a merged identity. It's a profound experience."[74] The abduction contact experiencers are a real-life example of dual identity that reveal not only the wonders of such advanced technology, but the challenges it presents.

Abductees seem to have great difficulty reconciling their dual alien-human identity and sometimes ETs have trouble getting them to recognize their ET side. Abductee's complaints to what are apparently their ET colleagues that they have no right to abduct them have been firmly rebuked.[75] Sometimes ETs have to go to great lengths to get abductees like Jim Sparks to see their inner ET and to remember their original purpose. Sparks called his experience an "alien boot camp." In the foreword to Sparks' book *The Keepers*, John Mack wrote, "The purpose of this schooling seems to be twofold: to create a hybrid race as an "insurance policy" for the future, and to awaken us to our destructiveness, so that we may halt the devastation we are bringing to Earth."[76]

The implications are clear. If mankind can't wake up in time to clean up its act it will be replaced. Hybrids will repopulate the planet. One way or the other, the error that occurred in human evolution on Earth will be corrected. According to one of Mack's abductees, the universe is an interconnected "tapestry" of life that is "self-correcting." It may be that our own local Singularity is part of the process. The development of open source technology, including cryptocurrencies that can't be manipulated by central banks, and quantum technology that can't be hacked, may make it much more difficult, if not impossible, for the elites to continue to rig the system. At the same time, exponentially evolving technology connects us in new ways, extending our senses and expanding our consciousness.

We now find ourselves in the same situation that we were over four hundred years ago when Galileo pointed his telescope at Jupiter and proved that the Earth was not the center of the universe around which everything revolved. But this time things are a little different. The stakes are high and time is short. Kurzweil's most recent estimate is that we will hit the Singularity in 2029.[77] That means the ultimate paradigm shift is just about a decade away. If we successfully navigate our Singularity without becoming killer robots that turn the Earth's surface into gray goo we will join the Great Cosmic Civilization. If it goes the other way there are alien-human hybrids waiting in the wings.[78] Amidst the folly of too-big-to-fail scams, frauds, hustles, rackets and cons, how it all plays out is anyone's guess.

AFTERWORD

Ironically, it seems Singularity theorists like Google Director of Engineering Ray Kurzweil don't read much non-fiction science fiction. If they did they'd understand that we're not going to be the first to hit the Singularity and so we're not going to be the ones to colonize the galaxy. That ship has sailed. The process began long ago, somewhere else. But Kurzweil, Kaku and their colleagues don't know that. They don't know because the astronomical community doesn't recognize LaViolette's discovery that Pulsars are stellar cores that have been moved around the galaxy and placed into strategic positions to serve as radio beacons by an advanced extraterrestrial civilization.

One would think that after 2003 when a group of radio astronomers found that the Crab pulsar had properties that can't be explained by the standard pulsar model there would be a crisis in radio astronomy like there was when the Ptolemaic model broke down. One would think there'd be a modern-day Copernicus in there somewhere searching for an alternative. But there isn't. Not when the alternate model is extraterrestrial intelligence and the prospect of paradigm shift.

As a result, Singularity theorists don't know that radio astronomy has confirmed LaViolette's theory, which, in turn, fulfills Kurzweil's prediction that if the Singularity had already happened elsewhere there would be an artificial grouping of stars somewhere in the heavens. Such is the "half-way cleverness" of man as the great British philosopher Bertrand Russell put it.

It's hard to see things changing anytime soon. LaViolette's work is a threat to the status quo. If his findings gained traction it would cause great embarrassment to radio astronomers much like cold fusion did to nuclear fusion engineers. Pons and Fleischmann's announcement was like a gut punch to the nuclear fusion community. "It was shocking and insulting to the hot fusion people as if they had been told that their television set had not been able to run for decades because they had neglected to plug it in," wrote MIT science writer Eugene Mallove.[1]

SETI astronomers would suffer similar crushing humiliation. It seems unlikely they'd be willing to admit they've been overlooking ET radio signals since 1967. So here we are again mired in a flawed paradigm destined to fail. But this time we won't spend another 1,300 years tweaking a crumbling model. The closer we get to our own local Singularity - which should occur around 2029 based on Kurzweil's estimate - the more obvious it will be that the current worldview is just as illusory as Ptolemy's epicycles.

When this happens we'll experience the ultimate paradigm shift and with it the single greatest expansion of consciousness in human history. Every change in worldview causes an expansion of consciousness that transforms our reality. The shift from flat Earth to spherical Earth enabled us to sail around the globe without fear of falling off. The transition from Earth-centered universe to Sun-centered solar system led us to venture out into space in search of our place in the cosmos.

The Singularity will literally usher in a New World- if we can take it. It's impossible to imagine what it's going to be like to live in a world where everyone's as smart as Tesla or Einstein and the new iPhone is a brain implant that wirelessly connects every mind in the world to every other mind as well as to the Internet, a vast, virtual world within the real world in which it's possible to cheat death indefinitely. Luckily, we don't need our imagination to know what this world will be like. The UFO phenomenon is a manifestation of a post-Singularity civilization. The close encounter experiencers studied by John Mack have one foot in this world, which is much like Kurzweil's vision of our future, only even more incredible.

After our local Singularity we won't expand out into space at light speed or better as establishment Singularity theorists expect. Instead, we'll find that space is occupied by a post-Singularity civilization and that we're the newest member of a Galactic Federation of planets. Once our little outpost fully matures we'll be entrusted with the development of a new world. Like the self-replicating robots in Fermi paradox theorist's model for galactic colonization, we'll spread to a new planet and start from scratch, thus continuing the process of expansion and evolution of life in the universe.

There's just one problem: We're defective. We may not make it to the Singularity. We have a Big Brain but we don't really know how to use it. Spiritualists teach that an error in our evolution has prevented us from accessing its full range of capabilities.

"Man's ordinary state of consciousness is not the highest level of consciousness of which he is capable. In fact, it is so defective that the condition has been defined as little better than somnambulism. Man does not really know what he is doing or where he is going. He lives in dreams. He inhabits a world of delusions and, because of these delusions, he makes dangers for himself and others," wrote the late scientist, Robert S. de Ropp, disciple of esoteric spiritual masters, P. D. Ouspensky and G. I. Gurdjieff.[2] De Ropp used an age-old story he called *The Myth of the Mad King* to sum up our fundamental malfunction. Various cultures tell a version of the story about a king gone mad who mistakes the squalor of the dungeon for the throne. His delusions are such that he sees the rags, refuse and bones as his crown jewels and he reacts incredulously when told otherwise by his servants. We are like the king in the story and our ET benefactors are like the king's servants trying to shake us from our delusions. Mack's alien abductees tell us that these extraterrestrial beings are attempting to foment a transformation of consciousness in humanity in order to prevent the destruction of nature on Earth. They've warned us that we're killing our planet, but like the mad king we go on with our quarterly earnings reports, bridal showers, the Super Bowl and so forth. Meanwhile, we're turning the surface of our planet into gray goo just like the hypothetical self-replicating carbon nanobots that Fermi's paradox theorists like to muse about. "The Earth, our home, is beginning to look like an immense pile of filth," wrote Pope Francis in his recent encyclical.[3] Indeed.

One can make a case that the importance of the scientific consensus on global warming induced climate change is diminished by paradigm shifts of the past. They've been wrong before and they may be wrong yet again. Maybe we'll wind up in a new ice age instead of the ultimate Burning Man barbeque? But it's undeniable that we are trashing this planet. How long will it be before our beaches look like city dumps and the oceans seem more like some sort of toxic Italian salad dressing? What happens when airpocalypse is the norm in China? That's nothing to say of Three Mile Island, Chernobyl, Fukushima or any of the chemical and nuclear waste produced by the military-industrial complex. To not see this as a dungeon is to be the mad king.

So far our ET overlords have been unsuccessful in their efforts to persuade us not to destroy ourselves. According to former Canadian Defense Minister Paul Hellyer, it's the same international banking cabal enforcing UFO secrecy that's behind all the world's problems. [4] It's important to note that this is the same crowd that thwarted Tesla and tried to enlist Major General Smedley Butler in an attempt to overthrow the government of the United States in order to establish a fascist dictatorship in concert with Nazi Germany.

It seems the mad kings of Earth have successfully warded off the heavens. Or have they? Corso told Trudeau that, despite fears about alien invasion, he thought the Roswell crash might be a gift like the "gift of fire." [5] The prospect of software that writes new software and neural network systems that learn from their experiences in the real world convinced him that we would develop a symbiotic relationship with this alien technology/silicon-based life-form. In other words, we'd experience a technological Singularity.

If we consider Tesla a first, failed, attempt at establishing a fully functioning post-Singularity galactic colony, then maybe the Roswell crash was plan B. Perhaps it went something like this: *Tesla was our von Neumann probe. The visions he received from extraterrestrials were like instructions one of our probes might receive from mission control. Tesla even described himself as a "self-propelled automaton entirely under the control of external influences" and used himself as a model to build the telautomaton, his remote-controlled boat that he considered the first nonbiological life-form[6]. He literally meets the definition of self-reproducing robot. But something has seriously gone wrong down on "the farm," as Corso put it.*

We have not fully evolved. Our pseudo-civilization, plagued by warfare, reflects our lack of development. Hostility towards the super-civilization from which we spring is a malfunction not unlike that of the HAL 9000 computer in *2001: A Space Odyssey*.

So mission control comes up with a workaround. It uses our militarism as a delivery system. It stages a crash, complete with a crew of "humanoid robots" allowing the technology to fall into our hands, knowing it would be developed for defense against what we mistakenly believe are hostile aliens from another planet. It's a brilliant ploy. They even got us to use Tesla's notes.

Mission control knows that the Singularity is a self-corrective process. As we merge with our technology we'll become much more than just halfway clever. Nanobots will not only supercharge our intellectual faculties turning us into Tesla and Einstein with the memory of Rainman and Sheldon Cooper, they'll also augment the portions of our brain that give us mystical and spiritual experiences. We'll all experience the enlightenment of the Buddha, the compassion of the Christ and the godly attributes of (insert preferred religious/spiritual figure here). We'll finally have full access to higher levels of consciousness. We'll awaken as individual nodes in a global brain. Like Mack's subjects we'll feel a "heightened reverence for nature" and a connection with all of creation. We'll finally experience the transformation in consciousness that will enable us to fully mature as a galactic species.

In the New World – if we make it - we'll see that the Earth is a palace that we've turned into a dungeon. We'll clean up our mess and green the deserts. And we'll all become aware of the extraterrestrial presence and the greater galactic civilization. We will have experienced the last, great paradigm shift and an explosion of super-consciousness.

It will be a thunderous paradigm shift of Ptolemaic proportions for the scientific community, which will be subject to relentless, merciless revision. In the aftermath of the Singularity, science will finally be truly self-correcting. To get an idea of how this paradigm shift might unfold imagine the shock and disbelief if Einstein's theory of relativity and the Big Bang were suddenly revealed to be as mythical as Ptolemy's epicycles. Now imagine that really happens. The Brookings Institute report is going to prove prophetic. The post-Singularity world will shred cornerstone theories of the scientific establishment.

The possibility that the theory of relativity is wrong is currently unthinkable, but as the Roswell Incident showed, the future is Tesla's. He flat-out rejected the idea of curved space-time as delusional, condemning it as "futile and destined to oblivion." He said only a field of force could explain the motion of astronomical objects. Tesla tied gravity to electromagnetism and called it the most important phenomenon in the universe. He developed a unified field theory called the Dynamic Theory of Gravity based on his experiments. Unfortunately, he died before he was able to give the world mathematical details of his theory, which reportedly remains classified.[7]

If Tesla had been able to publish his theory it might have changed the course of history. According to Mallove, the growing body of evidence for low-energy nuclear reactions shows that Tesla was right- relativity is wrong.[8] What's more, Paul LaViolette has also concluded that relativity is an illusion. In fact, he disproved the Big Bang theory in a paper published in the *Astrophysical Journal* in 1986. LaViolette suggested a new model of the universe he calls continuous creation cosmology based on his theory of subquantum kinetics.[9]

If it's true that our cosmology is completely wrong, once again, the closer we get to the Singularity the more obvious it will become. The same is true of LaViolette's pulsars and the extraterrestrial presence. It won't take a thousand years or even a hundred years this time. In the blink of an eye, our collective worldview will change. Maybe far more than even Tesla imagined.

A new worldview will be shaped by where the original Singularity occurred. Did it happen somewhere else in our galaxy or did it happen in another galaxy somewhere else in the universe? Could it have happened in another dimension or another universe altogether? Are we the product of a much older planetary civilization that is colonizing the galaxy or is the entire universe the product of a post-Singularity civilization? Has the cosmos been designed specifically to bring about beings like us? Just how far down the rabbit hole are we and what will the new worldview look like?

Physicist Seth Lloyd says the universe is a quantum computer, which brings to mind the sci-fi classic *The Matrix*.[10] As fantastic as it sounds, it could be that we will come to understand ourselves to be the inhabitants of a computer-generated world designed by a post-Singularity civilization. Imagine yourself as a real-life avatar and God as the ultimate database. The idea of an all-seeing, all-knowing entity, which sounds absurd to 20th century intellectuals, might just have its roots in something akin to the NSA's worldwide cyber-surveillance system exposed by Edward Snowden that enables the agency to know everything one does online.

This is admittedly some far-out, non-fiction, science fiction. In fact, it's so far out we may need another new literary genre. Call it science-fiction existentialism. Because Nietzsche, Sartre and all that nihilistic hand ringing over the abyss is going to turn out to be just a lot of pre-Singularity angst.

ENDNOTES

INTRODUCTION

[1] Cox, *Subpoena the Roswell 'whistle-blower'*, Herald-Tribune, Thursday, July 19, 2012 http://devoid.blogs.heraldtribune.com/13141/subpoena-the-roswell-whistle-blower/?tc=ar; Friedman, *Roswell Really Happened, Says Former CIA Agent*, Time Magazine, July 11, 2012 http://newsfeed.time.com/2012/07/11/roswell-really-happened-says-former-cia-agent/

CHAPTER I – PARADOX

[1] Jones, *Where is Everybody? An Account of Fermi's Question*, Los Alamos National Laboratory, Los Alamos, Dec. 1985, p.1-3

[2] Villard, Williams, *Hubble's Deepest View of the Universe Unveils Bewildering Galaxies across Billions of Years*, Hubblesite.org, Jan. 15, 1996, http://hubblesite.org/newscenter/archive/releases/1996/01/

[3] see *Hubble's Greatest Discoveries*, Hubblesite.org, http://hubblesite.org/newscenter/press_resources/hubbles_greatest_discoveries.php

[4] Savage, Villard, Christensen, Stiles, *Hubble's Deepest View Ever of the Universe Unveils Earliest Galaxies*, Hubblesite.org, March 4, 2004, http://hubblesite.org/newscenter/archive/releases/2004/07/text/

[5] Mackie, *To see the Universe in a Grain of Taranaki Sand*, North and South Magazine, New Zealand, May 1999, http://astronomy.swin.edu.au/~gmackie/billions.html

[6] Kaku, *Kaku on Life Beyond Earth*, mkaku.org, Aug. 17, 2017, http://mkaku.org/home/tag/alien-intelligence/

[7] Sagan, Cosmos, Episode XI: The Persistence of Memory, Cosmos Studios, 1980

[8] See *NASA Wilkinson Microwave Anisotropy Probe*, http://map.gsfc.nasa.gov/universe/uni_age.html

[9] Webb, *If the Universe is Teeming with Aliens… Where is Everybody? Fifty Solutions to the Fermi Paradox and the Problem of Extraterrestrial Life*, Copernicus Books, New York, 2010, p.19-21

[10] Barrow & Tipler, *The Anthropic Cosmological Principle*, Oxford University Press, New York, 1988, p.578-580

[11] Kaku, *Hyperspace: A Scientific Odyssey Through Parallel Universes, Time Warps, and the 10th Dimension*, Anchor Books, New York, March 1995, p.308-9; Davies, *Are*

We Alone? Philosophical Implications of the Discovery of Extraterrestrial Life, BasicBooks, New York, 1995, p.66-8

[12] Shklovsky & Sagan, *Intelligent Life in the Universe*, Dell Publishing, New York, 1966, p.373, 441-7, 485-8

[13] Freitas, *Fermi's Paradox: A Real Howler*, Isaac Asimov's Science Fiction Magazine 8, Sept, 1984, p.30-44, http://www.rfreitas.com/Astro/FermiHowler1984.htm; Webb, *If the Universe is Teeming with Aliens... Where is Everybody?* p.1-2; Frietas, *Extraterrestrial Intelligence in the Solar System: Resolving the Fermi Paradox*, Journal of the British Interplanetary Society 36, Nov. 1983, p.496-500, http://www.rfreitas.com/Astro/ResolvingFermi1983.htm

[14] Davidson, *Carl Sagan: A Life*, John Wiley & Sons, New York, 1999, p.346-54

[15] Ruppelt, *The Report On Unidentified Flying Objects*, Doubleday, New York, 1956, p.47-51, Online version available at http://www.nicap.org/rufo/contents.htm

[16] Dolan, *UFOs and the National Security State: An Unclassified History, Volume One: 1941-1973*, Keyhole Publishing Company, Rochester, Apr. 2000, p.108-9, 113-5

[17] Ruppelt, *The Report On Unidentified Flying Objects*, p.52-4

[18] Dolan, *UFOs and the National Security State: An Unclassified History*, p.123

[19] Swords, Powell, Svahn, Olmos, Chalker, Greenwood, Thieme, Aldrich & Purcell, *UFOs and Government: A Historical Inquiry*, Anomalist Books, San Antonio, July 5, 2012, p.81

[20] Swords, *Clyde Tombaugh, Mars, and UFOs*, Journal of Scientific Exploration, Vol. 13, No. 4, 1999, p.685-694, http://www.scientificexploration.org/journal/volume-13-number-4-1999

[21] Marrs, *Alien Agenda*, HarperCollins Publishers, New York, 1997, p.137-144

[22] Keyhoe, *Aliens From Space*, Signet, New York, 1974, p.130-1

[23] Cameron, *More on the 1954 UFO Satellites*, presidentialufo.com, Nov. 29, 2012, http://www.presidentialufo.com/dwight-d-eisenhower/476-more-on-the-1954-ufo-satellites

[24] Dolan, *UFOs and the National Security State: An Unclassified History*, p.43

[25] Dolan, *UFOs and the National Security State: An Unclassified History*, p.28-30

[26] Carey & Schmitt, *Witness to Roswell*, New Page Books, Franklin Lakes, 2009, p.86

[27] Dolan, *UFOs and the National Security State: An Unclassified History*, p.49-67

[28] Carey & Schmitt, *Witness to Roswell*, p185-195

[29] Friedman, *Top Secret/Majic*, Marlowe & Company, New York, 1996, p.17-8

[30] Carey & Schmitt, *Witness to Roswell*, p.40

[31] CNN Larry King Live, *Roswell Truth Debated*, July, 4, 2008, http://transcripts.cnn.com/TRANSCRIPTS/0807/04/lkl.01.html; *Former astronaut: Man not alone in universe*, CNN, April 20, 2009,

http://www.cnn.com/2009/tech/04/20/ufo.conference/index.html; Carey & Schmitt, *Witness to Roswell*, p.15-8

[32] Carey & Schmitt, *Witness to Roswell*, p.175-183

[33] Friedman, *Top Secret/Majic*, p.20-3, 222-9

[34] Friedman, *Top Secret/Majic*, p.55

[35] Friedman, *Top Secret/Majic*, p.20-2, 61, 209-210

[36] Friedman, *Update on Operation Majestic 12 Documents*, StantonFriedman.com, 2004, p.2, http://www.stantonfriedman.com/index.php?ptp=articles&fdt=2004.04.15&prt=2; Friedman, *Top Secret/Majic*, p.152-3

[37] Dolan, *UFOs and the National Security State: An Unclassified History*, p.82-6

[38] Friedman, *Top Secret/Majic*, p.150-160; Friedman, *Update on Operation Majestic 12 Documents*, p.4

[39] Carey & Schmitt, *Witness to Roswell*, p.30; Hansen, *The Missing Times: News Media Complicity in the UFO Cover-up*, Xlibris, Bloomington, 2000, p.242

[40] Dolan, *UFOs and the National Security State: An Unclassified History*, p.60-1

[41] Dolan, *UFOs and the National Security State: An Unclassified History*, p.171-5

[42] Carlson, *Alien Armada*, Washington Post, July 21, 2002, http://www.washingtonpost.com/ac2/wp-dyn?pagename=article&node=&contentId=A31625-2002Jul19

[43] Dolan, *UFOs and the National Security State: An Unclassified History*, p.128

[44] Dolan, *UFOs and the National Security State: An Unclassified History*, p.198; Hansen, *The Missing Times*, p.167-170

[45] *Report on Scientific Advisory Panel on Unidentified Flying Objects Convened by Office of Scientific Intelligence, CIA*, Jan. 14-18, 1953 Tab A p.26, http://www.cufon.org/cufon/robert.htm

[46] *Report on Scientific Advisory Panel on Unidentified Flying Objects Convened by Office of Scientific Intelligence, CIA*, Jan. 14-18, 1953, p.20-21, http://www.cufon.org/cufon/robert.htm

[47] Hansen, *The Missing Times*, p.167-171, 254; Dolan, *UFOs and the National Security State: An Unclassified History*, p.393

[48] Hansen, *The Missing Times*, p.15-33

[49] Hansen, *The Missing Times*, p.235-246

[50] Hansen, *The Missing Times*, p.237-9

[51] Howe, *CIA Origin of National Enquirer?* Earthfiles.com, 2007, http://www.earthfiles333.com/earthfiles/EarthfilesPodcast/A8B062F2-8342-49B4-8014-C108C1FBE963.html

[52] Hansen, *The Missing Times*, p.145

[53] Hansen, *The Missing Times*, p.34

[54] Friedman, *Top Secret/Majic*, p.113-4

[55] Dolan, *UFOs and the National Security State: An Unclassified History*, p.144, 146

[56] Friedman, *Top Secret/Majic*, p.86-102; Dolan, *UFOs and the National Security State: The Cover-up Exposed, 1973-1991*, Keyhole Publishing Company, Rochester, September 2009, p.401

[57] Knapp, *Nuclear physicist searches for evidence in Roswell UFO case*, March 28, 2014, http://www.8newsnow.com/story/25101190/i-team

[58] Dolan, *UFOs and the National Security State: An Unclassified History*, p.43; http://www.majesticdocuments.com

[59] Friedman, *Top Secret/Majic*, p.47-8

[60] Greer, *Disclosure: Military and Government Witnesses Reveal the Greatest Secrets in Modern History*, Crossing Point Inc., Crozet, 2001, p.18, 28, 188; Darlington, *Area 51: The Dreamland Chronicles*, Henry Holt & Company, New York, 1997, p.67; *UFOs and the National Security State: The Cover-up Exposed, 1973-1991*, Keyhole Publishing Company, Rochester, September 2009, p.409-410

[61] Jones, *Where is Everybody? An Account of Fermi's Question*, p.2

[62] Dolan, *UFOs and the National Security State: An Unclassified History*, p.434; Dolan, *Twelve Government Documents That Take UFOs Seriously*, Dec. 5, 2009, http://www.richarddolanpress.com/#!twelve-government-documents/cg96

[63] Dolan, *UFOs and the National Security State: The Cover-up Exposed*, p.17-8; Stringfield, *Situation Red*, Fawcett Crest Books, New York, 1977, p.40-2

Chapter 2 – ROSWELL

[1] Jones, *Where is Everybody? An Account of Fermi's Question*, p.2

[2] Dolan, *UFOs and the National Security State: An Unclassified History*, p44-6

[3] Carey & Schmitt, *Witness to Roswell*, p.36

[4] Carey & Schmitt, *Witness to Roswell*, p.66

[5] Carey & Schmitt, *Witness to Roswell*, p.81-86; Marrs, *Alien Agenda*, p.90; Dolan, *UFOs and the National Security State: An Unclassified History*, p.52-5

[6] Carey & Schmitt, *Witness to Roswell*, , p.88, 137-9, 252

[7] Carey &Schmitt, *Witness to Roswell*, p.205-7

[8] Marrs, *Alien Agenda*, p.93; Carey & Schmitt, *Witness to Roswell*, p.199-201, 215

[9] Pflock, *Roswell: Inconvenient Facts and the Will to Believe*, Prometheus Books, Amherst, June 2001, p.113, 114, 117; Zimmerman, *Affidavit of Earl L. Zimmerman*, Nov. 2, 1993, http://www.roswellproof.com/zimmerman.html

[10] Carey & Schmitt, *Witness to Roswell*, p.139, 269

[11] Carey & Schmitt, *Witness to Roswell*, p.86, 124-5

[12] Carey & Schmitt, *Witness to Roswell*, p.103

[13] Dolan, *UFOs and the National Security State: An Unclassified History*, p.52

[14] Carey & Schmitt, *Witness to Roswell*, p.98

[15] Carey & Schmitt, *Witness to Roswell*, p.97, 123

[16] Dolan, *UFOs and the National Security State: An Unclassified History*, p.3; Carey & Schmitt, *Witness to Roswell*, p.217

[17] Dolan, *UFOs and the National Security State: An Unclassified History*, p.53; Carey & Schmitt, *Witness to Roswell*, p.67, 69-70

[18] Carey & Schmitt, *Witness to Roswell*, p.56-7, 67

[19] Carey & Schmitt, *Witness to Roswell*, p.42

[20] Carey & Schmitt, *Witness to Roswell*, p.57; Friedman, *Top Secret/Majic*, p.15-6; Dolan, *UFOs and the National Security State: An Unclassified History*, p.62

[21] Carey & Schmitt, *Witness to Roswell*, p.252

[22] Friedman, *Top Secret/Majic*, p.19

[23] Dolan, *UFOs and the National Security State: An Unclassified History*, p.52; Carey & Schmitt, *Witness to Roswell*, p.125-6

[24] Carey & Schmitt, *Witness to Roswell*, p.163-183

[25] Carey & Schmitt, *Witness to Roswell*, p.33, 100, 126-130, 176-183; Dolan, *UFOs and the National Security State: An Unclassified History*, p.53

[26] Friedman & Berliner, *Crash at Corona*, Marlowe & Company, New York, 1995, p.xv.

[27] Carey & Schmitt, *Witness to Roswell*, p.46

[28] Carey & Schmitt, *Witness to Roswell*, p.30

[29] Carey & Schmitt, *Witness to Roswell*, p.61, 78; Roswell Daily Record, *Harassed Rancher who Located 'Saucer' Sorry He Told About It*, July 9, 1947, p.1 - front page

[30] Dolan, *UFOs and the National Security State: An Unclassified History*, p.59-60

[31] Carey & Schmitt, *Witness to Roswell*, p.30, 36

[32] Carey & Schmitt, *Witness to Roswell*, p.97

[33] Rudiak, http://www.Roswellproof.com; Carey & Schmitt, *Witness to Roswell*, p. 297

[34] Carey & Schmitt, *Witness to Roswell*, p.245-251

[35] Carey & Schmitt, *Witness to Roswell*, p.251-4

[36] Marrs, *Alien Agenda*, p.96-7; Dolan, *UFOs and the National Security State: An Unclassified History*, p.55

[37] Dolan, *UFOs and the National Security State: An Unclassified History*, p.132

[38] Dolan, *UFOs and the National Security State: An Unclassified History*, p.144

[39] Dolan, *UFOs and the National Security State: The Cover-up Exposed*, p.140-1

[40] Dolan, *UFOs and the National Security State: An Unclassified History*, p.58-9

[41] Dolan, *UFOs and the National Security State: An Unclassified History*, p.59-60

[42] Carey & Schmitt, *Witness to Roswell*, p.67-70

[43] Dolan, *UFOs and the National Security State: An Unclassified History*, p.53, 60-62; Carey & Schmitt, *Witness to Roswell*, p.53, 54, 55-6, 78, 209; *Harassed Rancher who Located 'Saucer' Sorry He Told About It*, Roswell Daily Record, July 9, 1947, p.1 - front page headline

[44] Carey & Schmitt, *Witness to Roswell*, p. 54-5, 69, 75-7

[45] Dolan, *UFOs and the National Security State: An Unclassified History*, p.65; Carey & Schmitt, *Witness to Roswell*, p.205-8

[46] Carey & Schmitt, *Witness to Roswell*, p.240-1

[47] Dolan, *UFOs and the National Security State: An Unclassified History*, p.59-61

[48] Carey & Schmitt, *Witness to Roswell*, p.30

[49] Carey & Schmitt, *Witness to Roswell*, p.36

[50] Corso & Birnes; *The Day After Roswell*, Pocket Books, first hardcover printing, New York, July 1997, Back matter

[51] Corso & Birnes; *The Day After Roswell*, Pocket Books, first hardcover printing, New York, July 1997, p.x

[52] Ressner & Handy, *Roswell or Bust*, Time Magazine, June 23, 1997, http://www.time.com/time/magazine/ article/0,9171,986566,00.html

[53] Jacobson, CongressDaily, *The Senator and the UFOs*, GovernmentExecutive.com, National Journal Group, June 4, 1997, http:www.govexec.com/dailyfed/0697/060497t4.htm

[54] Broad, *Senator Regrets Role in Book on Aliens*, The New York Times, June 5, 1997, http://www.nytimes.com/1997/06/05/us/senator-regrets-role-in-book-on-aliens.html

[55] Corso & Birnes, *The Day After Roswell*, Pocket Books, New York, 1998, p.276

[56] COMETA, *UFOs and Defense: What Should We Prepare For?* VSD Magazine, France, July 1999, p.52; https://archive.org/details/TheCometaReport/page/n1 (English translation)

[57] Salla, *Colonel Philip Corso and his Critics: Crossing the Rubicon between Objective Criticism and Debunking – Part 2*, Exopolitics Journal, April 2006, p.207, http://www.exopoliticsjournal.com/journal-vol-1-3-Salla.pdf; http://www.virtuallystrange.net/ufo/updates/2001/oct/m31-002.shtml

[58] Pflock, *Pflock on Corso*, Mutual UFO Network UFO Journal, number 404, Dec. 2001, p.22, http://www.scribd.com/doc/21435155/Mutual-UFO-Network

[59] Dolan, *The CIA, Official History, and You: A Study of Gerald Haines and UFOs*, UFO Magazine, Dec/Jan. 2001; http://keyholepublishing.com/Haines.htm

[60] Corso & Birnes, *The Day After Roswell*, p.27, 37-9

[61] Corso & Birnes, *The Day After Roswell*, p.40; All POW-MIA, *Senate Select Committee 49*, http://aiipowmia.com/ssc/ssc49.html; Douglass, Jr., *Remembering*

Those We Left Behind, Dec. 18, 2002,
http://aiipowmia.com/sea/douglassremember.html

[62] Corso & Birnes, *The Day After Roswell*, p.95, 226, 228

[63] Bassett, *Lt. Col. Philip J. Corso: Biography and Accomplishments*, FOIA documents, Paradigm Research Group, 2004,
http://www.paradigmresearchgroup.org/Awards/Corso_Philip.htm; Clear Channel Communications, *Interview with Col. Philip J. Corso*, Coast to Coast AM radio program with Art Bell, 7/23/97

[64] Corso & Birnes, *The Day After Roswell*, p.4, 44, 55, 86-7

[65] Corso & Birnes, *The Day After Roswell*, p.31-5; Clear Channel Communications, *Interview with Col. Philip J. Corso*, Coast to Coast AM radio program with Art Bell, 7/23/97

[66] Corso & Birnes, *The Day After Roswell*, p.44, 55

[67] Corso & Birnes, *The Day After Roswell*, p.45-6, 95

[68] Corso & Birnes, *The Day After Roswell*, p.40, 92-3

[69] Corso & Birnes, *The Day After Roswell*, p.93

[70] Corso & Birnes, *The Day After Roswell*, p.45

[71] Corso & Birnes, *The Day After Roswell*, p.87

[72] Corso & Birnes, *The Day After Roswell*, p.55, 60, 86

[73] Corso & Birnes, *The Day After Roswell*, p.71

[74] Corso & Birnes, *The Day After Roswell*, p.72-6

[75] Corso & Birnes, *The Day After Roswell*, p.64

[76] Corso & Birnes, *The Day After Roswell*, p.73-8

[77] Friedman, *Top Secret/Majic*, p.22, 82-5, 229;
http://www.majesticdocuments.com/pdf/truman_forrestal.pdf

[78] Friedman, *Top Secret/Majic*, p.41-55

[79] Corso & Birnes, *The Day After Roswell*, p.81-2

[80] Corso & Birnes, *The Day After Roswell*, p.60

[81] Corso & Birnes, *The Day After Roswell*, p.61-4, 77

[82] Corso & Birnes, *The Day After Roswell*, p.82

[83] Corso & Birnes, *The Day After Roswell*, p.64

[84] Dolan, *UFOs and the National Security State: An Unclassified History*, p.434

[85] Maccabee, *UFO-FBI Connection*, Llewellyn Publications, St. Paul, 2000, p.286-8; Dolan, *UFOs and the National Security State: An Unclassified History*, p.80-1

[86] Corso & Birnes, *The Day After Roswell*, p.67

[87] Corso & Birnes, *The Day After Roswell*, p.66

[88] Corso & Birnes, *The Day After Roswell*, p.68-9

[89] Corso & Birnes, *The Day After Roswell*, p.85

[90] Corso & Birnes, *The Day After Roswell*, p.84

[91] Corso & Birnes, *The Day After Roswell*, p.92-5

[92] Corso & Birnes, *The Day After Roswell*, p.96

[93] Corso & Birnes, *The Day After Roswell*, p.96-7

[94] Corso & Birnes, *The Day After Roswell*, p.114-5

[95] Corso & Birnes, *The Day After Roswell*, p.126

[96] Corso & Birnes, *The Day After Roswell*, p.116-8

[97] Corso & Birnes, *The Day After Roswell*, p.103

[98] Corso & Birnes, *The Day After Roswell*, p.110, 117-9

[99] Corso & Birnes, *The Day After Roswell*, p.117

[100] Corso & Birnes, *The Day After Roswell*, p.104, 117-9

[101] Corso & Birnes, *The Day After Roswell*, p.254-73; Swartz, *The Lost Journals of Nikola Tesla*, Global Communications, New Brunswick, 2011, p.146-7

[102] Corso & Birnes, *The Day After Roswell*, p.119-120

[103] Corso & Birnes, *The Day After Roswell*, p.109-110

[104] Corso & Birnes, *The Day After Roswell*, p.47-50

[105] Corso & Birnes, *The Day After Roswell*, p.121

[106] Corso & Birnes, *The Day After Roswell*, p.97, 145

[107] Corso & Birnes, *The Day After Roswell*, p.130

[108] Corso & Birnes, *The Day After Roswell*, p.49

[109] Corso & Birnes, *The Day After Roswell*, p.141-7

[110] Corso & Birnes, *The Day After Roswell*, p.4, 125-6

[111] Dolan, *UFOs and the National Security State: An Unclassified History*, p.143-6; Dolan, *UFOs and the National Security State: The Cover-up Exposed*, p.278

[112] Trudeau, *Engineer Memoirs: Lieutenant General Arthur G. Trudeau*, U.S. Army, Feb. 1986, p.293-342, http://www.usace.army.mil/About/History/Bookshelf.aspx

[113] Dateline, *Space Cadets*, NBC television, June 24, 1997

[114] Clear Channel Communications, *Interview with Bill Birnes*, Coast to Coast AM radio program with George Knapp, 7/2/2006; Kent, *The Roswell EBE/UFO Interface*, UFO Magazine, Birnes, Vol. 17. 4 Aug-Sept, 2002, p.67

[115] Biberman, *Electro-Optical Imaging: System Performance and Modeling*, SPIE Publications, Jan, 2001, preface xv, preface available online @ http://spie.org/x648.html?product_id=832715&origin_id=x653; Van Atta, Baker, Bovey, Cannon, Collopy, Epstein, Goldstein, Gutmanis, Harwood, Hong, Hull, Kindberg, Lippitz, Macheret, Nunn, White, *Science and Technology in Development Environments – Industry and Department of Defense Case Studies*, Institute for Defense Analyses, Nov. 2003, p. XIII-13 available online at http://handle.dtic.mil/100.2/ADA429056

[116] Carey & Schmitt, *Witness to Roswell*, p.275-284

[117] Dolan, *UFOs and the National Security State: An Unclassified History*, p.55, 63; Dolan, *UFOs and the National Security State: The Cover-up Exposed*, p.278

[118] Corso & Birnes, *The Day After Roswell*, p.169-170, 278

[119] Salla, *Colonel Philip Corso and his Critics: Crossing the Rubicon between Objective Criticism and Debunking – Part 1*, Exopolitics Journal, January 2006, p.116-27, http://www.bibliotecapleyades.net/exopolitica/esp_exopolitics_ZZO.htm; Philip J. Corso's Department of the Army Form 66, Officer Qualification Record: http://www.cufon.org/cufon/corso_da66.htm

[120] *Majestic Twelve Project, Annual Report*, p.10, http://www.majesticdocuments.com/pdf/mj12_fifthannualreport.pdf

[121] Wood & Wood, *Another Look at Majestic*, MUFON UFO Journal, March 1999, p.15, http://www.majesticdocuments.com/pdf/anotherlookatmajestic.pdf

[122] Salla, *Colonel Philip Corso and his Critics: Crossing the Rubicon between Objective Criticism and Debunking – Part 1*, p.128-9

[123] Fox, *UFOs: 50 Years of Denial?* Quick Fox Productions, 1997

[124] Sauter & Sanders, *The Men We Left Behind: Henry Kissinger, the Politics of Deceit and the Tragic Fate of Pows After the Vietnam War*, National Press Books, Washington, D.C., May 1993; Nelan, Hwang, Thompson, Lost Prisoners of War: Sold Down the River?, Time Magazine, Sept 30, 1996, http://content.time.com/time/magazine/article/0,9171,985224,00.html; Greer, *Disclosure*, p.463

[125] Corso & Birnes, *The Day After Roswell*, p.55; Clear Channel Communications, *Interview with Col. Philip J. Corso*, Coast to Coast AM radio program with Art Bell, 7/23/97

[126] Clear Channel Communications, *Interview with Col. Philip J. Corso*, Coast to Coast AM radio program with Art Bell, 7/23/97

[127] Cameron, *Extraterrestrial Politics Part 1 – The Rockefeller Initiative to the Clinton White House*, PresidentialUFO.com, Aug. 2, 2009, http://www.presidentialufo.com/bill-clinton/105-extraterrestrial-politics-part-1-rockefeller-initiative-to-the-clinton-white-house; *Cameron, Clinton, UFOs and the Single Bullet Theory*, PresidentialUFO.com, April 6, 2014, http://www.presidentialufo.com/bill-clinton/544-clinton-ufos-and-the-single-bullet-theory

[128] Bassett, *The Paradigm Clock Time Change Chronicle*, http://www.paradigmresearchgroup.org/timechangechronicle.html

[129] McClendon, *Lid Coming Off Government Cover-up on UFOs*, McClendon News Service, March 30, 1998, http://www.paradigmresearchgroup.org/McClendon_Articles.html

[130] Clear Channel Communications, *Interview with Bill Birnes,* Coast to Coast AM radio program with George Knapp, 7/2/2006

[131] COMETA, *UFOs and Defense: What Should We Prepare For?* p.52

[132] Kean, *UFO theorists gain support abroad, but repression at home,* The Boston Globe, May 21, 2000, http://www.disclosureproject.org/lkean-bostonglobe-may-21-2000.shtml

[133]Hellyer, *Paul Hellyer Speaks: Complete Transcript of his speech delivered on September 25 at the 2005 Toronto Exopolitics Symposium,* UFO Magazine, Dec/Jan 2006, p.36-39, http://www.jerrypippin.com/UFO%20Magazine%20Hon.%20Paul%20Hellyer.pdf: Salla, *Former Canadian Defense Minister Speaks Out on Extraterrestrial Visitors & Government Secrecy,* exopolitics.org, Sept. 29, 2005, https://web.archive.org/web/20121003154725/http://exopolitics.org/Exo-Comment-38.htm

[134] Corso & Birnes, *The Day After Roswell,* p.136, 156-171; O'Brien & King, *Bush unveils vision for moon and beyond,* CNN.com, Jan 15, 2004, http://www.cnn.com/2004/TECH/space/01/14/bush.space/

[135] *Former Canadian Minister of Defence Asks Canadian Parliament To Hold Hearings On Relations With Alien "Et" Civilizations,* PRWeb.com, Nov. 24, 2005, http://exopolitics.blogs.com/exopolitics/2005/11/former_canadian.html; *Senate pressured to hold hearings on ET,* Edmonton Sun, Nov. 26, 2005, http://exopolitics.blogs.com/exopolitics/2005/11/edmonton_sun_se.html

[136] Corso & Birnes, *The Day After Roswell,* p.290

Chapter 3 - DISCLOSURE

[1] Hubbell, *Friends in High Places,* William Morrow and Company, New York, Nov. 1997, p.282

[2] *Remarks by the President and First Lady at the Lighting of the Christmas Tree,* Office of the Press Secretary, Nov. 30, 1995

[3] Cameron, *Extraterrestrial Politics Part 3 – Rockefeller continues his effort to get UFO Disclosure,* Presidentialufo.com, Aug. 2, 2009, *http://www.presidentialufo.com/bill-clinton/107-extraterrestrial-politics-part-3-rockefeller-continues-his-effort-to-get-ufo-disclosure*

[4] McClendon, *Lid Coming Off Government Cover-up on UFOs,* http://www.paradigmresearchgroup.org/McClendon_Articles.html

[5] Cameron, *Extraterrestrial Politics Part 5 – White House interest (Including John Podesta),* Presidentialufo.com, Aug. 3, 2009, *http://www.presidentialufo.com/bill-clinton/109-extraterrestrial-politics-part-5-white-house-interest-including-john-podesta*

[6] Corso & Birnes, *The Day After Roswell*, p.75

[7] McClendon, *Pressure is Building for Congressional Hearings on UFOs*, McClendon News Service, July 1, 1998,
http://www.paradigmresearchgroup.org/McClendon_Articles.html

[8] COMETA, *UFOs and Defense: What Should We Prepare For?* p.55

[9] Bourdais, *The French Report on UFOs and Defense: A Summary*, The Center for UFO Studies, Chicago, http://www.cufos.org/cometa.html

[10] COMETA, *UFOs and Defense: What Should We Prepare For?* p.33
Kean, *UFO theorists gain support abroad, but repression at home*,
http://www.disclosureproject.org/lkean-bostonglobe-may-21-2000.shtml

[11] COMETA, *UFOs and Defense: What Should We Prepare For?* p.31

[12] COMETA, *UFOs and Defense: What Should We Prepare For?* p.55

[13] COMETA, *UFOs and Defense: What Should We Prepare For?* p.38-42, 71

[14] COMETA, *UFOs and Defense: What Should We Prepare For?* p.38-9

[15] COMETA, *UFOs and Defense: What Should We Prepare For?* p.41-2, 75-7

[16] Dolan, *UFOs and the National Security State: An Unclassified History*, p.460

[17] COMETA, *UFOs and Defense: What Should We Prepare For?* p.58; Dolan, *UFOs and the National Security State: An Unclassified History*, p.217

[18] Dolan, *UFOs and the National Security State: An Unclassified History*, p.455-7

[19] COMETA, *UFOs and Defense: What Should We Prepare For?* p.57

[20] Corso & Birnes, *The Day After Roswell*, p.64, 67, 86-7

[21] COMETA, *UFOs and Defense: What Should We Prepare For?* p.77-9

[22] COMETA, *UFOs and Defense: What Should We Prepare For?* p.78

[23] Dolan, *UFOs and the National Security State: An Unclassified History*, p.270-1; Dolan, *UFOs and the National Security State: An Unclassified History, Volume One: 1941-1973*, Revised Edition, Hampton Roads Publishing Company, Newburyport, April 2002, p.191

[24] Corso & Birnes, *The Day After Roswell*, p.89-91

[25] COMETA, *UFOs and Defense: What Should We Prepare For?* p.78

[26] COMETA, *UFOs and Defense: What Should We Prepare For?* p.52

[27] COMETA, *UFOs and Defense: What Should We Prepare For?* p.57

[28] Corso & Birnes, *The Day After Roswell*, p.131

[29] COMETA, *UFOs and Defense: What Should We Prepare For?* p.55-9

[30] COMETA, *UFOs and Defense: What Should We Prepare For?* p.71-2; Bourdais, *The French Report on UFOs and Defense: A Summary*, The Center for UFO Studies, Chicago, http://www.cufos.org/cometa.html

[31] Hansen, *The Missing Times*, p.174-5

[32] Kean, *UFO theorists gain support abroad, but repression at home*,
http://www.disclosureproject.org/lkean-bostonglobe-may-21-2000.shtml

[33] Barkin, *Now is the Time to Tackle Corruption in Government*, New Hampshire Union Leader, 5/11/2006, http://www.progressivestates.org/journalists/246/now-is-the-time-to-tackle-corruption-in-government

[34] Phillips, Arrogant Capital: Washington, Wall Street, and the Frustration of American Politics, Back Bay Books, New York, 1995

[35] Taibbi, *Wall Street's Big Win*, Rolling Stone Magazine, Aug. 4, 2010, http://www.rollingstone.com/politics/news/17390/188551

[36] Ratigan, *The Great Con Job*, The Dylan Ratigan Show, MSNBC, April 7, 2010

[37] Celente, *The History of the Future: Trends 2012*, The Trends Journal, Autumn, 2009, p.21

[38] Huffington Post, *Ex-Cigna Exec Wendell Potter: 'I Don't Think Co-ops Have A Chance To Succeed Or Compete'*, Sept. 15, 2009, http://www.huffingtonpost.com/2009/09/15/wendell-potter-public-opt_n_287733.html

[39] Taibbi, *Sick and Wrong: How Washington is screwing up health care reform – and why it may take a revolt to fix it*, Rolling Stone Magazine, April 5, 2010, www.rollingstone.com/politics/news/12697/64819

[40] bio Steven Bassett, Paradigm Research Group, http://www.paradigmresearchgroup.org/stephenbassett.html; Cox, *X-it the X-conference?* Herald-Tribune, Dec. 31, 2009, http://devoid.blogs.heraldtribune.com/10445/x-it-the-x-conference/

[41] Clear Channel Communications, *Interview with Col. Philip J. Corso*, Coast to Coast AM radio program with Art Bell, 7/23/97

[42] Greer, *Hidden Truth – Forbidden Knowledge*, Crossing Point Inc., Crozet, April 28, 2006, p.73, 78, 95-6

[43] Greer, *The Disclosure Project Press Conference*, National Press Club, May 9, 2001, http://www.disclosureproject.org/media.shtml; http://speedstream.netro.ca/netrostream113/npcc.wmv; http://www.youtube.com/

[44] Cameron, *Extraterrestrial Politics Part 1*, http://www.presidentialufo.com/bill-clinton/105-extraterrestrial-politics-part-1-rockefeller-initiative-to-the-clinton-white-house

[45] Cameron, *Extraterrestrial Politics Part 2 – CIA Director James Woolsey gets a UFO Briefing*, Aug. 3, 2009, http://www.presidentialufo.com/bill-clinton/106-extraterrestrial-politics-part-2-cia-director-james-woolsey-gets-a-ufo-briefing

[46] Greer, *Extraterrestrial Contact: The Evidence and Implications*, Crossing Point Inc., Crozet, 1999, p.xvii

[47] Cameron, *Extraterrestrial Politics Part 5*, http://www.presidentialufo.com/bill-clinton/109-white-house-interest-including-john-podesta

[48] IPCC, 2013: *Summary for Policymakers*,
http://www.climatechange2013.org/images/report/WG1AR5_SPM_FINAL.pdf;
Rice, *Science group says climate change worsening, dangerous*, USAtoday.com, Aug.
27, 2014, http://www.usatoday.com/story/news/2014/08/26/climate-change-report-united-nations/14638079/; Goodell, *Global Warming is Very Real*, Rolling Stone
Magazine, Sept. 26, 2014, http://www.rollingstone.com/politics/news/global-warming-is-very-real-20130912?page=3; Barboza, *Scientists warn of global
warming's abrupt changes*, LAtimes.com, March 18, 2014,
http://www.latimes.com/science/la-me-0319-climate-change-20140319-story.html#axzz2wRPaArvH

[49] Sample, *Scientists Offered Cash to Dispute Climate Study*, The Guardian UK, Feb.
2, 2007

[50] Townsend & Harris, *Now the Pentagon tells Bush: climate change will destroy us*,
The Guardian, Feb. 22, 2004,
http://www.guardian.co.uk/environment/2004/feb/22/usnews.theobserver;
http://www.climate.org/topics/PDF/clim_change_scenario.pdf

[51] Beaumont & Walters, *Greenspan admits that Iraq was about oil, as death put at
1.2m*, theguardian.com, Sept. 15, 2007,
http://www.theguardian.com/world/2007/sep/16/iraq.iraqtimeline; *Australia 'has
Iraq oil interest'*, BBC News, July 5, 2007, http://news.bbc.co.uk/2/hi/asia-pacific/6272168.stm; WashingtonsBlog, *Top REPUBLICAN Leaders Say Iraq War
Was Really about Oil*, washingtonsblog.com, March 19, 2013,
http://www.washingtonsblog.com/2013/03/top-republican-leaders-say-iraq-war-was-really-for-oil.html

[52] Kunstler, *The Long Emergency*, Atlantic Monthly Press, New York, 2005, p.24, 49

[53] Cameron, *President Bush UFO Story*, PresidentialUFO.com, Aug. 2, 2009
http://www.presidentialufo.com/george-h-w-bush/103-president-bush-ufo-story;
Dolan, *UFOs and the National Security State: The Cover-up Exposed*, p.439

[54] Cameron, *Bush Says UFO Promise Still On*, Presidentialufo.com, Aug. 9, 2009,
http://www.presidentialufo.com/george-w-bush/188-bush-says-ufo-promise-still-on

[55] Cameron, *Dick Cheney*, Presidentialufo.com, Aug. 8, 2009,
http://www.presidentialufo.com/george-w-bush/183-dick-cheney

[56] Greer, *Disclosure*, p.79-93

[57] Greer, *Disclosure*, p.112-127

[58] Greer, *Disclosure*, p.375-383

[59] Greer, *Disclosure*, p.379

[60] Greer, *Disclosure*, p.167-175

[61] Greer, *Disclosure*, p.176-9

[62] Greer, *Disclosure*, p.429-432

[63] Greer, *Disclosure*, p.413-9

[64] Greer, *Disclosure*, p.307-322

[65] Greer, *Disclosure*, p.325-344

[66] Greer, *Disclosure*, p.497-510

[67] Greer, *Disclosure*, p.504

[68] Corso & Birnes, *The Day After Roswell*, p.229-234

[69] Greer, *Disclosure*, p.254-261

[70] Greer, *Hidden Truth – Forbidden Knowledge*, p.199-200

[71] Kolber, *Deafening Silence: Media Response to the May 9th Event and its implications Regarding the Truth of Disclosure*, Uncensored Magazine, Auckland, New Zealand, Issue 2, Jan.-March 2006, p.77; http://www.disclosureproject.org/docgallery.shtml

[72] *Task Force on Greater CIA Openness*, http://www.disclosureproject.org/docs/pdf/CIAMemo.pdf

[73] Carr, *Resurrecting a Disgraced Reporter*, The New York Times, Oct. 2, 2014, http://www.nytimes.com/2014/10/05/movies/kill-the-messenger-recalls-a-reporter-wrongly-disgraced.html; Parry, *The Sordid Contra-Cocaine Saga*, Consortium News, Oct. 10, 2014, http://consortiumnews.com/2014/10/09/the-sordid-contra-cocaine-saga/; Devereaux, *Managing a Nightmare: How the CIA Watched Over the Destruction of Gary Webb*, The Intercept, Sep. 25, 2014, https://firstlook.org/theintercept/2014/09/25/managing-nightmare-cia-media-destruction-gary-webb/

[74] Greer, *Hidden Truth – Forbidden Knowledge*, p.200-1

[75] Greer, *ABC News Defrauding: Inside the ABC News Documentary Hoax*, Disclosureproject.org, Aug. 8, 2005, http://www.disclosureproject.org/articles/abcnewsdefrauding.htm

[76] Bennett, *Not a Bird or a Plane?* Newsweek, Jan. 4, 2007, http://www.msnbc.msn.com/id/16472286/site/newsweek/; http://www.paradigmresearchgroup.org/News_Items-2.htm#1-4-07%20N

[77] Daily Mail, *Experts call on US government to reopen UFO investigations*, Dailymail.co.uk, Nov. 13, 2007, http://www.dailymail.co.uk/news/article-493407/Experts-US-government-reopen-UFO-investigations.html; Morgan, *Former pilots and officials call for new U.S. UFO probe*, Reuters, Nov. 12, 2007

[78] Hanna, *UFOs eyed nukes, ex-Air Force personnel say*, CNN, Sep. 27, 2010, http://news.blogs.cnn.com/2010/09/27/ufos-showed-interest-in-nukes-ex-air-force-personnel-say/; Boyle, *Aliens have landed… in the headlines*, MSNBC, Sep. 27, 2010, http://cosmiclog.msnbc.msn.com/_news/2010/09/27/5189195-aliens-have-landed-in-the-headlines; FoxNews.com, *Aliens Are Monitoring Our Nukes, Worry Ex-Air Force Officers*, Sep. 23, 2010, http://www.foxnews.com/scitech/2010/09/23/aliens-monitoring-nukes-worry-ex-air-force-officers/; Stanglin, *Ex-Air Force officers calls*

UFOs and nukes a real 'security concern', USA Today, Sep. 27, 2010, http://content.usatoday.com/communities/ondeadline/post/2010/09/ex--air-force-officers-discuss-ufos-and-nuclear-missiles-at-national-press-club/1; Firth, *'We saw a bright glowing object like an eye': U.S. airman's startling testimony about UFO encounter near UK nuclear base*, Daily Mail, UK, Sep. 28, 2010, http://www.dailymail.co.uk/sciencetech/article-1315620/US-airman-Charles-Halts-UFO-testimony-encounter-near-UK-nuclear-base.html; Bloxham, *Aliens have deactivated British and US nuclear missiles, say US military pilots*, Daily Telegraph, UK, Sep.28, 2010, http://www.telegraph.co.uk/news/newstopics/howaboutthat/ufo/8026971/Aliens-have-deactivated-British-and-US-nuclear-missiles-say-US-military-pilots.html; *Former airmen claim alien visits*, UPI, Sep. 27, 2010, http://www.upi.com/Odd_News/2010/09/27/Former-airmen-claim-alien-visits/UPI-28911285617028/

[79] King, *Former Air Force officers discuss UFO sightings*, AirForceTimes, Gannet, Sep. 27, 2010, http://archive.airforcetimes.com/article/20100927/NEWS/9270306/Former-Air-Force-officers-discuss-UFO-sightings; U.S. Air Force, *Unidentified Flying Objects and Air Force Project Blue Book*, U.S. Air Force, April, 25, 2003, http://www.af.mil/AboutUs/FactSheets/Display/tabid/224/Article/104590/unidentified-flying-objects-and-air-force-project-blue-book.aspx

[80] Kelly, *UFO visits? Hmmm. Cookies? Yummm.*, The Washington Post, Sep. 28, 2010, http://www.washingtonpost.com/wp-dyn/content/article/2010/09/27/AR2010092706362.html; Strong, *Leslie Kean, UFOs, and the need for timely and responsible UFO reporting*, TucsonCitizen.com, Oct. 9, 2010, http://tucsoncitizen.com/paranormal/2010/10/09/leslie-kean-ufos-and-the-need-for-timely-and-responsible-ufo-reporting/

Chapter 4 – PARADIGM

[1] Mackenzie, *After 50 Years The Cover-Up Conspiracy Goes On*, The Sunday Express, June 16, 2002, p.20-21, https://www.paradigmresearchgroup.org/Webpages/After%2050%20Years%20The%20Cover-Up%20Conspiracy%20Goes%20On%20-%20UFO%20Evidence.htm

[2] Cox, *National media sidestep UFOs*, Florida Today, May 7, 2002, https://www.paradigmresearchgroup.org/News_Items-4.htm

[3] Price, *Arizonans say the truth about UFO is out there*, USA Today, March 18, 1997, http://www.freedomofinfo.org/media/ArizonanssaythetruthaboutUFO.pdf; MUFON, *Phoenix Lights – 1997*, https://www.mufon.com/phoenix-lights---

1997.html; Hook, *What were those lights in the Phoenix sky?* CNN.com, June 19, 1997, http://www.cnn.com/US/9706/19/ufo.lights/

[4] Sagan & Druyan, *Cosmos*, Ballentine Books, New York, Dec. 10, 2013, p.7-10, 48-52; 148

[5] Kuhn, *The Structure of Scientific Revolutions*, The University of Chicago Press, Chicago, 1996, 3rd edition, p.67-69

[6] Langford, *Galileo, Science, and the Church*, Ann Arbor Paperbacks, University of Michigan Press, 1971, p.35-40

[7] Powell, *Defending Giordano Bruno: A Response from the Co-Writer of "Cosmos,"* Discovermagazine.com, March 13, 2014
http://blogs.discovermagazine.com/outthere/2014/03/13/cosmos-giordano-bruno-response-steven-soter/#.WyxQT6knbSw

[8] Davies, *Are We Alone?* p.4-6

[9] Kuhn, *The Structure of Scientific Revolutions*, p.xxiii, 92

[10] Naik, *Mistakes in Scientific Studies Surge*, The Wall Street Journal, Aug. 10, 2011,
http://www.wsj.com/articles/SB10001424052702303627104576411850666582080

[11] Harris, *Study Says Drug's Dangers were Apparent Years Ago*, The New York Times, Nov. 5, 2004,
http://www.nytimes.com/2004/11/05/business/05drug.html?pagewanted=print&position=&_r=0; Horton, *Vioxx, the implosion of Merck, and aftershocks at the FDA*, The Lancet, Vol. 364, No. 9450, Dec. 4, 2004, p.1995-1996,
http://www.thelancet.com/journals/lancet/article/PIIS0140-6736%2804%2917523-5/fulltext?version=printerFriendly

[12] Adams, *Reputation of the FDA in shambles after Vioxx Scandal; calls for wholesale FDA reform gain momentum*, NaturalNews.com Nov. 6, 2004,
http://www.naturalnews.com/002157.html

[13] Mallove, *MIT and Cold Fusion: A Special Report*, Infinite Energy Magazine, Issue 24, 1999, p.4; *Interview with Eugene Mallove*, Coast to Coast AM radio program with George Noory, 2/3/2004

[14] Mallove, *MIT and Cold Fusion: A Special Report*, p.11-15

[15] Amos, *Arthur C. Clarke demands cold fusion rethink*, BBC News, Sept. 11, 2000,
http://news.bbc.co.uk/2/hi/in_depth/sci_tech/2000/festival_of_science/919953.stm

[16] Plotkin, *Data Versus Dogma: The Continuing Battle Over Cold Fusion*, Pure Energy Systems News Service, April 26, 2004,
http://pesn.com/2004/04/26/ColdFusionDogma.html

[17] Clarke, *The Futurists*, Random House, New York, 1972, p.144; Hansen, *The Missing Times*, p.298

[18] Cerf, Navaski, *The Experts Speak: The Definitive Compendium of Authoritative Misinformation*, Villard, Aug. 4, 1998, p.256

[19] Hansen, *The Missing Times*, p.45; Milton, Alternative Science: Challenging the Myths of the Scientific Establishment, Park Street press, 1996

[20] LaViolette, *Evidence Against the Expanding Universe Hypothesis*, Starburstfoundation.org, 2017, http://starburstfound.org/sqk-cosmology/

[21] Horgan, *The End of Science*, Addison-Wesley Publishing Company, Reading, 1996, p.109

[22] Swartz, *The Lost Journals of Nicola Tesla*, p.93-5

[23] Klein, *This Changes Everything: Capitalism Vs. The Climate*, Simon & Schuster, New York, 2014, p. 73-74

[24] see IPCC, http://www.ipcc.ch

[25] IPCC press release Nov. 2, 2014, http://www.ipcc.ch/pdf/ar5/prpc_syr/11022014_syr_copenhagen.pdf; Carrington, *IPCC: rapid carbon emission cuts vital to stop severe impact of climate change*, Guardian.com, Nov. 2, 2014, http://www.theguardian.com/environment/2014/nov/02/rapid-carbon-emission-cuts-severe-impact-climate-change-ipcc-report; Davenport, *Pentagon signals security risks of climate change*, The New York Times, Oct. 13, 2014, http://www.nytimes.com/2014/10/14/us/pentagon-says-global-warming-presents-immediate-security-threat.html?_r=1

[26] Klein, *This Changes Everything*, p.41, 43, 45; Harrabin, *Harrabin's Notes: Getting to the Bottom of Climategate*, BBC News, July 5, 2010, http://www.bbc.co.uk/news/10507144; McDonald, *New Study shows Climategate scientists were right*, CBCNews, Oct. 21, 2011, http://www.cbc.ca/newsblogs/technology/quirks-quarks-blog/2011/10/new-study-shows-climategate-scientists-were-right.html

[27] Buncombe and Castle, *Exxon Spends Millions to Cast Doubt on Warming*, The Independent UK, Dec. 7, 2006, http://www.independent.co.uk/news/world/europe/exxon-spends-millions-to-cast-doubt-on-warming-427404.html; Sample, *Scientists Offered Cash to Dispute Climate Study*, The Guardian UK, Feb. 2, 2007, http://www.guardian.co.uk/environment/2007/feb/02/frontpagenews.climatechange

[28] Gillis, Schwartz, *Deeper Ties to Corporate Cash for Doubtful Climate Researcher*, The New York Times, Feb. 21, 2015, http://www.nytimes.com/2015/02/22/us/ties-to-corporate-cash-for-climate-change-researcher-Wei-Hock-Soon.html?_r=1

[29] Pelley, *Bush Administration Rewrites Science on Global Warming*, CBS News, March 19, 2006, http://www.archive.truthout.org:81/issues_06/032206ec.shtml; Kennedy, *The Junk Science of George W. Bush*, The Nation, March 8, 2004, http://truth-out.org/archive/component/k2/item/47302:robert-f-kennedy-jr--the-junk-science-of-george-w-bush; Gerard, *The Political Corruption of Science*,

Truthout.com, August 7, 2006, http://www.truthout.org/cgi-bin/artman/exec/view.cgi/63/21643

[30] Oreskes & Conway, *Merchants of Doubt: How a Handful of Scientists Obscured the Truth on Issues from Tobacco Smoke to Global Warming*, Bloomsbury Press, New York, May 24, 2011, p.9

[31] Gore, *Climate of Denial: Can science and the truth withstand the merchants of poison?* Rolling Stone, June 22, 2011,

http://www.rollingstone.com/politics/news/climate-of-denial-20110622

[32] Bassett, *Biography and Accomplishments*, Paradigm Research Group, http://www.paradigmresearchgroup.org/Awards/Balducci_Corrado.htm; Greer, *Disclosure*, p.64-7

[33] Balducci, *UFOs and Extraterrestrials... A Problem for the Church? Rome, 2002*; Balducci, *UFOlogy and Theological Clarifications*, Pescara, June 8, 2001, http://www.pufoin.com/pufoin_perspective/et_church.php

[34] Harris, *The Vatican Officially Proclaims that Extraterrestrial Life most Probably Exists!* Exopolitics.com, May 13, 2008, http://exopolitics.blogs.com/exopolitics/2008/07/exopoliticsco-1.html

[35] Shimron, *Star-gazing priest takes a timeout*, The News & Observer, Sept. 17, 2006, http://www.newsobserver.com/2006/09/17/33718/star-gazing-priest-takes-a-timeout.html

[36] Corrales, *Vatican Astronomer – 'It's Madness To Believe Man Is Alone'*, El Mundo Newspaper, Spain, Jan. 7, 2002, http://www.rense.com/general18/believe.htm

[37] Thavis, *Vatican astronomer says if aliens exist, they may not need redemption*, Catholic News Service, May 14, 2008 http://www.catholicnews.com/data/stories/cns/0802629.htm

[38] Derbyshire, *I'd love to baptise ET, says Vatican's stargazer*, Daily Mail, Sep. 17, 2010, http://www.dailymail.co.uk/sciencetech/article-1312922/Pope-astronomer-Guy-Consolmagno-Aliens-souls-living-stars.html

[39] Dolan and Zabel, *A.D. After Disclosure: The People's Guide to Life After Contact*, Keyhole Publishing Company, Rochester, Oct. 25, 2010, p.222-3, iPad Kindle edition Loc. 2507 of 6178; Thomas, *Alien life could be found within 40 years, says royal astronomer*, DailyMail.com, Sept. 6, 2012, http://www.dailymail.co.uk/news/article-2199586/Alien-life-40-years-says-royal-astronomer.html

[40] Brookings Institution, *Proposed Studies on the Implications of Peaceful Space Activities for Human Affairs*, Committee on Science and Astronomics, U.S. House of Rep. 87th Congress, 1961, p.225

[41] Corso & Birnes, *The Day After Roswell*, p.131

[42] Twining, *AMC opinion concerning "Flying Disks,"* Sept. 23, 1947, National Archives Record Group 341;
http://www.majesticdocuments.com/pdf/twiningopinionamc_23sept47.pdf

[43] Dolan, *UFOs and the National Security State: An Unclassified History*, p.434

[44] Maccabee, *UFO-FBI Connection*, p.286-8

[45] Corso & Birnes, *The Day After Roswell*, p.64-8, 75-81; Dolan, *UFOs and the National Security State: An Unclassified History*, p.80-2

[46] Mullis, *Dancing Naked In The Mind Field*, Pantheon Books, New York, 1998, p.130-136

[47] Hall, *Donald Edward Keyhoe biography*, http://cevsite.com/keyhoe.htm

[48] Keyhoe, *The Flying Saucers Are Real*, Fawcett Publications, New York, 1950, p.8

[49] Keyhoe, *The Flying Saucer Conspiracy*, Henry Holt and Company, New York, 1955

[50] *Top Secret U.S.A.F. Memo*, Nov. 4, 1948, National Archives, declassified on July, 31, 1997; available online @
http://www.majesticdocuments.com/official.documents.nara.php;
http://www.majesticdocuments.com/pdf/usaf_swedish4nov48.pdf

[51] Dolan, *UFOs and the National Security State: An Unclassified History*, p.102-3

[52] Dolan, *UFOs and the National Security State: An Unclassified History*, p.152-3, 210-1, 216-8

[53] Friedman, *Top Secret/Majic*, p.26-32

[54] Dolan, *UFOs and the National Security State: An Unclassified History*, p.171-7

[55] Randle, *Invasion Washington UFOs Over The Capitol*, 2001 HarperCollins Publishers, New York, p.71

[56] Ruppelt, *The Report On Unidentified Flying Objects*, p.168,
http://www.nicap.org/rufo/rufo-12.htm

[57] Dolan, *UFOs and the National Security State: An Unclassified History*, p.167

[58] Keyhoe, *Flying Saucers From Outer Space*, Permabooks, Garden City, 1954, p.70, 95

[59] Carlson, *Alien Armada*, Washington Post, July 21, 2002,
http://www.washingtonpost.com/ac2/wp-dyn?pagename=article&node=&contentId=A31625-2002Jul19

[60] Dolan, *UFOs and the National Security State: An Unclassified History*, p.93-4

[61] Keyhoe, *Flying Saucers From Outer Space*, p.20-1

[62] Ruppelt, *The Report On Unidentified Flying Objects*, p.31-7

[63] Marrs, *Alien Agenda*, p.105

[64] Keyhoe, *The Flying Saucers Are Real*, p.6-8, 17, 21, 38-44, 168-175

[65] Dolan, *UFOs and the National Security State: An Unclassified History*, p.486-7

[66] Dolan, *UFOs and the National Security State: An Unclassified History*, p.128-9, 132, 162-168

[67] Maccabee, *UFO-FBI Connection*, p.149-156

[68] Keyhoe, *The Flying Saucers Are Real*, p.112

[69] Maccabee, *UFO-FBI Connection*, p.160

[70] Dolan, *UFOs and the National Security State: An Unclassified History*, p.102-3, 110-1

[71] Keyhoe, *The Flying Saucer Conspiracy*, p.38-56

[72] Dolan, *UFOs and the National Security State: An Unclassified History*, p.193-202

[73] *Report on Scientific Advisory Panel on Unidentified Flying Objects convened by Office of Scientific Intelligence, CIA*, Jan. 14-18, 1953, p.7-9, 15, Tab A, http://www.cufon.org/cufon/robert.htm

[74] Keyhoe, *Aliens From Space*, Signet, New York, 1974, p.68-71

[75] Hansen, *The Missing Times*, p.254

[76] CIA, *CIA Memorandum: Task Force Report on Greater CIA Openness*, Dec. 1991, p.6, http://www.disclosureproject.org/docs/pdf/CIAMemo.pdf

[77] Howe, Linda Moulton, *CIA Origin of National Enquirer*, Earthfiles.com, May 11, 2007, http://www.earthfiles.com/news.php?ID=1244&category=Environment; Hansen, *The Missing Times*, p.167-172

[78] Dolan, *UFOs and the National Security State: An Unclassified History*, p.28-30, 169-170, 196-9, 200

[79] Friedman, *Top Secret/Majic*, p.5

[80] Vallee, Goudie,, Klotz, *The "Pentacle Memorandum" Including Text of Correspondence from Dr. Jaquess Vallee*, Aug. 17, 1993, http://www.cufon.org/cufon/pentacle.htm

[81] Vallee, *Forbidden Science: Journals 1957-1969*, North Atlantic Books, Second edition, Berkeley, 1992, p.281-2

[82] Dolan, *UFOs and the National Security State: An Unclassified History*, p.102, 152-155, 210-1, 217, 270-346; Keyhoe, *The Flying Saucer Conspiracy*, p.13, 25

[83] COMETA, *UFOs and Defense: What Should We Prepare For?* p.58

[84] Corso & Birnes, *The Day After Roswell*, p.91

[85] Greer, *Disclosure*, p.230-5

[86] Greer, *Disclosure*, p.236-7

[87] Corso & Birnes, *The Day After Roswell*, p.233

[88] Keyhoe, *Aliens From Space*, p.196-7; Dolan, *UFOs and the National Security State: An Unclassified History*, p.362-3

[89] Filer, *Filer's Files #46*, National UFO Center, Medford, NJ, Nov. 14, 2013, https://nationalufocenter.com/2013/11/filers-files-46-2013-ufo-tidbits/

[90] Dolan, *UFOs and the National Security State: An Unclassified History*, p.371-405; Keyhoe, *Aliens From Space*, p.87-106

[91] Dolan, *UFOs and the National Security State: An Unclassified History*, p.376-8

[92] Vallee, *Forbidden Science,* p.173-6

[93] Dolan, *UFOs and the National Security State: An Unclassified History*, p.391-4

[94] Marrs, *Alien Agenda*, p.150-1

[95] Vallee, *Forbidden Science*, p.193

[96] Dolan, *UFOs and the National Security State: An Unclassified History*, p.400, 402, 407, 424-5

[97] Keyhoe, *Aliens From Space*, p.124-5

[98] Keyhoe, *Aliens From Space*, p.107-12

[99] Hynek, *The UFO Experience*, Marlowe & Company, New York, 1998, p.195

[100] Dolan, *UFOs and the National Security State: An Unclassified History*, p.431-441

[101] Ledger & Stiles, *Dark Object: The World's Only Government-Documented UFO Crash*, Dell Publishing, Random House, Inc., New York, NY, 2001, p.51-4

[102] Marrs, *Alien Agenda*, p.151-2

[103] Keyhoe, *Aliens From Space*, p.145

[104] Dolan, *UFOs and the National Security State: An Unclassified History*, p.480

[105] Dolan, *UFOs and the National Security State: An Unclassified History*, p.293, 399

[106] Vallee, *Forbidden Science,* p.186

[107] Dolan, *UFOs and the National Security State: An Unclassified History*, p.422

[108] Dolan, *UFOs and the National Security State: An Unclassified History*, p.441-4

[109] see *Statement by Dr. James E. McDonald,* submitted to the House Committee on Science and Astronautics at July 29, 1968, *Symposium on Unidentified Flying Objects*, p.17-31 http://nicap.org/books/1968Sym/1968_UFO_Symposium.pdf

[110] Keyhoe, *Aliens From Space*, p.148-54

[111] Dolan, *UFOs and the National Security State: An Unclassified History*, p.449

[112] Saunders, *UFOs? Yes! Where the Condon Committee Went Wrong*, World Pub. Company, New York, 1969, p.129; Dolan, *UFOs and the National Security State: An Unclassified History*, p.112

[113] Dolan, *UFOs and the National Security State: An Unclassified History*, p.412-3; Marrs, *Alien Agenda*, p.151-5

[114] Dolan, *UFOs and the National Security State: An Unclassified History*, p.456-7, 460

[115] Greer, *Unacknowledged: An exposé of the World's Greatest Secret*, A & M Publishing, L. L. C., West Palm Beach, FL, 2017, p.252-5, iPad edition

[116] Berliner, *UFO Briefing Document*, Dell publishing, New York, June 2000, p.87-90; Greer, *Disclosure*, p.167-175; Dolan, *UFOs and the National Security State: The Cover-up Exposed*, p.84-6, 95-9

[117] Berliner, *UFO Briefing Document*, p.105-111; Greer, *Disclosure*, p.307-322; Dolan, *UFOs and the National Security State: The Cover-up Exposed*, p.233-244

[118] Greer, *Disclosure*, p.79-93; Dolan, *UFOs and the National Security State: The Cover-up Exposed*, p.375-380

[119] Berliner, *UFO Briefing Document*, p.139-144; Dolan, *UFOs and the National Security State: The Cover-up Exposed*, p.500-2; Kean, *UFOs: Generals, Pilots and Government Officials Go on the Record*, Harmony Books, New York, 2010, p.24-40

[120] see MUFON, *Phoenix Lights – 1997*, https://www.mufon.com/phoenix-lights---1997.html; Kean, *Former Arizona Governor Now Admits Seeing UFO*, 2007, http://www.fifesymington.com/former-arizona-governor-now-admits-seeing-ufo; Kean, *UFOs: Generals, Pilots and Government Officials Go on the Record*, p.247-264

[121] Casler, *UFO reported in area again, after 50 years*, The Washington Times, August 7, 2002, http://www.washingtontimes.com/news/2002/aug/7/20020807-035733-8089r/; Vogel, *F-16s Pursue Unknown Craft Over Region*, Washington Post, July 26, 2002, http://www.washingtonpost.com/archive/local/2002/07/27/f-16s-pursue-unknown-craft-over-region/b1fd943e-0430-43cc-a9ff-3d840ff69de3/

[122] Hilkevitch, *In the sky! A bird? A plane? A… UFO?* Chicago Tribune, Jan 1, 2007, http://articles.chicagotribune.com/2007-01-01/travel/chi-0701010141jan01_1_craig-burzych-controllers-in-o-hare-tower-united-plane

[123] Kean, *UFOs: Generals, Pilots and Government Officials Go on the Record*, p.65-72; Kean, *Unsettling, unidentified incursion at O'Hare*, Providence Journal, Feb. 25, 2007, http://www.projo.com/opinion/contributors/content/CT_kean25_02-25-07_KI4G47E.4f3aef6.html; Bennett, *Not a Bird or a Plane?* Newsweek, Jan 4, 2007, http://www.paradigmresearchgroup.org/News_Items-2.htm

[124] Von Fremd, *UFO Investigators Flock to Stephenville, Texas,* ABC News, Jan. 18, 2008, http://www.abcnews.go.com/GMA/story?id=4142232&page=1; Mount, *UFOs? Nope. They were fighter jets, Air Force says,* CNN.com, Jan. 23, 2008, http://www.cnn.com/2008/US/01/23/airforce.ufo/index.html?eref=yahoo

[125] Goodwyn, *Air Force Alters Texas UFO Explanation*, NPR, Jan. 24, 2008, http://www.npr.org/templates/story/story.php?storyid=18375952; Cox, *USAF still silent on Stephenville*, Herald Tribune, August 15, 2008, http://www.heraldtribune.com/article/20080815/BLOG32/187004538&title=USAF_still_silent_on_Stephenville

[126] *Unidentified Flying Objects And Air Force Project Blue Book*, Official Website of the United States Air Force, http://www.af.mil/information/factsheets/factsheet.asp?fsid=188

[127] Keyhoe, *The Flying Saucers Are Real*, p.52

[128] Hynek, *The UFO Experience*, p.6

[129] Brookings Institution, *Proposed Studies on the Implications of Peaceful Space Activities for Human Affairs*, p.225

[130] Marrs, *Alien Agenda*, p.154

[131] Mackenzie, *After 50 Years The Cover-Up Conspiracy Goes On*, The Sunday Express, UK, June 16, 2002, p.20-21

[132] Keyhoe, *Aliens From Space*, p.113-7

[133] Ledger & Styles, *Dark Object: The World's Only Government-Documented UFO Crash*, Dell Publishing, Random House Inc., New York, NY, 2001, p.112-24

[134] see PlanetQuest @ http://planetquest.jpl.nasa.gov/

[135] AFP, *First planet with water is spotted outside Solar System*, Agence France Press, July 11, 2007, http://macaudailytimes.com.mo/archive-2007-2009/first-planet-with-water-is-spotted-outside-solar-system.html

[136] Reuters, *Alien encounters 'within twenty years'*, Thompson Reuters, June 27, 2011, http://www.guardian.co.uk/science/2011/jun/27/alien-encounters-twenty-years-russian-astronomer

[137] Blake, *Alien life certain to exist on Earth-like planet, scientists say*, The Telegraph, UK, Sept. 30, 2010, http://www.telegraph.co.uk/science/space/8033930/Alien-life-certain-to-exist-on-Earth-like-planet-scientists-say.html

[138] Choi, *New Estimate for Alien Earths: 2 Billion in Our Galaxy Alone*, Space.com, March 21, 2011, http://www.space.com/11188-alien-earths-planets-sun-stars.html

[139] Hynek, *The UFO Experience*, p.234

Chapter 5 – ASTROENGINEERING

[1] Greer, *Disclosure*, p.467-474

[2] Valone, *Harnessing the Wheelwork of Nature: Tesla's Science of Energy*, Adventures Unlimited Press, Kempton, 2002, p.41-3; Ancient Aliens, *The Tesla Experiment*, Season 7, May 29, 2015, http://www.history.com/shows/ancient-aliens/episodes/season-7

[3] Seifer, *Wizard: The Life and Times of Nikola Tesla, Biography of a Genius*, Citadel Press, New York, 1998, p.195

[4] Seifer, *Wizard: The Life and Times of Nikola Tesla*, p.230-3; Cheney, *Tesla: Man out of Time*, Simon & Shuster, New York, 1981, p.188

[5] Valone, *Harnessing the Wheelwork of Nature*, p.44-5

[6] Seifer, *Wizard: The Life and Times of Nikola Tesla*, p.283-307

[7] Swartz, *The Lost Journals of Nikola Tesla*, p.126; Seifer, *Wizard: The Life and Times of Nikola Tesla*, p.200-3

[8] Swartz, *The Lost Journals of Nikola Tesla*, p.18-9

[9] Seifer, *Wizard: The Life and Times of Nikola Tesla*, p.11; Swartz, *The Lost Journals of Nikola Tesla*, p.41

[10] Seifer, *Wizard: The Life and Times of Nikola Tesla,* p.220-2; Cheney, *Tesla: Man out of Time,* p.188-192; Swartz, *The Lost Journals of Nikola Tesla,* p.23-4

[11] Valone, *Harnessing the Wheelwork of Nature,* p.139; *Tesla's Discovery: Nobel Prize Winner,* The New York Times, Nov. 7, 1915, p.17, http://query.nytimes.com/mem/archive-free/pdf?res=9F02E0DF113CE733A25754C0A9679D946496D6CF; Swartz, *The Lost Journals of Nikola Tesla,* p.163

[12] *Tesla at 75,* Time Magazine, July 20, 1931, p.27-28; Seifer, *Wizard: The Life and Times of Nikola Tesla,* p.421

[13] Swartz, *The Lost Journals of Nikola Tesla,* p.22; Seifer, *Wizard: The Life and Times of Nikola Tesla,* p.xiii; Storm, *Return of the Dove,* M. Storm Productions, Baltimore, 1956

[14] Seifer, *Wizard: The Life and Times of Nikola Tesla,* p.425, 446-462

[15] Swartz, *The Lost Journals of Nikola Tesla,* p.146-7; Corso & Birnes, *The Day After Roswell,* p.251-273

[16] Corso & Birnes, *The Day After Roswell,* p.272-3

[17] Cheney, *Tesla: Man out of Time,* p.138-139

[18] Cheney, *Tesla: Man out of Time,* p.230

[19] see Macrae, *John von Neumann: The Scientific Genius Who Pioneered the Modern Computer, Game Theory, Nuclear Deterrence and Much More,* Pantheon Books, New York, 1999; Regis, *Johnny Jiggles the Planet,* The New York Times, Nov. 8, 1992, http://www.nytimes.com/1992/11/08/books/johnny-jiggles-the-planet.html

[20] Kaku, *Hyperspace,* p.276-7

[21] Kaku, *Visions: How Science Will Revolutionize the 21st Century, Doubleday,* New York, 1997, p.17-19; Kaku, *Hyperspace,* p.278; Kaku, *Physics of the Future: How Science Will Shape Human Destiny and Our Daily Lives by the Year 2100,* Doubleday, New York, 2011, p.329-346

[22] Friedman, *Is the Inflection Point Near?* The New York Times, March 7, 2009 http://www.nytimes.com/2009/03/08/opinion/08friedman.html?_r=1; Celente, *The Global Ponzi Scheme is Collapsing,* Trends Research Institute, March 30, 2011, http://geraldcelentechannel.blogspot.com/2011/03/gerald-celente-global-ponzi-scheme-is.html; Barraud & Grumet, *Prophets of Doom,* History Channel, Jan. 5, 2011; see synopsis for *Prophets of Doom* @ http://survivalandprosperity.com/tag/nathan-hagens/; http://planetponzi.com/

[23] Kaku, *Physics of the Future,* p.339-44

[24] see Lovelock, *The Revenge of Gaia,* Basic Books, New York, June 2007; Lovelock, *The Earth is about to catch a morbid fever that may last as long as 100,000 years,* Independent.co.uk, Jan. 16, 2006,

https://www.independent.co.uk/voices/commentators/james-lovelock-the-earth-is-about-to-catch-a-morbid-fever-that-may-last-as-long-as-100000-years-5336856.html

[25] see *Energy Efficiency & Renewable Energy*, U.S. Dept. of Energy, http://www1.eere.energy.gov/ba/pba/intensityindicators/index.html; Flavin, *Low-Carbon Energy: A Roadmap*, WorldWatch Institute, http://www.worldwatch.org/node/5948 http://www.worldwatch.org/bookstore/publication/worldwatch-report-178-low-carbon-energy-roadmap

[26] Ratigan, *Debate Sparked Over US Nuclear Industry*, The Dylan ratigan Show, March 15, 2011 http://www.dylanratigan.com/2011/03/15/debate-sparked-over-us-nuclear-industry/

[27] Liptak, *Justices, 5-4, Reject Corporate Spending Limit*, The New York Times, Jan. 21, 2010, http://www.nytimes.com/2010/01/22/us/politics/22scotus.html

[28] Alter, *High-Court Hypocrisy*, Newsweek Magazine, Jan. 22, 2010, http://www.thedailybeast.com/newsweek/2010/01/22/high-court-hypocrisy.html

[29] Harkinson, *Revolving Door: Climate Edition*, Mother Jones, Dec. 14, 2009, http://motherjones.com/blue-marble/2009/12/how-bush-insiders-are-influencing-climate-debate; see MostCorrupt.com, *Most Corrupt agencies: Environmental Protection Agency (EPS)*, http://mostcorrupt.com/Agencies--EPA.htm

[30] Kurzweil, *The Singularity Is Near: When Humans Transcend Biology*, The Viking Press, New York, Sept. 22, 2005, p.10; John von Neumann, paraphrased by Stanislaw Ulam, *Tribute to John von Neumann*, Bulletin of the American Mathematical Society 64.3, pt. 2 (May 1958): 1-49

[31] Kurzweil, *The Singularity Is Near*, p.35-6, 56

[32] Kurzweil, *The Singularity Is Near*, Front Flap; http://www.singularity.com/aboutthebook.html

[33] Kaku, *Physics of the Future*, p.11

[34] Webb, *If the Universe is Teeming with Aliens... Where is Everybody?* p.134-7, (Loc 1879 of 4042 iPad Kindle)

[35] Kurzweil, *The Singularity Is Near: When Humans Transcend Biology*, The Viking Press, New York, Sept. 22, 2005, p.364

[36] Greer, *Disclosure*, p.523-6

[37] see Greer, *Disclosure: Military and Government Witnesses Reveal the Greatest Secrets in Modern History*, Crossing Point Inc., Crozet, 2001

[38] Greer, *Disclosure*, p.547-552; LaViolette, *Secrets of Antigravity Propulsion: Tesla, UFOs and Classified Aerospace Technology*, Bear & Company, Rochester, 2008, p.66-7, 142-3

[39] Greer, *Disclosure*, p.497-509

[40] Greer, *Disclosure*, p.237

[41] Greer, *Disclosure*, p.524-6

[42] See LaViolette's bio @ http://starburstfound.org/bio-for-paul-laviolette/

[43] see *Purpose of the Starburst Foundation*, http://starburstfound.org/purpose-of-starburst-foundation/

[44] Greer, *Disclosure*, p.552

[45] LaViolette, *Decoding the Message of the Pulsars: Intelligent Communication From the Galaxy*, Bear & Company, Rochester, 2006, p.1-2

[46] see Stanley Kubrick Collection, Stanley Kubrick's 2001: A Space Odyssey, Special Features, *Arthur C. Clarke press conference*, 1968, Turner entertainment Co., 1999

[47] LaViolette, *Decoding the Message of the Pulsars*, p.1-6

[48] LaViolette, *Decoding the Message of the Pulsars*, p.8-14

[49] Davidson, *Carl Sagan: A Life*, p.238

[50] LaViolette, *Decoding the Message of the Pulsars*, p.3; Collyns, *Did Spacemen Colonize the Earth?* Henry Regnery Company, Chicago 1976, p.160

[51] Clear Channel Communications, *Interview with Dr. Paul LaViolette*, Coast to Coast AM radio program with George Noory, 12/27/2005

[52] Capra, *The Web of Life*, Anchor Books, New York, October 1997, p.37

[53] Clear Channel Communications, *Interview with Dr. Paul LaViolette*, 12/27/2005; LaViolette, *Earth Under Fire*, Bear & Company, Rochester, 1997, 2005

[54] LaViolette, *Decoding the Message of the Pulsars*, p.58-68

[55] LaViolette, *Decoding the Message of the Pulsars*, p.10

[56] LaViolette, *Decoding the Message of the Pulsars*, p.14-5

[57] LaViolette, *Decoding the Message of the Pulsars*, p.24-5

[58] LaViolette, *Decoding the Message of the Pulsars*, p.71-2

[59] LaViolette, *Decoding the Message of the Pulsars*, p.26

[60] LaViolette, *Decoding the Message of the Pulsars*, p.30

[61] LaViolette, *Decoding the Message of the Pulsars*, p.75

[62] LaViolette, *Decoding the Message of the Pulsars*, p.85

[63] LaViolette, *Decoding the Message of the Pulsars*, p.58, 76

[64] Clear Channel Communications, *Interview with Dr. Paul LaViolette*, 12/27/2005

[65] LaViolette, *Decoding the Message of the Pulsars*, p.87; LaViolette, *Decoding the Message of the Pulsars: Intelligent Communication From the Galaxy*, Bear & Company, Rochester, 2006, iPad 2 edition, p.122-3

[66] LaViolette, *Decoding the Message of the Pulsars*, p.142

[67] Davidson, *Carl Sagan: A Life*, p.238, 242

[68] Clear Channel Communications, *Interview with Dr. Paul LaViolette*, 12/27/2005

[69] see SETI Institute projects @ http://www.seti.org/seti-institute/projects

[70] Shostak, *SETI and Intelligent Design*, Space.com, Dec. 1, 2005,
http://www.space.com/1826-seti-intelligent-design.html

[71] Jastrow & Thompson, *Astronomy: Fundamentals and Frontiers*, John Wiley & Sons, New York, 1977, p.198

[72] LaViolette, *Decoding the Message of the Pulsars*, p.3-6

[73] see SETI Institute The Allen Telescope Array: Science Capabilities @
http://www.seti.org/seti-institute/project/allen-telescope-array-science-operations

[74] Corso & Birnes, *The Day After Roswell*, p.84

[75] Dolan, *UFOs and the National Security State: An Unclassified History*, p.325;
Friedman, *Top Secret/Majic*, p.48-9

[76] Davidson, *Carl Sagan: A Life*, p.226-7, 346-9; Dolan, *UFOs and the National Security State: An Unclassified History*, p.352

[77] Dolan, *UFOs and the National Security State: The Cover-up Exposed*, p.467-8

[78] Greer, *Disclosure*, p.474

[79] see Starburst Foundation: *Subquantum Kinetics Predictions and their Subsequent Verification* @ http://starburstfound.org/predictions-part-2/; *Superwave Predictions ad their Subsequent Verifications* @ http://starburstfound.org/predictions-part-1/

[80] LaViolette, *[58.07] Evidence that Radio Pulsars may be Artificial Beacons of ETI Origin*, American Astronomical Society, Jan. 2000
http://aas.org/archives/BAAS/v31n5/aas195/12.htm; see *DVD video of Dr. Paul LaViolette's historic announcement to the American Astronomical Society*, Starlane Publications, 2001, http://etheric.com/the-talk-of-the-galaxy/;
http://www.amazon.com/Talk-Galaxy-T-Pulsar-Laviolette/dp/B00005RDVE/ref=sr_1_1?ie=UTF8&qid=1325739299&sr=8-1

[81] LaViolette, *Decoding the Message of the Pulsars*, p.87

[82] Benford, Benford & Benford, *Messaging with Cost-Optimized Interstellar Beacons*, Astrobiology, Volume 10 number 5, http://www.liebertonline.com/toc/ast/10/5

[83] Cooper, *The frugal alien's beacon*, Astronomy Now, June 8, 2010,
http://www.astronomynow.com/news/n1006/08SETI/

[84] Lemonick, *Listening for aliens, what would ET do?* Time magazine, July 27, 2010,
http://www.time.com/time/health/article/0,8599,2006631,00.html

[85] LaViolette, *Regarding idea priority: Response of the Astrobiology journal*,
StarburstFoundation.org, Nov. 10, 2010, http://starburstfound.org/seti2blog/

[86] LaViolette, *Secrets of Antigravity Propulsion*, p.260-295

[87] LaViolette, *Decoding the Message of the Pulsars*, p.163-4

[88] LaViolette, *Decoding the Message of the Pulsars*, p.39, 85

[89] LaViolette, *Decoding the Message of the Pulsars*, p.52

[90] LaViolette, *Decoding the Message of the Pulsars*, p.52-3

[91] LaViolette, *Decoding the Message of the Pulsars*, p.39

[92] LaViolette, *Decoding the Message of the Pulsars*, p.40-1

[93] Clear Channel Communications, *Interview with Dr. Paul LaViolette*, 12/27/2005;
LaViolette, *Decoding the Message of the Pulsars*, p.41

[94] LaViolette, *Decoding the Message of the Pulsars*, p.40

[95] Clear Channel Communications, *Interview with Dr. Paul LaViolette*, 12/27/2005

Chapter 6 – MOON

[1] LaViolette, *Decoding the Message of the Pulsars*, p.107-8

[2] LaViolette, *Decoding the Message of the Pulsars*, p.108-9

[3] Hoagland, *The Monuments of Mars: A City on the Edge of Forever*, 4th Edition,
North Atlantic Books, Berkeley, 1996, p.29-38

[4] Choi, *New Evidence for Cold Ocean on Early Mars*, Space.com, Aug. 28, 2011,
http://www.space.com/12761-ancient-mars-cold-ocean-evidence.html; *Signs of
Ancient Ocean on Mars Spotted by European Spacecraft*, Space.com, Feb. 6, 2012,
http://www.space.com/14483-mars-ancient-ocean-evidence-european-probe.html

[5] Di Achille & Hynek. *Ancient Ocean on Mars supported by global distribution of
deltas and valleys*. Nature, 2010; *Ancient Ocean May Have Covered Third of Mars*,
ScienceDaily.com, June 13, 2010,
http://www.sciencedaily.com/releases/2010/06/100613181245.htm

[6] Hoagland, *The Curious Case of the NASA Crinoid Cover-up*,
Enterprisemission.com, Mar. 8, 2004,
http://www.enterprisemission.com/_articles/03-08-2004/crinoid_cover-up.htm

[7] see JPL Mars Exploration website @
http://marsrovers.jpl.nasa.gov/gallery/all/opportunity_m034.html

[8] Hoagland, *The Curious Case of the NASA Crinoid Cover-up*, Mar. 8, 2004,

[9] Chaikin, *Clarke's Believe It or Not, Space.com*, Feb. 25, 2001,
http://www.space.com/peopleinterviews/clarke_believe_010227.html

[10] Foulke, *The Banyan Trees of Mars*, Popular Science, Dec.17, 2001,
http://www.popsci.com/military-aviation-space/article/2001-12/banyan-trees-mars;
Hoagland, *Sir Arthur Ups the Ante*, Enterprisemission.com, 2001,
http://www.enterprisemission.com/sir.htm; http://www.times-
archive.co.uk/news/pages/tim/2000/09/16/timopnope01001.html; Hoagland, *Dark
Mission: The Secret History of NASA*, Feral House, Los Angeles, 2007, p.322-323; see
Mars Global Surveyor image M0804688 @ Malin Space Science Systems,
http://www.msss.com/moc_gallery/m07_m12/maps/M08/M0804688.gif

[11] Foulke, *The Banyan Trees of Mars*, Popular Science, Dec.17, 2001,
http://www.popsci.com/military-aviation-space/article/2001-12/banyan-trees-mars

[12] Clarke, *2???: A Real Space Odyssey*, Aviation Week & Space Technology, Mar. 24, 2003, p.52-3

[13] Moskowitz, *Minerals Needed for Life Found on Mars*, Space.com, Jun. 26, 2008, http://www.space.com/5566-minerals-needed-life-mars.html

[14] NASA, *Found it! Ice on Mars*, Science.nasa.gov, May 28, 2002, http://science.nasa.gov/science-news/science-at-nasa/2002/28may_marsice/

[15] Baldwin, *Liquid water on Mars might taste salty*, Astronomy Now, Aug. 4, 2011, http://astronomynow.com/news/n1108/04mars/

[16] *Scientist claims Mars has 'contemporary' life*, Indo-Asian News Service, Aug. 10, 2008, http://www.ndtv.com/convergence/ndtv/story.aspx?id=NEWEN20080060938

[17] Than, *Life on Mars Found by NASA's Viking Mission? New analysis suggest robots discovered microbes in 1976*, National Geographic, April 13, 2012, http://news.nationalgeographic.com/news/2012/04/120413-nasa-viking-program-mars-life-space-science/

[18] *Scientist claims Mars has 'contemporary' life*, Indo-Asian News Service, Aug. 10, 2008, http://www.ndtv.com/convergence/ndtv/story.aspx?id=NEWEN20080060938

[19] Hoagland, *World-Class Astrobiologist Says "NASA's Hiding Current Life on Mars!"* Enterprisemission.com, 2008, http://www.enterprisemission.com/Chandra-NASA-Accusation.htm; Hoagland, *Sir Arthur Ups the Ante*, Mar. 9, 2001

[20] Hoagland, *The Europa Enigma*, Star & Sky Magazine, Jan. 1980, http://www.enterprisemission.com/europa.html

[21] see Press Release: *NASA Startling Discoveries at Jupiter, From On-going Galileo Probe, Confirm Detailed Predictions Made 17 Years Before by Angstrom Science Medal Winner, Richard Hoagland*, Enterprisemission.com, April 14, 1997, http://www.enterprisemission.com/tem-0002.html; Kelly, The Week That Was, April 12, 1997, http://articles.nydailynews.com/1997-04-12/entertainment/18034672_1_europa-suicide-bombing-last-month-mayor-giuliani

[22] Hoagland, *Sir Arthur Ups the Ante*, Enterprisemission.com, Mar. 9, 2001; Clarke, *2010: Odyssey Two*, Ballantine Books, 1997, p.291, 294

[23] see Richard C. Hoagland Biographical Information @ http://www.enterprisemission.com/hoagland.html

[24] Hoagland, *The Monuments of Mars: A City on the Edge of Forever*, 4th Edition, Frog Ltd., North Atlantic Books, Berkeley, 1987, 1992, 1996, p.3-28

[25] Hoagland, *Dark Mission*, p.285-308; Van Flandern, *Proof That the Cydonia Face on Mars Is Artificial*, Meta Research, 1998, http://metaresearch.org/solar%20system/cydonia/proof_files/proof.asp

[26] Van Flandern, *On Improbable Claims*, Meta Research, 1996-2012, http://metaresearch.org/media%20and%20links/press/on-improbable-claims.asp

[27] see http://ida.wr.usgs.gov/fullres/divided/m04002/m0400291a.jpg

[28] Hoagland, *Detailed Examination of Apparent Architectural Features on Mars*, Enterprisemission.com, 2001, http://www.enterprisemission.com/archet.htm

[29] Nicks, *Opening a Martian "Can of Worms."* Enterprisemission.com, 2001, http://www.enterprisemission.com/can.htm; Van Flandern, *"Glassy Tubes on Mars are Sand Dunes?* Meta Research, 2001, http://www.metaresearch.org/home/viewpoint/archive/010313glassytubes/meta-in-news010313.asp; Bara, *The Glass Tubes of Mars Revisited*, MikeBara.com, June 9, 2014, http://mikebara.blogspot.com/2014/06/the-glass-tubes-of-mars-revisited.html

[30] Leathley, *A Visit to the Red Planet, Three-Foot Tall Mysterious Hominids and Future Robots*, The Journal, Newcastle, England, UK, Jan. 7, 2005, https://www.questia.com/newspaper/1G1-126774221/a-visit-to-the-red-planet-three-foot-tall-mysterious

[31] Van Flandern, *The Exploded Planet Hypothesis 2000*, Meta Research, 2000, http://www.metaresearch.org/solar%20system/eph/eph2000.asp

[32] Vander Ploeg, *Astrophysicist: Giant Spaceships are Orbiting Mars*, UFODigest.com, April 7, 2011, http://www.ufodigest.com/article/scientist-claims-mars-moon-phobos-hollow; Davidson, *Carl Sagan: A Life*, p.148, 251

[33] Wright, *The dust of crashing illusions*, The Herald, Herald & Times Group, HeraldScotland.com, Nov. 4, 1999, http://www.heraldscotland.com/sport/spl/aberdeen/the-dust-of-crashing-illusions-1.264181

[34] see European Space Agency Mars Express Blog, *Radio science result from 2008 Phobos Flyby now accepted for publication* @ http://webservices.esa.int/blog/post/7/1085; http://www.agu.org/journals/pip/gl/2009GL041829-pip.pdf; Kolyuka, Y. F., Efimov, A. E., Kudryavtsev, S. M., Margorin, O. K., Tarasov, V. P., & Tikhonov, V. F., *Refinement of the Gravitational Constant of PHOBOS from PHOBOS-2 Tracking Data*, Soviet Astronomy Letters, Vol.16, NO.2 Mar/April, 1990, p.168, http://articles.adsabs.harvard.edu//full/1990SvAL...16..168K/0000168.000.html; Hoagland, *For the World is Hollow… and I Have Touched the Sky Part 1*, Enterprisemission.com, 2010, http://www.enterprisemission.com/Phobos.html

[35] Dolan, *UFOs and the National Security State: The Cover-Up Exposed*, p.469-471

[36] Hoagland, *For the World is Hollow… and I Have Touched the Sky Part 2*, Enterprisemission.com, 2010, http://www.enterprisemission.com/Phobos2.html; *News Update: European Space Agency to Contact Mars' Phobos-Grunt Probe Today*, The Daily Galaxy, Nov. 28, 2011, http://www.dailygalaxy.com/my_weblog/2011/11/news-update-european-space-agency-to-contact-mars-phobos-gunt-probe-today.html

[37] *Mars' Moon Phobos is Slowly Falling Apart*, NASA, Nov. 10, 2015, http://www.nasa.gov/feature/goddard/phobos-is-falling-apart

[38] Hoagland, *For the World is Hollow… and I Have Touched the Sky Part 2*, Enterprisemission.com, 2010

[39] *Buzz Aldrin stokes the mystery of the monolith on Mars*, Daily Mail, UK, Aug. 6, 2009, http://www.dailymail.co.uk/sciencetech/article-1204254/Has-mystery-Mars-Monolith-solved.html

[40] see Ward & Brownlee, *Rare Earth: Why Complex Life is Uncommon in the Universe*, Copernicus Books, New York, 2000

[41] Jastrow, *Red Giants and white Dwarfs: The Evolution of Stars, Planets and Life*, Harper & Row, New York, 1967, p.72-73

[42] Ubell, *The Moon is More of a Mystery Than Ever*, The New York Times Magazine, April 16, 1972, p.32; Marrs, *Alien Agenda*, p.2

[43] Knight & Butler, *Who Built the Moon?* Watkins Publishing, London, 2006, p.49-51, 69; NASA, *Earth's Moon: In Depth*, http://solarsystem.nasa.gov/planets/moon/indepth

[44] Hartmann, *Origin of the Moon*, Lunar and Planetary Institute, Houston, 1986

[45] Knight & Butler, *Who Built the Moon?* p.44-57

[46] see NASA, *Lunar History* @ http://lunar.ksc.nasa.gov/history/moonh.html; Taylor, *Origin of the Earth and Moon*, NASA, Feb 21, 2012, http://solarsystem.nasa.gov/scitech/display.cfm?ST_ID=446

[47] Choi, *Moon's Birth May Have Vaporized Most of Earth, Study Shows*, Space.com, New York, Sept. 13, 2016, http://www.space.com/34044-moon-birth-may-have-vaporized-earth.html

[48] Knight & Butler, *Who Built the Moon?* p.56

[49] Clear Channel Communications, *Interview with Christopher Knight & Alan Butler*, Coast to Coast AM radio program with George Noory, Dec. 7, 2005

[50] Marrs, *Alien Agenda*, p.13-5; Wilson, *Secrets of our Space Ship Moon*, Sphere Books Ltd., London, 1980, p.13-4, 26-8

[51] Keyhoe, *The Flying Saucer Conspiracy*, p.70-8

[52] Wilson, *Secrets of our Space Ship Moon*, p.33, 35-9

[53] Wilson, *Our Mysterious Spaceship Moon*, Sphere Books Ltd., London, 1976, p.22-61

[54] Wilson, *Secrets of our Space Ship Moon*, p.48-51; Marrs, *Alien Agenda*, p.18-21

[55] Hoagland, *Dark Mission*, p.113-198

[56] Marrs, *Alien Agenda*, p.15-17; Ecker, *Long Saga of Lunar Anomalies*, UFO 10, no. 2, Mar/Apr 1995, p.23

[57] see *Apollo 13 Mission*, Lunar and Planetary Institute, Houston, TX, http://www.lpi.usra.edu/lunar/missions/apollo/apollo_13/experiments/

[58] Knight & Butler, *Who Built the Moon?* p.72

[59] Marrs, *Alien Agenda*, p.2-3, 6-7; Wilson, *Secrets of our Space Ship Moon*, p.100-2, 107

[60] Wilson, *Secrets of our Space Ship Moon*, p.173-4

[61] Marrs, *Alien Agenda*, p.10; Wilson, *Secrets of our Space Ship Moon*, p.11-2, 161

[62] *Secrets of our Space Ship Moon*, p.59-66

[63] Marrs, *Alien Agenda*, p.7; Sullivan, *Seismic Net Set to Find Source of Tremors as Moon Nears*, New York Times, Aug. 4, 1972, p.1

[64] Marrs, *Alien Agenda*, p.9; Shelton, *Winning the Moon*, Little, Brown, New York, 1970, p.58

[65] *Secrets of our Space Ship Moon*, Dell, New York, 1979, p.177-79

[66] Marrs, *Alien Agenda*, p.4; Ubell, *The Moon is More of a Mystery Than Ever*, The New York Times Magazine, April 16, 1972, p.50-51; *Secrets of our Space Ship Moon*, Dell, New York, 1979, p.115-22, 131

[67] Knight & Butler, *Who Built the Moon?* p.63

[68] Marrs, *Alien Agenda*, p.4-5; Wilson, *Secrets of our Space Ship Moon*, p.153-6

[69] Knight & Butler, *Who Built the Moon?* p.63-5

[70] Hoagland, *The Monuments of Mars: A City on the Edge of Forever*, 2001, North Atlantic Books, Berkeley, p.xv-xvii

[71] Marrs, *Alien Agenda*, 1997, p.9; Shelton, *Winning the Moon*, p.9; Wilson, *Secrets of our Space Ship Moon*, p.87

[72] Knight & Butler, *Who Built the Moon?* p.244

[73] Clear Channel Communications, *Interview with Christopher Knight & Alan Butler*, Dec. 7, 2005

[74] Kaku, *The Physics of Extraterrestrial Civilizations: How advanced could they possibly be?* Mkaku.org, 2012, http://mkaku.org/home/?page_id=246; Davies, *Are We Alone?* p.41

[75] Barrow & Tipler, *The Anthropic Cosmological Principle*, p.579-81

[76] Tipler, *Extraterrestrial Beings Do Not Exist*, Quarterly Journal of the Royal Astronomical Society, Vol. 21, number 267, 1981

[77] Knight & Butler, *Who Built the Moon?* p.79-85

[78] Knight & Butler, *Who Built the Moon?* p.94-101

[79] Ward & Brownlee, *Rare Earth: Why Complex Life is Uncommon in the Universe*, Copernicus Books, New York, 2004, Back Matter

[80] Ward & Brownlee, *Rare Earth*, p.xx, 222

[81] Ward & Brownlee, *Rare Earth*, p.50

[82] Knight & Butler, *Who Built the Moon?* p.137-41

[83] Knight & Butler, *Who Built the Moon?* p.137, 248

[84] Knight & Butler, *Who Built the Moon?* p.106; Comins, *Voyages to the Earth That Might Have Been*, HarperCollins, New York, 1993; Comins, *What if the Earth Had Two Moons?* St. Martins Press, New York, April 2010, p.15

[85] Knight & Butler, *Who Built the Moon?* p.88-9, 106-7

[86] Kurzweil, *The Singularity Is Near: When Humans Transcend Biology*, Penguin Books, New York, 2006, p.364

[87] Knight & Butler, *Who Built the Moon?* p.138

Chapter 7 – INTERFACE

[1] Webre, *Exopolitics: Politics, Government, and Law in the Universe*, Universebooks, Vancouver, 2005, p.9; Jung, *Dr. Carl Jung on Unidentified Flying Objects*, Flying Saucer Review, vol. 1, no. 2, 1955; Jung & Hall (translator), *Flying Saucers: A Modern Myth of Things Seen in the Skies*, 1958, republished Princeton, NJ, Princeton University Press, 1979; Creighton, *Dr. Carl Jung And The UFOs: The Real Story!* Flying Saucer Review, Volume 46/4 Winter 2001, p7-11

[2] Webre, *Exopolitics*, p.11

[3] Woodward, *The Washington, DC, Area Jet Chase of July 26, 2002*, International UFO Reporter, Winter 2002-3, Vol. 27, No. 4, p.3-7, 22-5

[4] Webre, *Is UFO orb over Dome of the Rock in Jerusalem a context communication by ET?* Examiner.com, Jan. 30, 2011, http://exopolitics.blogs.com/exopolitics/2011/01/is-ufo-orb-over-dome-of-the-rock-in-jerusalem-a-context-communication-by-et-or-a-cgi-hoax-.html; *'UFO' Hovers over Jerusalem's Dome of the Rock Shrine*, The Sun, Feb. 3rd, 2011, http://www.foxnews.com/tech/2011/02/03/ufo-jerusalems-dome-rock-baffles-experts/

[5] Dolan, *UFOs and the National Security State: The Cover-up Exposed*, p.559

[6] Dolan, *UFOs and the National Security State: The Cover-up Exposed*, p.560

[7] Webre, *Exopolitics*, p.5-17

[8] Jacobs, *The Threat The Secret Agenda: What the Aliens Really Want... and How They Plan to Get It*, Simon & Schuster, New York, 1998, p.216-7

[9] Marrs, *Alien Agenda*, p.188-195

[10] Keyhoe, *Aliens From Space*, p.198-9

[11] Marrs, *Alien Agenda*, p.201-212

[12] Sagan, *Cosmos*, Random House, New York, 1980, p. 30-31, Sagan, *Carl Sagan's Cosmic Connection: An Extraterrestrial Perspective*, Cambridge University Press, New York, 2000, p.43

[13] Dolan, *UFOs and the National Security State: An Unclassified History*, p.284

[14] Marrs, *Alien Agenda*, p.196

[15] Dolan, *UFOs and the National Security State: An Unclassified History*, p.282

[16] Dolan, *UFOs and the National Security State: An Unclassified History*, p.335-341; see Friedman & Marden, *Captured! The Betty and Barney Hill UFO Experience*, New Page Books, Franklin Lakes, 2007

[17] Dolan, *UFOs and the National Security State: An Unclassified History*, p.337

[18] Friedman & Marden, *Captured! The Betty and Barney Hill UFO Experience*, p.87

[19] Dolan, *UFOs and the National Security State: An Unclassified History*, p.338-9

[20] Marrs, *Alien Agenda*, p.198; Friedman & Marden, *Captured! The Betty and Barney Hill UFO Experience*, p.66-7

[21] Dolan, *UFOs and the National Security State: An Unclassified History*, p.340

[22] Friedman & Marden, *Captured! The Betty and Barney Hill UFO Experience*, p.88, 124

[23] Friedman & Marden, *Captured! The Betty and Barney Hill UFO Experience*, p.137-8

[24] Friedman & Marden, *Captured! The Betty and Barney Hill UFO Experience*, p.131, 236

[25] Friedman & Marden, *Captured! The Betty and Barney Hill UFO Experience*, p.155

[26] Friedman & Marden, *Captured! The Betty and Barney Hill UFO Experience*, p.192; Marrs, *Alien Agenda*, p.200

[27] Friedman & Marden, *Captured! The Betty and Barney Hill UFO Experience*, p.196-7

[28] Friedman & Marden, *Captured! The Betty and Barney Hill UFO Experience*, p.185-200

[29] Marrs, *Alien Agenda*, p.199

[30] Friedman & Marden, *Captured! The Betty and Barney Hill UFO Experience*, p.234-244

[31] Friedman & Marden, *Captured! The Betty and Barney Hill UFO Experience*, p.237-40

[32] Dolan, *UFOs and the National Security State: The Cover-Up Exposed*, p.102-8; Marrs, *Alien Agenda*, p.218-22

[33] Dolan, *UFOs and the National Security State: The Cover-Up Exposed*, p.104

[34] Dolan, *UFOs and the National Security State: An Unclassified History*, p.291

[35] Dolan, *UFOs and the National Security State: An Unclassified History*, p. 437-8, 481

[36] Dolan, *UFOs and the National Security State: The Cover-Up Exposed*, p.80-3

[37] Fowler, *The Watchers: The Secret Design Behind UFO Abductions*, Bantam Books, New York, 1990, p.4

[38] Marrs, *Alien Agenda*, p.216

[39] Dolan, *UFOs and the National Security State: The Cover-Up Exposed*, p.389

[40] Fowler, *The Watchers*, p.333

[41] Fowler, *The Watchers*, p.338-9

[42] Fowler, *The Watchers*, p.340-1

[43] Fowler, *The Watchers*, p.344-8

[44] Marrs, *Alien Agenda*, p.216

[45] Fowler, *The Watchers*, p.353

[46] Fowler, *The Andreasson Affair: The Documented Investigation of a Woman's Abduction Aboard a UFO*, Bantam Books, New York, 1980, p.x; Marrs, *Alien Agenda*, p.217

[47] Dolan, *UFOs and the National Security State: The Cover-Up Exposed*, p.65

[48] Dolan, *UFOs and the National Security State: The Cover-Up Exposed*, p.263, 388-390

[49] Marrs, *Alien Agenda*, p.222-5

[50] Dolan, *UFOs and the National Security State: The Cover-Up Exposed*, p.392-3; Strieber, *Communion: A True Story*, Avon Books, New York, 1987, p.76

[51] Hopkins, *Witnessed: The True Story of the Brooklyn Bridge UFO Abductions*, Pocket Books, New York, 1996, p.173; Sparks, *The Keepers: An Alien Message for the Human Race*, Wild Flower Press, Columbus, 2008, p.22

[52] Marrs, *Alien Agenda*, p.230

[53] Dolan, UFOs and the National Security State: The Cover-Up Exposed 1973-1991, Keyhole Publishing Company, Rochester, 2009, p.394; Mack, *Abduction: Human Encounters with Aliens REVISED EDITION*, Ballentine Books, New York, May 1995, p.4

[54] Jacobs, *The Threat*, p.18-9, 80

[55] Fowler, *The Watchers*, p.5, 328

[56] Jacobs, *The Threat*, p.251

[57] Mack, *Abduction: Human Encounters with Aliens*, p.7-8

[58] Deardorff, *Is there an alien strategy?* MUFON UFO Journal, Sept. 2002, No. 413, p.12-3

[59] Mack, *Passport to the Cosmos: Human Transformation and Alien Encounters*, Crown Publishers, New York, 1999, p.10

[60] Mack, *Abduction: Human Encounters with Aliens*, p.411

[61] Marrs, *Alien Agenda*, p.227-230; Honan, *Harvard Investigates a Professor Who Wrote of Space Aliens*, The New York Times, May 4, 1995, http://www.nytimes.com/1995/05/04/us/harvard-investigates-a-professor-who-wrote-of-space-aliens.html

[62] Mack, *Abduction: Human Encounters with Aliens*, p.x

[63] Sagan, *The Demon-Haunted World: Science as a Candle in the Dark*, Ballentine Books, New York, Feb. 25, 1997, p.64-195; Chiten, *Touched*, Blind Dog Films, Feb. 20, 2003

[64] Jacobs, *Secret Life: Firsthand Accounts of UFO Abductions*, New York, Simon & Schuster, 1992, p.12; Jacobs, *The Threat*, p.212

[65] Mack, *Abduction: Human Encounters with Aliens*, p.10

[66] Mack, *Passport to the Cosmos*, p.268-81

[1] Barrow & Tipler, *The Anthropic Cosmological Principle*, p.580

[2] Jacobs, *The Threat*, p.61, 96

[3] Jacobs, *The Threat*, p.122-5

[4] Kurzweil, *The Singularity Is Near: When Humans Transcend Biology*, Penguin Books, New York, 2005, p. 358; Woollaston, *We'll be uploading our entire MINDS to computers by 2045 and our bodies will be replaced by machines within 90 years*, Google expert claims, Dailymail.com.uk, June 19, 2013, http://www.dailymail.co.uk/sciencetech/article-2344398/Google-futurist-claims-uploading-entire-MINDS-computers-2045-bodies-replaced-machines-90-years.html

[5] Kurzweil, *The Singularity Is Near*, p.316

[6] Fowler, *The Watchers*, p.184

[7] Kurzweil, *The Singularity Is Near*, p.4

[8] Sparks, *The Keepers*, p.4

[9] Sparks, *The Keepers*, p.181

[10] Sparks, *The Keepers*, p.196

[11] Mack, *Passport to the Cosmos*, 1999, p.261; Dolan and Zabel, *A.D. After Disclosure*, iPad Kindle edition Loc. 2527; Mack, *Abduction: Human Encounters with Aliens*, p.22

[12] Marrs, *Alien Agenda*, p. 216, 234; Fowler, *The Andreasson Affair*, p.137-8

[13] *Study: Billions of Earth-size Planets in Milky Way*, Associated Press, Jan. 8, 2013, http://abcnews.go.com/Technology/study-billions-earth-size-planets-milky/comments?type=story&id=18152982#.UYDMT4Wfvyt

[14] Dolan & Zabel, *A. D. After Disclosure: When the Government Finally Reveals the Truth About Alien Contact*, New Page Books, Pompton Plains, May 22, 2012, p.128

[15] Corso & Birnes, *The Day After Roswell*, p.99

[16] Dolan, *UFOs and the National Security State: The Cover-Up Exposed*, p.395

[17] Fowler, *The Watchers II: Exploring UFOs and the Near-Death Experience*, Wild Flower Press, 1995, p.95-109

[18] Mack, *Abduction: Human Encounters with Aliens*, p.17

[19] Fowler, *The Watchers*, p.209

[20] Mack, *Passport to the Cosmos*, p.62-84

[21] Mack, *Passport to the Cosmos*, p.81

[22] Mack, *Passport to the Cosmos*, p.57

[23] Fowler, *The Watchers*, p.182

[24] Mack, *Passport to the Cosmos*, p.15

[25] Fowler, *The Watchers*, p.172-190

[26] Fowler, *The Watchers*, p.347

[27] Mack, *Passport to the Cosmos*, p.16-7, 81, 207-8

[28] Kurzweil, *The Age of Spiritual Machines: When Computers Exceed Human Intelligence*, Penguin Books, New York, 2000, p.152-153

[29] Mack, *Passport to the Cosmos*, p.78, 81-2

[30] Mack, *Abduction: Human Encounters with Aliens*, p.22; Mack, *Passport to the Cosmos*, p.276

[31] Schnabel, *Remote Viewers: The Secret History of America's Psychic Spies*, Dell Publishing, New York, 1997, p.183-192

[32] Dolan, *UFOs and the National Security State: The Cover-Up Exposed*, p.67

[33] Morehouse, *Remote Viewing: The Complete User's Manual for Coordinate Remote Viewing*, Sounds True, May 28, 2011, p.27

[34] Schnabel, *Remote Viewers*, p.215-9

[35] Schnabel, *Remote Viewers*, p.358

[36] Dolan, *UFOs and the National Security State: The Cover-Up Exposed*, p. 67-71

[37] Schnabel, *Remote Viewers*, p.234-256

[38] Marrs, *Alien Agenda*, p. 318-21

[39] Greer, *Disclosure*, p.183-190

[40] McMoneagle, *The Ultimate Time Machine*, Hampton Roads Publishing Company, Inc. 1998, Charlottesville, p.32-3

[41] Mack, *Abduction: Human Encounters with Aliens*, p.207, 318-9, 327-8, 411, 413-4, 415, 420; Mack, *Passport to the Cosmos*, p.68, 91-2, 112-3, 123-4, 276,

[42] Brown, *Cosmic Voyage: A Scientific Discovery of Extraterrestrials Visiting Earth*, Penguin Books, New York, Jan. 1996, 129-137, 194-201

[43] Webre, *Exopolitics*, p. 23-30, 57

[44] Webre, *Exopolitics*, p.16-7, 31

[45] Friedman, *Flying Saucers and Science: A Scientist Investigates the Mystery of UFOs*, Franklin Lakes, 2008, p.145-6

[46] Kaku, *Physics of the Future*, p.271 iPad iBooks; Kaku, *Physics of the Future*, p106-109

[47] LaViolette, *Decoding the Message of the Pulsars*, p.39-40

[48] Kaku, *Physics of the Future*, p121; Rosenberg & Markoff, *The Pentagon's 'Terminator Conundrum': Robots That Could Kill on Their Own*, The New York Times, Oct. 26, 2016, https://www.nytimes.com/2016/10/26/us/pentagon-artificial-intelligence-terminator.html

[49] Butler, *War is a Racket*, Round Table Press, New York, 1935, p.1-2; Butler, *War is a Racket*, Feral House, Los Angeles, 2003, p.35

[50] Ward, *Ollie and Old Gimlet Eye*, American Heritage.com, American Heritage Magazine, Nov. 1987, Volume 8, Issue 7, http://web.archive.org/web/20070913215113/http://www.americanheritage.com/articles/magazine/ah/1987/7/1987_7_14.shtml

[51] Butler, *War is a Racket*, Feral House, Los Angeles, 2003, p.41-50

[52] Schmidt, *Maverick Marine: General Smedley D. Butler and the contradictions of American military history*, The University Press of Kentucky, July 2, 1998, p.2, 231

[53] Young, *Cheney's Halliburton Made $39.5 billion on Iraq War*, International Business Times, Businessinsider.com, March 20, 2013, http://www.businessinsider.com/halliburton-company-got-395billion-iraq-2013-3

[54] BBC, *Halliburton admits $6 million kickbacks*, BBC.com, Jan 2, 2004, http://news.bbc.co.uk/2/hi/business/3425043.stm

[55] Barlett & Steele, *Billions over Baghdad*, Vanity Fair magazine, Oct 2007, http://www.vanityfair.com/politics/features/2007/10/iraq_billions200710

[56] Horgan, *The End of War*, McSweeney's Books, San Francisco, 2011, p.28-60, 113-43 (iPad eBook edition)

[57] Webre, *Exopolitics*, p.16

[58] Fowler, *The Andreasson Affair*, p.132-3

[59] Mack, *Abduction: Human Encounters with Aliens*, p.410

[60] Hoare, *Research ship finds the world's oceans are 'plasticized'*, CNN.com, May 22, 2012, http://edition.cnn.com/2012/05/21/world/asia/algalita-eco-solutions/index.html

[61] Aguilar, *The Great Garbage Patch of the Pacific*, Aljazeera.com, March 10, 2013, http://www.aljazeera.com/indepth/opinion/2013/03/20133911393486789.html

[62] Milman, *Yachtsman Describes Horror at 'Dead', Rubbish Strewn Pacific Ocean*, thegaurdian.com, Oct. 23, 2013, http://www.theguardian.com/environment/2013/oct/21/yachtsman-describes-horror-at-dead-rubbish-strewn-pacific-ocean

[63] Denyer, *Choking smog paralyzes cities in northeast china, closing schools, airports*, Washingtonpost.com, Oct. 22, 2013, http://www.washingtonpost.com/world/choking-smog-paralyzes-cities-in-northeast-china-closing-schools-airports/2013/10/22/ba2c46d6-3b04-11e3-b0e7-716179a2c2c7_story.html; Wainwright, *Inside Beijing's Airpocalypse- A city made 'almost uninhabitable' by pollution*, The Guardian, Dec. 16, 2014, https://www.theguardian.com/cities/2014/dec/16/beijing-airpocalypse-city-almost-uninhabitable-pollution-china

[64] Taibbi, *Griftopia: Bubble Machines, Vampire Squids, and the Long Con That Is Breaking America*, Spiegel & Grau, New York, 2010, p.234-8

[65] *Looming Ecological Credit Crunch?* Sciencedaily.com, Nov. 6, 2008, http://www.sciencedaily.com/releases/2008/11/081105192704.htm; *Living Planet Report 2008*, http://assets.panda.org/downloads/lpr_2008.pdf

[66] Mack, *Passport to the Cosmos*, p.46, 91; Sparks, *The Keepers*, p.137-43

[67] Sparks, *The Keepers*, p.165-7, 198

[68] Webre, *Exopolitics*, p.71

[69] Fowler, *The Watchers*, p.349

[70] Fowler, *The Watchers*, p.25

[71] Daly, *Fukushima isn't the only nuclear plant leaking radioactive water*, The Christian Science Monitor, Aug. 13, 2013

[72] Mack, *Abduction: Human Encounters with Aliens*, p.411-5; Mack, *Passport to the Cosmos*, p.241

[73] Mack, *Abduction: Human Encounters with Aliens*, p.178-9, 207

[74] Kurzweil, *The Singularity Is Near*, p. 381-2

[75] Dolan, *UFOs and the National Security State: The Cover-Up Exposed*, p.393; Sparks, *The Keepers*, p.22; Hopkins, *Witnessed*, p.173

[76] Sparks, *The Keepers*, p.xvii

[77] Weston, *Super humans who are sexier, stronger and smarter will arrive by 2029 as brains begin to fuse with machines, Google expert claims*, Dailymail.co.uk, March 16. 2017, http://www.dailymail.co.uk/sciencetech/article-4319436/Singularity-create-super-humans-Google-expert-claims.html

[78] Mack, *Passport to the Cosmos*, p.113; Sparks, *The Keepers*, p.194

AFTERWORD

[1] Mallove, *MIT and Cold Fusion: A Special Report*, p.7

[2] De Ropp, *The Master Game: Pathways to Higher Consciousness Beyond the Drug Experience*, Dell Publishing, New York, 1968, p.50, 49-51

[3] Pantsios, *Pope Francis' Encyclical Urges Swift Action on Climate Change Ahead of Paris Climate Talks*, EcoWatch, http://ecowatch.com/2015/06/18/pope-encyclical-action-climate-change/

[4] Coyle, *Cabal keeping UFO secrets to blame for world's woes, says former cabinet minister Paul Hellyer*, thestar.com, Apr. 11, 2015, http://www.thestar.com/news/gta/2015/04/11/cabal-keeping-ufo-secrets-to-blame-for-worlds-woes-says-former-cabinet-minister-paul-hellyer.html

[5] Corso & Birnes, *The Day After Roswell*, p.187-9

[6] Seifer, *Wizard: The Life and Times of Nikola Tesla*, p.202

[7] Swartz, *The Lost Journals of Nikola Tesla*, p.125-6

[8] Mallove, *Breaking Through Editorial: The Einstein Myths- Of Space, Time, and Aether*, Infinite Energy Magazine, Issue #38, July-August 2001, p.29-83, http://www.infinite-energy.com/iemagazine/issue38/einstein.html; Mallove, *Breaking Through Editorial: Nikola Tesla- Man of Three Centuries*, Infinite Energy Magazine, Issue #48, p.5-9, http://www.infinite-energy.com/iemagazine/issue48/nikolaman.html

[9] LaViolette, *Subquantum Kinetics: A Systems Approach to Physics and Cosmology*, Starlane publications, Nov. 22, 2010; LaViolette, *SQK Cosmology*, Starburstfound.org, http://starburstfound.org/sqk-cosmology/3/; LaViolette, *Is the Universe Really Expanding?* Astrophysical Journal Part 1, vol. 301, Feb. 15, 1986, p544-553, http://cdsads.u-strasbg.fr/cgi-bin/nph-bib_query?bibcode=1986ApJ...301..544L&db_key=AST&data_type=HTML&format=&high=43cbd8cf4e25584

[10] see Lloyd, *Programming the Universe: A Quantum Computer Scientist Takes on the Cosmos*, Vintage Books, 2006; Wired, *Life, the Universe, and Everything*, Wired.com, March 2006, http://archive.wired.com/wired/archive/14.03/play.html?pg=4

BIBLIOGRAPHY

Balducci, M. C. (2001). *Ufology and Theological Clarifications.* Pescara.

Balducci, M. C. (2002). *UFOs and Extraterrestrials... A Problem for the Church?* Rome.

Barrow, J. D., & Tipler, F. J. (1988). *The Anthropic Cosmological Principle.* New York, NY, USA: Oxford University Press.

Bassett, S. (1997, April 15). *Paradigm Research Group.* Retrieved May 9, 2001, from Paradigm Research Group Portal: http://www.paradigmresearchgroup.org/index-2.html

Bassett, S. (1998, April 30). *The Paradigm Clock Time Change Chronicle.* Retrieved November 1, 2006, from PRG Paradigm Research Group: http://www.paradigmresearchgroup.org/timechangechronicle.html

Berliner, D. (2000). *UFO Briefing Document.* New York, NY, USA: Dell Publishing.

Birnes, W. J. (2006, July 2). Coast to Coast AM. (G. Knapp, Interviewer)

Brookings Institution. (1961). *Proposed Studies on the Implications of Peaceful Space Activities for Human Affairs.* Washington DC: U.S. Government Printing Office.

Cameron, G. (2002, March 21). *The President's UFO Website.* Retrieved September 1, 2009, from PresidentialUFO.com: http://www.presidentialufo.com

Carey, T. J., & Schmitt, D. R. (2009). *Witness to Roswell.* Franklin Lakes, NJ, USA: New Page Books.

Carey, T. J., Earl, F., Rooney, J., & Schmitt, D. R. (2008, July 4). Roswell Truth Debated. (L. King, Interviewer)

Cheney, M. (1981). *Tesla: Man Out of Time.* New York, NY, USA: Simon & Shuster.

Chiten, L. (Director). (2003). *Touched* [Motion Picture].

COMETA. (1999). *UFOs and Defense: What Should We Prepare For?* Paris: G.S. Presse Communication.

Corso, C. P. (1997, July 23). Coast to Coast AM. (A. Bell, Interviewer)

Corso, C. P., & Birnes, W. J. (1997). *The Day After Roswell.* New York, NY, USA: Pocket Books.

Davidson, K. (1999). *Carl Sagan: A Life.* New York, NY, USA: John Wiley & Sons, Inc.

Davies, P. (1995). *Are We Alone? Philosophical Implications of the Discovery of Extraterrestrial Life.* New York, NY, USA: Basic Books.

Dickinson, T. (1974). *The Zeta Reticuli Incident.* Houlton, Maine: Astromedia.

Dolan, R. M. (2000, December 1). *The CIA, Official History, and you: A Study of Gerald Haines and UFOs.* Retrieved February 1, 2009, from Richarddolanpress.com: http://www.richarddolanpress.com/#!cia-official-history-and-you/ce73

Dolan, R. M. (2009, December 15). *Twelve Government Documents That Take UFOs Seriously.* Retrieved January 1, 2010, from Richarddolanpress.com: http://www.richarddolanpress.com/#!twelve-government-documents/cg96

Dolan, R. M. (2000). *UFOs and the National Security State: An Unclassified History, Volume One: 1941-1973.* Rochester, NY, USA: Keyhole Publishing Company.

Dolan, R. M. (2009). *UFOs and the National Security State: The Cover-up Exposed, 1973-1991.* Rochester, NY, USA: Keyhole Publishing Company.

Dolan, R. M., & Zabel, B. (2010). *A.D. After Disclosure: The People's Guide to Life After Contact.* Rochester, NY, USA: Keyhole Publishing Company.

Fowler, R. E. (1980). *The Andreasson Affair: The Documented Investigation of a Woman's Abduction Aboard a UFO.* New York, NY, USA: Bantam Books.

Fowler, R. E. (1990). *The Watchers: The Secret Design Behind UFO Abduction.* New York, NY, USA: Bantam Books.

Fox, J. (Director). (1997). *UFOs: 50 Years of Denial?* [Motion Picture].

Friedman, S. T. (2008). *Flying Saucers and Science: A Scientist Investigates the mystery of UFOs.* Franklin Lakes, NJ, USA: The Career Press.

Friedman, S. T. (1996). *Top Secret/Majic.* New York, NY, USA: Marlowe & Company.

Friedman, S. T. (2004, April). *Update on Operation Majestic 12 Documents.* Retrieved June 1, 2004, from StantonFriedman.com: http://www.stantonfriedman.com/index.php?ptp=articles&fdt=2004.04.15&prt=1

Friedman, S. T., & Berliner, D. (1995). *Crash at Corona: The U.S. Military Retrieval and Cover-up of a UFO* (5th Edition ed.). New York, NY, USA: Marlowe & Company.

Friedman, S. T., & Marden, K. (2007). *Captured! The Betty and Barney Hill UFO Experience.* Franklin Lakes, NJ, USA: New Page Books.

Greer, D. S. (2001). Disclosure Project Press Conference. *Disclosure: Military and Government Witnesses Reveal the Greatest Secrets in Modern History.* Washington DC: National Press Club.

Greer, D. S. (2001). *Disclosure: Military and Government Witnesses Reveal the Greatest Secrets in Modern History.* Crozet, VA, USA: Crossing Point, Inc.

Greer, D. S. (2006). *Hidden Truth - Forbidden Knowledge.* Crozet, VA: Crossing Point Inc.

Greer, D. S. (2000, August 15). *The Disclosure Project.* Retrieved May 9, 2001, from DisclosureProject.org: http://www.disclosureproject.org/

Hansen, T. (2000). *The Missing Times: News Media Complicity in the UFO Cover-up.* Bloomington, IN, USA: Xlibris.

Hellyer, P. T. (2006, December/January). Paul Hellyer Speaks. *UFO Magazine* , pp. 36-39.

Hoagland, R. C. (1998, December 4). *Enterprise Mission: Now Hear This.* Retrieved March 8, 2004, from Enterprise Mission: http://www.enterprisemission.com/

Hoagland, R. C. (2001). *The Monuments of Mars: A City on the Edge of Forever* (5th Edition ed.). Berkeley, CA: North Atlantic Books.

Hoagland, R. C., & Bara, M. (2007). *Dark Mission: The Secret History of NASA.* Los Angeles, CA, USA: Feral House.

Hopkins, B. (1981). *Missing Time: A Documented Study of UFO Abductions.* New York, NY, YSA.

Hopkins, B. (1996). *Witnessed: The True Story of the Brooklyn Bridge UFO Abductions.* New York, NY, USA: Pocket Books.

Hynek, J. A. (1998). *The UFO Experience.* New York, NY, USA: Marlowe & Company.

Jacobs, D. M. (1998). *The Threat: The Secret Agenda: What the Aliens Really Want... and How They Plan to Get It.* New York, NY, USA: Simon & Schuster.

Jones, E. M. (1985). *Where is Everybody? An Account of Fermi's Question.* Los Alamos: Los Alamos National Laboratory.

Kaku, M. (1995). *Hyperspace: A Scientific Odyssey Through parallel Universes, Time Warps and the 10th Dimension*. New York, NY, USA: Anchor Books.

Kaku, M. (2011). *Physics of the Future: How Science Will Shape Human Destiny and Our Daily Lives by the Year 2100*. New York, NY, USA: Doubleday.

Kaku, M. (1997). *Visions: How Science Will Revolutionize the 21st Century*. New York, NY, USA: Doubleday.

Kean, L. (2000, May 21). UFO Theorists gain support abroad, but repression at home. *The Boston Globe* .

Kean, L. (2010). *UFOs: Generals, Pilots and Government Officials Go on the Record*. New York, NY, USA: Harmony Books.

Keller, T. (2010). A Look at Ben Rich, a man who kept secrets of stealth and space travel. *MUFON UFO Journal* (505), 3-5.

Keyhoe, D. E. (1974). *Aliens From Space*. New York, NY, USA: Signet.

Keyhoe, D. E. (1954). *Flying Saucers From Outer Space*. Garden City, NY, USA: Permabooks.

Keyhoe, D. E. (1955). *The Flying Saucer Conspiracy*. New York, NY, USA: Henry Holt & Company.

Keyhoe, D. E. (1950). *The Flying Saucers Are Real*. New York, NY, USA: Fawcett Publications.

Knight, C., & Butler, A. (2006). *Who Built the Moon?* London, England, UK: Watkins Publishing.

Kolber, J. (2006, January-March). Deafening Silence: Media Response to the May 9th Event and its Implications Regarding the Truth of Disclosure. *Uncensored Magazine* , p. 77.

Kuhn, T. S. (1996). *The Structure of Scientific Revolutions*. Chicago, IL, USA: The University of Chicago Press.

Kurzweil, R. (2000). *The Age of Spiritual Machines: When Computers Exceed Human Intelligence*. New York, NY, USA: Penguin Books.

Kurzweil, R. (2005). *The Singularity Is Near: When Humans Transcend Biology*. New York, NY, USA: The Viking Press.

LaViolette, P. A. (2006). *Decoding the Message of the Pulsars: Intelligent Communication From the Galaxy*. Rochester, VT, USA: Bear & Company.

LaViolette, P. A. (2005). *Earth Under Fire: Humanity's Survival of the Ice Age*. Rochester, VT, USA: Bear & Company.

LaViolette, P. A. (2008). *Secrets of Antigravity Propulsion: Tesla, UFOs and Classified Aerospace Technology.* Rochester, VA, USA: Bear & Company.

LaViolette, P. A. (2007, September 6). *The Starburst Foundation: Science for Survival A Non-profit Scientific Research Institute.* Retrieved October 1, 2011, from The Starburst Foundation: http://starburstfound.org/

Maccabee, B. (2000). *UFO-FBI Connection.* St. Paul, MN, USA: Llewelln Publications.

Mack M. D., J. E. (1995). *Abduction: Human Encounters with Aliens REVISED EDITION.* New York, NY, USA: Ballantine Books.

Mack M. D., J. E. (1999). *Passport to the Cosmos: Human Transformation and Alien Encounters.* New York, NY, USA: Crown Publishers.

Mallove, E. F. (2003, March/April). Breaking Through Editorial: Nikola Tesla: Man of Three Centuries. *Infinite Energy Magazine*, pp. 5-9.

Mallove, E. F. (2001, July/August). Breaking Through Editorial: The Einstein Myths- Of Space, Time and Aether. *Infinite Energy Magazine*, pp. 6-12.

Mallove, E. (1999, March/April). MIT and Cold Fusion: A Special Report. *Infinite Energy Magazine*, pp. 64-119.

Marrs, J. (1997). *Alien Agenda: Investigating the Extraterrestrial Presence Among Us.* New York, NY, USA: HarperCollins Publishers.

McClendon, S. (1998). *Lid Coming Off Government Cover-up on UFOs.* Washington DC: McClendon News Service.

McClendon, S. (1998). *Pressure is Building for Congressional Hearings on UFOs.* Washington DC: McClendon News Service.

McMoneagle, J. (1998). *The Ultimate Time Machine.* Charlottesville, VA: Hampton Roads Publishing Company, Inc.

Mullis, K. (1998). *Dancing Naked in the Mind Field* (First Edition ed.). New York, NY, USA: Pantheon Books.

Randle, K. D. (2001). *Invasion Washington: UFOs Over the Capitol.* New York, NY, USA: HarperCollins Publishers.

Robertson, H. P. (1953). *Report on Scientific Advisory Panel on Unidentified Flying Objects Convened by Office of Scientific Intelligence.* Washington DC: CIA.

Rudiak, D. (2002, November 13). *Roswell Proof: What really happened.* Retrieved December 10, 2003, from Roswellproof.com: http://www.roswellproof.com/

Ruppelt, E. J. (1956). *The Report on Unidentified Flying Objects.* New York, NY, USA: Doubleday & Company, Inc.

Sagan, C. (Writer), & Malone, A. (Director). (1980). *Cosmos* [Motion Picture].

Sagan, C. (1997). *The Demon-Haunted World: Science as a Candle in the Dark.* New York: Ballentine Books.

Sagan, C., & Druyan, A. (2013). *Cosmos.* New York, NY, USA: Ballentine Books.

Salla, M. (2006). Colonel Philip Corso and his Critics: Crossing the Rubicon between Objective Criticism and Debunking. *Exopolitics Journal* , 194-211.

Salla, M. (2005, September 29). *Former Canadian Defense Minister Speaks Out on Extraterrestrial Visitors & Government Secrecy.* Retrieved December 1, 2005, from Exopolitics: https://web.archive.org/web/20121003154725/http://exopolitics.org/Exo-Comment-38.htm

Schnabel, J. (1997). *Remote Viewers: The Secret History of America's Psychic Spies.* New York, NY, USA: Dell Publishing.

Seifer, M. J. (1998). *Wizard: The Life and Times of Nikola Tesla.* New York, NY, USA: Citadel Press.

Sparks, J. (2008). *The Keepers: An Alien Message for the Human Race.* Columbus, NC, USA: Wild Flower Press.

Strieber, W. (1988). *Confirmation: The Hard Evidence of Aliens Among Us.* New York, NY, USA: St. Martin's Press.

Swartz, T. R. (2011). *The Lost Journals of Nikola Tesla.* New Brunswick, NJ, USA: Global Communications.

Twining, N. (1947). *AMC Opinion Concerning "Flying Discs".* Dayton: Air Material Command.

Vallee, J. (1992). *Forbidden Science: Journals 1957-1969.* Berkeley, CA, USA: North Atlantic Books.

Vallee, J., & Aubeck, C. (2010). *Wonders in the Sky: Unexplained Aerial Objects from Antiquity to Modern Times.* New York, NY, USA: Jeremey P. Tarcher/Penguin.

Valone, T. (2002). *Harnessing the Wheelwork of Nature: Tesla's Science of Energy.* Kempton, IL, USA: Adventures Unlimited Press.

Webb, S. (2010). *If the Universe is Teeming with Aliens... Where is Everybody? Fifty Solutions to the Fermi Paradox and the Problem of Extraterrestrial Life.* New York, NY: Copernicus Books.

Webre, A. L. (2005). *Exopolitcs: Politics, Government and Law in the Universe.* Vancouver, BC, Canada: Universebooks.

Wilson, D. (1976). *Our Mysterious Spaceship Moon.* London, Great Britain: Sphere Books Limited.

Wilson, D. (1980). *Secrets of Our Spaceship Moon.* London, Great Britain: Sphere Books Limited.

Wood, R. M., & Wood, R. S. (1999, March). Another Look at Majestic. *MUFON UFO Journal*, 15.

Wood, R. M., & Wood, R. S. (1999, September 1). *The Majestic Documents: Evidence That We Are Not Alone.* Retrieved November 1, 2001, from The Majestic Documents: http//www.majesticdocuments.com/

INDEX

ABOUT THE AUTHOR

Steve S. Lazarus graduated from Cal. State University, Chico in 1985 with a BA in Communications and a Minor in Philosophy. He is a direct first-hand, close encounter eyewitness who has been active in the Disclosure movement since 1997.

167, 178, 245, 290-291,

Manufactured by Amazon.ca
Bolton, ON